BEST OF THE
NEW HAM
COMPANION

Selected *QST* articles on all
aspects of ham radio—from
the beginner's perspective

Published by: **The American Radio Relay League**
225 Main Street
Newington, CT 06111-1494
USA

Edited by: **Steve Ford, WB8IMY**
Compiled by: **Richard Roznoy, K1OF**

BENEDICTINE UNIVERSITY AT MESA LIBRARY

D1228071

Copyright © 1997 by

The American Radio Relay League, Inc.

Copyright secured under the Pan-American Convention

International Copyright secured

This work is publication No. 220 of the Radio Amateur's Library, published by the League. All rights reserved. No part of this work may be reproduced in any form except by written permission of the publisher. All rights of translation are reserved.

Printed in USA

Quedan reservados todos los derechos

First Edition

ISBN: 0-87259-600-1

Contents

Foreword

Acknowledgments

3. Antennas

4. Digital Modes

5. General Interest

Foreword

Starting out in Amateur Radio can be a challenge—there is so much to learn. Almost every beginner has questions, and not surprisingly, many ask the same questions. This book provides answers to many of those questions in a simple, straightforward manner. The most informative and popular articles from the "New Ham Companion" and "The Doctor Is IN" sections of *QST* are combined for easy reading in this book.

All aspects of getting on the air are covered:

• Operating practices

• Understanding and building simple antennas

• Useful station accessories you can build

• How to operate 2-meter repeaters

• SWLing, specialized modes—and much more

This book is a valuable resource for all newly licensed hams. At a glance you can find the answers to almost any question a newcomer might ask. Who can't benefit from a down-to-earth review of the basics or a review of current operating practices? By reading this book you can get on the air with the satisfaction of knowing you are doing it right.

We've included a handy feedback form at the back to make it as convenient as possible to provide us with your comments and suggestions. We'd love to hear from you.

David Sumner, K1ZZ

Executive Vice President

Newington, Connecticut

February 1997

Acknowledgments

In introducing a new section of *QST*, in the February 1993 issue, Steve Ford, WB8IMY, wrote, in part: "As a new ham, you'll find information you can use every day. Our authors will provide handy operating hints, easy construction articles, practical advice and entertaining personal experiences." As this is written, four years later, Steve remains at the helm of "The New Ham Companion," although he now also serves as *QST* Managing Editor. The contents of this book are a testament to Steve's ability to write and edit articles that will appeal to all hams, regardless of experience or license class.

The Editor also wishes to thank all the authors whose work appears in this book. A perusal of the contents page will show that some prolific authors have several articles represented. It is our hope that by compiling these articles into one volume, they will be that much more useful to the ham community.

A word of caution: Addresses, telephone numbers, prices, Web addresses and other information is published exactly as they appeared originally in *QST*. This type of information is subject to change, and may no longer be valid.

About the American Radio Relay League

The seed for Amateur Radio was planted in the 1890s, when Guglielmo Marconi began his experiments in wireless telegraphy. Soon he was joined by dozens, then hundreds, of others who were enthusiastic about sending and receiving messages through the air—some with a commercial interest, but others solely out of a love for this new communications medium. The United States government began licensing Amateur Radio operators in 1912.

By 1914, there were thousands of Amateur Radio operators—hams—in the United States. Hiram Percy Maxim, a leading Hartford, Connecticut, inventor and industrialist saw the need for an organization to band together this fledgling group of radio experimenters. In May 1914 he founded the American Radio Relay League (ARRL) to meet that need.

Today ARRL, with more than 170,000 members, is the largest organization of radio amateurs in the United States. The League is a not-for-profit organization that:
* promotes interest in Amateur Radio communications and experimentation
* represents US radio amateurs in legislative matters, and
* maintains fraternalism and a high standard of conduct among Amateur Radio operators.

At League headquarters in the Hartford suburb of Newington, the staff helps serve the needs of members. ARRL is also International Secretariat for the International Amateur Radio Union, which is made up of similar societies in more than 100 countries around the world.

ARRL publishes the monthly journal *QST*, as well as newsletters and many publications covering all aspects of Amateur Radio. Its headquarters station, W1AW, transmits bulletins of interest to radio amateurs and Morse code practice sessions. The League also coordinates an extensive field organization, which includes volunteers who provide technical information for radio amateurs and public-service activities. ARRL also represents US amateurs with the Federal Communications Commission and other government agencies in the US and abroad.

Membership in ARRL means much more than receiving QST each month. In addition to the services already described, ARRL offers membership services on a personal level, such as the ARRL Volunteer Examiner Coordinator Program and a QSL bureau.

Full ARRL membership (available only to licensed radio amateurs) gives you a voice in how the affairs of the organization are governed. League policy is set by a Board of Directors (one from each of 15 Divisions). Each year, half of the ARRL Board of Directors stands for election by the full members they represent. The day-to-day operation of ARRL HQ is managed by an Executive Vice President and a Chief Financial Officer.

No matter what aspect of Amateur Radio attracts you, ARRL membership is relevant and important. There would be no Amateur Radio as we know it today were it not for the ARRL. We would be happy to welcome you as a member! (An Amateur Radio license is not required for Associate Membership.) For more information about ARRL and answers to any questions you may have about Amateur Radio, write or call:

ARRL Educational Activities Dept
225 Main Street
Newington CT 06111-1494
(860) 594-0200
Prospective new amateurs call:
800-32-NEW HAM (800-326-3942)
You can also contact us via e-mail: **ead@arrl.org**
or check out our World Wide Web site: **http://www.arrl.org/**

Falling in Love With Ham Radio
For Less Than $200

By Jeff M. Gold, AC4HF
1751 Dry Creek Rd
Cookeville, TN 38501

I'll never forget the thrill of talking to 18 DX stations in less than 45 minutes using a small battery, a piece of wire and a tiny transceiver. My low power *(QRP)* station fits very nicely in a small backpack and was assembled for less than $200!

After a year of grinding away at work, it was finally time for a vacation. Not only was I going to get some time off, I had an extra $200 to spend on a portable station. I saw an article about a new MFJ QRP transceiver that was small enough for backpacking. Because I didn't have enough time to build a rig before my vacation, I made some calls and finally found a dealer who had a preassembled model in stock at a discount price.

While waiting for the rig to arrive, I assembled a resonant dipole antenna. I used inexpensive #14 copper wire purchased from a local electrical wholesale store. At a cost of $20 for 500 feet, it was a bargain!

Some 1-inch PVC pipe scraps became the end and center insulators. I fed the antenna with RG-58 coaxial cable (you can get 50 feet of RG-58 with PL-259 end connectors from Radio Shack for about $14). I also visited my local hobby store and purchased a 7 amp-hour radio-controlled airplane battery ($18).

Within three days my new transceiver arrived. I wired a power cord from the bat-

---

You don't need huge antennas, hundreds of watts or an overstuffed bank account to enjoy Amateur Radio.

---

tery to the rig and put a connector on my straight key. I also grabbed some heavy fishing line and an old spark plug. They'd come in handy when it was time to install my antenna in the trees.

Time for a Test!

I still had two weeks to go before my vacation, so I figured I had better test the rig and see how it would perform. I packed the whole setup, including the antenna, into a backpack and headed for a nearby riverside recreational area. Operating CW QRP brought to mind a picture of spending two hours banging away at a key just to barely reach someone down the block. If my gloomy scenario came true, at least I could console myself with a swim!

I found a place by the river with tall trees and a picnic bench. Using my trusty spark plug as a throwing weight, I managed to get the fishing line high into the branches. Tying the ends of the antenna to the fishing line, I raised it as far off the ground as possible. The entire setup took 25 minutes.

With shaky hands I pushed the power button on my new rig. I heard something! This was getting exciting! I twisted the tuning knob and seemed to hear signals, but there was nothing distinct. Soon I realized that I was turning the knob too fast, going right past dozens of stations! Curbing my nervous excitement, I took out my pen and paper and started to explore the band.

Within minutes I heard an EA3 station in Spain. His signal was surprisingly strong. I gave him a call, but another station beat me to it. I waited patiently and tried again. Bingo! He gave me a 559 RST and said he wanted a serial number. Huh? Looks like there was a contest going on! I gave him 001 and recorded the number he sent to me. I worked a few more EA stations, contacted several Italian and English stations, and then worked four Russian stations in rapid-fire order.

My head was spinning! I never imagined I would be able to work DX so successfully with such a small, inexpensive radio. The CW filtering made reception a snap and it seemed that my signal was getting out pretty well. After a while I grew tired of contesting and wanted to just relax and talk to someone. I was eager to tell other hams that I was only putting out 3 watts with battery power and a portable antenna! I continued tuning around the band and found some US ops who wanted to chat. They all said my rig sounded great. In fact, my RST was equal to some stations with beam antennas and 100 watts output!

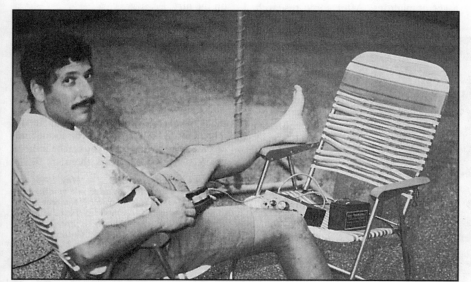

Working the world with a couple of watts is a relaxing experience. The author takes it easy as he enjoys a CW conversation. (*photos by Conard Murray, WS4S*)

From left to right: the MFJ transceiver, the author's homemade CW paddle key and a rechargeable battery. The portable antenna is visible in the background.

At first I only attempted to answer people who were calling CQ with reasonably strong signals—579 RST or better. I assumed that if a station wasn't at least a 579, there was no way he or she was going to hear me. Further experience proved that this was *not* the case. I've since enjoyed short contacts with DX stations that had only 449 signals and carried on longer conversations with equally weak stations.

On the Road

My portable station has traveled up Smoky Mountain trails, to lakes, to outdoor hamfests and even to a motel in Myrtle Beach where I strung my dipole between two buildings 60 feet apart! During my motel operation, I secured ropes to the fourth-floor railings and set up my station in plain sight. When people stopped by and asked what I was doing, I took off my headphones and let them listen, explaining what

they were hearing. I worked a good deal of DX and enjoyed some pleasant conversations.

On the last night, just as I was getting ready to tear down the station, a woman approached and began screaming questions. What was I doing? Was I a hit man, a spy perhaps? As it turned out, she was one of the motel owners!

I learned two important lessons from this jarring experience. One is to ask the owner of the motel for permission to set up a station (I haven't had any problems when I've asked). The other is to bring an alternative antenna if at all possible!

The Alternative Antenna

An article in the April 1992 issue of *CQ* magazine (pp 38-41) describes how to build a portable vertical antenna from PVC pipe sections. The antenna uses helically wound wire and costs next to nothing to make. PVC sells locally for $1.69 per 10-foot section. Since I already had the wire from the 500-foot roll I bought for my dipole, I tried the design. It worked so well that I decided to see if I could improve it.

My revised antenna is made from a heavier gauge PVC and uses ½-wavelength wire instead of the ¼-wavelength specified in the original design. The result is a superb portable antenna that assembles in only five minutes and performs much better than the ¼-wave version. Now I can set up anywhere and be on the air in less than five minutes!

Improving the Key

The only thing left to improve was the CW key. My nine-year-old son Danny, KD4HQV, has a General-class license and works CW exclusively. He never learned to use a straight key, but he's pretty good with a set of paddles. After some research, I found that none of the less expensive commercial paddles would be able to withstand the rigors of backpacking. The paddles that *did* meet the specifications were all priced at $100 or more.

I had only been a ham for about a year and I was not accustomed to being an inventor. Time to seek outside help. I posted "help" messages on electronic bulletin boards and took a good deal of

ridicule! Sarcastic comments suggesting the use of ironwood or two teaspoons were common, but they stimulated my creative thinking. I finally realized that CW paddles just make and break electrical contacts. I don't have an extensive background in electronics, but it sure sounded like an electronic switch to me!

I went to Radio Shack and bought momentary-contact switches (look for part #275-618). Grabbing an old Plexiglas desktop organizer, I sawed off one of the pen holder sections to use as a mounting platform. When I attached the switches they worked electrically, but were awkward to operate. Then I devised an elaborate system with nuts, bolts and tensioning devices attached to two pieces of plastic. After a couple of hours, I finally realized that it wasn't going to work!

Still, I refused to give up. I found some metal pieces that are used to hold slot positions in the back of IBM compatible computers. I drilled two holes in the Plexiglas pen holder and attached the thin metal strips. When I bent the metal into shape, I had working paddles which took only 10 minutes to finish. The entire paddle key was easily assembled in half an hour. After I mounted the switch assembly to a piece of pine, I tested the paddles and found that they worked fairly well—not too bad for about $4 and half an hour of work!

I was so encouraged that I proceeded to cut some smoked Plexiglas for the paddle ends. A heavy brass grounding strip (I bought it for $2 at a recent hamfest) was attached to the bottom for added weight. I included a strip of Velcro on the base to keep it from slipping.

Granted, it's not a high-quality paddle, but boy does it come close! My homemade paddles have survived many hours of operating as well as the bumps and jolts of backpacking. After the longest journeys, they need only a 30-second adjustment and I'm on the air!

It's Easier Than You Think

Commercial QRP transceiver kits are available for $100-$150. See the advertising section of *QST* for sources. Plans for an excellent backpacking rig are also available in the latest *ARRL Handbook*.

Running a low-power station *does not* mean inferior performance. All you need is a little more skill. Don't worry about finding someone to talk to. If you can hear them, chances are you can work them!

Jeff Gold was first licensed in May 1991 as a Technician Plus. He upgraded two months later to Extra Class. Jeff is an ARRL Volunteer Examiner in Cookeville, Tennessee. His educational background includes a Masters degree in Special Education from Manhattan College and a Bachelor's degree in Psychology from Adelphi University. Jeff's son Danny was licensed in July 1992 and holds a General-class license. He recently passed his 20-WPM CW test. Jeff is employed as Manager of Computer Support Services for Tennessee Technological University. ▭

The author's son Danny, KD4HQV, gets into the act, too. He enjoys making CW contacts with his father's portable station.

2-Meter FM FM FM FM FM FM DXing

VHF DX isn't just for CW and SSB operators. There's excitement to be found on FM, too.

By Steve Ford, WB8IMY
Assistant Technical Editor

To most VHFers, DXing means working stations hundreds or even thousands of miles away using SSB or CW. Why not FM? The reason has to do with signal strength and noise.

Due to the nature of FM reception, an FM signal must be fairly strong to be readable. This isn't true of SSB or CW. You can usually copy an SSB signal when it is quite weak, assuming that the frequency is free of interference. CW offers even better performance. Experienced CW operators can often decipher a signal that's barely audible above the noise. That's why CW is the preferred mode for moonbounce work.

The bottom line is that a CW or SSB signal will be readable at weaker levels and over greater distances than an FM signal. Does this mean that FM operators are frozen out of the DX game completely? Not at all. There's still plenty of DX to be worked on FM—if you know how to find it.

Waiting for *Tropo*

The DX activity you're likely to encounter on 2 meters is provided courtesy of Mother Nature in the form of *tropospheric propagation*, or just *tropo* for short. (No, the talking mouse on the Ed Sullivan Show was "Topo.")

The troposphere is the layer of the Earth's atmosphere where most of our weather takes place. Air masses at various temperatures and moisture densities have the potential to refract (bend) VHF signals so that communication is possible many miles—sometimes *hundreds* of miles—beyond your local horizon. A slow-moving high-pressure area, for example, is a prime candidate for tropo. Tropo can also occur when layers of cool air at the Earth's surface rest just below masses of warm air. (This type of tropo is known as *radiation inversion* and takes place primarily in the summer months.)

Violent weather can bring VHF DX, too. An advancing cold front may clash with a warm sector ahead of it. In addition to thunderstorms, it may create some fascinating tropo. Hurricanes and typhoons can also trigger tropo DX. In addition to stirring up the atmosphere over huge areas, these storms often block the movement of distant high-pressure zones. When a large dome of high pressure is lingering over your state, start checking your radio! Conditions may be right for a tropo opening.

Most tropo activity takes place in the summer and fall, although it can occur at other times of the year as well. A good tropo opening may last several hours, and sometimes several *days*. If you're hunting VHF DX, it pays to keep an eye on the weather reports. For more detailed information on weather-related DX conditions, see "The Weather That Brings VHF DX" by Emil Pocock, W3EP, in the May 1983 *QST*.

Hunting DX

If you suspect that the band is active, start prowling the repeater frequencies. Listen for bursts of activity from distant repeaters. They may offer your first clues that a band opening is at hand.

Generally speaking, it's best to avoid repeater DXing and concentrate on simplex contacts instead. When you hear a far-flung repeater, it's tempting to reach for your microphone. Yes, the repeater may indeed hear you—as may other repeaters operating on the same frequencies. Keep in mind that when a band opening is in progress, your signal is likely to travel much farther than you think. Sometimes you may hear several machines responding simultaneously to your transmissions. Often, however, you won't know that you're getting into more than one repeater. This gives you a unique opportunity to be a pain in the neck in several states at once!

Switch to 146.52 MHz or another simplex frequency instead. That's where you'll find the lion's share of 2-meter FM DX. If the frequency seems quiet, don't be shy. Go ahead and call a short CQ. You never know who will reply—or where they may be. If no one responds to your call, wait a few minutes and try again. You could also turn up your squelch control *just* to the point where the noise stops and busy yourself with another activity. If you hear voices or bursts of static, pay close attention. DX may be coming through!

Antennas for FM DX

Almost any kind of outdoor antenna will do the job for 2-meter FM DXing. Your best choice is a beam—the larger the better—mounted in the *vertically polarized* position. With a rotator to turn the antenna, you can maximize your transmitted and received signals for best effect.

Not everyone can afford a beam and a rotator, so an *omnidirectional* antenna is in order. Even a simple ground plane may work surprisingly well. I once contacted an FM station 200 miles away with a ground plane and about 30 W. Get your antenna as high above the ground as you can. If you're running low power (less than 10 W), you may want to consider adding an RF power amplifier.

But what if all you have is an H-T with a *rubber-duck* antenna? The solution is to get you—and your H-T—as high as possible. Tall buildings can be terrific locations for DXing, as can hilltops and mountains. If you have a friend who is a private pilot, see if he or she will take you aloft with your H-T. You'd be amazed at the DX you can work from about 5,000 feet. (Don't try to operate from a commercial airliner, however!)

Don't Take My Word for It

It's fine for me to extol the virtues of FM DXing, but I work at the ARRL. It's my business to promote all aspects of Amateur Radio. To gather some unbiased opinions I went to the CompuServe *Hamnet* forum and asked for input from anyone who had indulged in FM DXing. Here's a sample of the responses I received:

■ "Florida is the home of tropo. I have a 'pipeline' every morning from Clearwater Beach (30 km west of Tampa) to WB4BWS in Palm Harbor over by Cape Canaveral. My best FM DX on 2 meters is Gene, KD4NGB, in Warner Robins, Georgia. Not too shabby for a Yaesu 736R transceiver and a Comet vertical."—*Don Stoner, W6TNS/4*

■ "I was first licensed as G6NYY in the early 1980s. Back then I enjoyed a number of FM contacts with Dutch stations using 2.5 W and a 5-element Yagi. I was located in North Norfolk, England, so our conversations took place over a sea path of around 120 miles."—*Kevin Danks, G0DBL*

■ "This goes back more than 10 years, but on my first visit to Chicago, I took my 1-W Drake TR-22C transceiver to the top of the Sears Tower and worked a bunch of folks on 146.52 MHz across the lake in Michigan. I've also had good luck working FM simplex from the top of Cadillac Mountain in Bar Harbor, Maine." —*Rich Moseson, NW2L*

■ "I worked a station in North Carolina from the attic of my home in North Andover, Massachusetts on 146.52-MHz simplex with

NEW HAM COMPANION

a Yaesu FT-208 transceiver. This was during a hurricane off the Atlantic Coast, and the weather pattern was fantastic for tropo. That fellow in North Carolina must have worked thousands of New England stations on FM!''—*Rich Richmand, KA5S*

The VHF QSO Party

A great opportunity to test your FM DXing skill is just around the corner. The September VHF QSO Party is one of the hottest VHF contests of the year. It is held the weekend of September 10-11, and complete rules appeared in August *QST*. During the contest period you can expect to find activity on all VHF and UHF bands, with 2 meters being the most popular. Much of the activity will be taking place on SSB and CW, but you can count on hearing operators on FM, too.

You can't use 146.52-MHz simplex to make contest contacts, but all the other nationally recognized FM simplex frequencies are fair game. If you make at least 25 contacts you'll be eligible for a handsome participation pin. See the Complete rules in the August *QST* for details.

Remember: If you hear nothing, don't take "no" for an answer. Call "CQ contest" yourself! Other stations will be hunting for contacts, so you have to let them know you're on the air. Don't stay on one frequency after you've mined it for all it's worth. Jump to another frequency and try again. Depending on the activity in your area, you should bag 25 contacts in no time at all. And if tropo puts in an appearance, the sky's the limit!

Q **I'm a codeless Technician, so I'm limited to the bands above 50 MHz. Assuming that I can get my hands on some SSB or CW equipment and a good antenna system, what can I expect in terms of long-distance (DX) communication?**

A *Limited* to the bands above 50 MHz? Some limitation! Compared to the HF bands, you have more frequencies, less interference and fewer regulatory restrictions on the VHF, UHF and microwave bands. For many hams, this "limitation" is very liberating.

But what about DX? Long-distance communication above 50 MHz is certainly possible—and there are many ways to go about it.

❏❶*Tropospheric—or simply "tropo"— openings.* Tropo is the most common form of DX-producing propagation on the bands above 144 MHz. It comes in several forms, depending on local and regional weather patterns. Tropo may cover only a few hundred miles, or it may include huge areas of the country at once. The best times of year for tropo propagation are from spring to fall,

although they can occur anytime.

❏❶*Sporadic E* (abbreviated E$_s$) propagation is one of the most spectacular DX producers on the 50-MHz band. Where it may occur almost every day during late June, July and early August. A short E$_s$ season also occurs during December and January—just in time for the January VHF Sweepstakes! Sporadic E is more common in mid-morning and again around sunset during the summer months, but it can occur at any time and any date. E$_s$ also pops up at least once or twice a year on 2 meters in most areas. E$_s$ results from small patches of ionization in the ionosphere's E layer. E$_s$ signals are usually strong, but they may fade away without warning.

❏❶*Meteor scatter* communication uses the ionized trails meteors leave as they pass through the atmosphere. VHF radio signals can be bent (refracted) by these high-altitude meteor trails and return to Earth hundreds or even thousands of miles away. This ionization lasts only a second or so. It's so intense, though, that even 432-MHz signals can sometimes be refracted. Most meteor-scatter contacts are made on 6 and 2 meters.

Meteor-scatter contacts are possible at any time of year. Activity is greatest during the major meteor showers, especially the Perseids, which occurs in August. If you're running about 150 W to a single 8 or 11-element Yagi antenna, give meteor scatter a try.

❏❶*Aurora* (abbreviated Au) openings occur when the auroras are sufficiently ionized to refract radio signals. Auroras are caused by the Earth intercepting a massive number of charged particles from the Sun. Earth's magnetic field funnels these particles into the polar regions. The charged particles often interact with the upper atmosphere enough to make the air glow. Then we can see a visual aurora. The particles also provide an irregular, moving curtain of ionization that can propagate signals for many hundreds of miles.

Aurora-reflected signals have an unmistakable ghostly sound. CW signals sound hissy, SSB signals sound like a harsh whisper. FM signals refracted by an aurora are unreadable.

❏❶*EME, or Earth-Moon-Earth* (often called *Moonbounce*) is the ultimate VHF/UHF DX medium. Moonbouncers use the Moon as a reflector for their signals, and the contact distance is limited only by the diameter of the Earth (both stations must have line of sight to the Moon). As you've probably guessed, Moonbouncers have a particular obsession about knowing where the Moon is, especially when they can't see it because of cloud cover.

Moonbounce conversations between the USA and Europe or Japan are commonplace—at frequencies from 50 to 10,368 MHz. That's true DX! Hundreds of EME-capable stations are now active, some with gigantic antenna arrays. Their antenna systems make it possible for stations running

150 W and one or two Yagi antennas to work them. Activity is constantly increasing. In fact, the ARRL sponsors an EME contest, in which moonbouncers compete on an international scale.

❏❶*Satellites:* The low-orbiting birds such as RS-10, RS-12, RS-15 and OSCAR 20 can relay your signals over distances over hundreds of miles or more. Better yet, OSCARs 10 and 13 offer *hemispheric* coverage.

Q **Paul Huff, N8XMS, asks, "Is there any correlation between my S meter and the strength of the signal I report? Should I base my RST (or RS) report on the S-meter reading?"**

A There is usually little correlation between your S-meter reading and the RST (or RS) report that you provide. When you give an RST report, it is based on *your* evaluation of the other station's signal. You might use your S meter to help you, but don't depend on it. S meters measure only relative signal strength and the readings vary from one rig to another. I've witnessed tests where two radios of the same brand were hooked up to the same antenna and were monitoring the same signals. Both displayed different S-meter readings!

The RST system takes factors into account other than the strength of the signal. For example, you may hear an SSB signal that is very strong (+10 dB over 9 on your meter). Despite the strength and the meter indication, noise, interference or poor audio quality may make it difficult to understand what the person is saying. You wouldn't give this station a "5-9" report. A "3-9" would be more accurate.

Q **Floyd Schad, KA6DAU, asks, "Why is it legal for airline passengers to use a radiotelephone system while Amateur Radio activity from the same plane is illegal?"**

A There is a great difference between using a commercial radiotelephone system from an airliner and using, say, your 2-meter FM transceiver. The telephone systems used in airliners have passed rigid requirements for spurious signal emissions and compatibility with navigation avionics. The same cannot be said of Amateur Radio transceivers (or laptop computers and various entertainment devices, for that matter).

Even if an airline company took the extraordinary step of testing and "certifying" every brand of amateur transceiver for in-flight use, you'd still be hobbled by FCC Rules. The FCC states that you cannot operate an Amateur Radio station onboard an aircraft that is operating under *instrument flight rules* (IFR)—even if the pilot gives his or her permission. Airliners fly IFR virtually all the time.

BEEP...

What Did That Repeater Say?

We hear the *courtesy tone* almost every time we use the repeater. It's that innocuous beep that lets us know that the repeater is alive and, most importantly, that it has heard us. The courtesy tone also separates one person's comments from the comments of the next person. Other than that, we probably don't give the beep much thought. Too bad. There's a lot we can learn from that curious noise.

It's Called a "Courtesy Tone" for a Reason

Most repeaters have timing mechanisms which limit the lengths of transmissions. When you recall that only one person can use a repeater at a time, the idea makes perfect sense. Without some kind of limit, long-winded users would monopolize the machine for mind-numbing periods of time. The *time-out* function prevents this from happening. Basically, when a transmission ends, no one should speak again until the repeater sends the courtesy tone. The penalty for ignoring the courtesy tone can be severe. To paraphrase the late philosopher Joseph Campbell, repeaters are like ancient deities—all rules and no mercy!

Maybe you've heard someone talking on a repeater when, all of a sudden, their transmission stops. The repeater resets, beeps, and the next person starts his comments by saying something like, "Well, Chet, you talked too long again. The repeater timed out and we missed what you said after..." (You think Chet would learn after a while!)

But thank goodness for "forced" pauses! What if you needed the repeater during an emergency? Or, what if you were sitting in your car waiting to sign off after a long commute home? Either way, you don't want to wait while Joe Ham finishes his dissertation on Darwin's theory of evolution. Courtesy indeed.

Repeaters Have Tails

You may have heard someone talk about a repeater's "tail." What is it? Why is it important? And, what does it have to do with courtesy tones?

To answer those questions, we must first discuss a bit of repeater theory. (For additional discussion of repeater theory, see "Anatomy of a Repeater" by Steve Ford, WB8IMY, in the May 1995 *QST*.) We all know that repeaters receive on one frequency and simultaneously retransmit that same information on a different frequency. We also now know that, for a number of reasons, repeaters need to periodically reset themselves. The important thing to remember is that when the repeater resets, *the time-out timer resets as well.*

The resetting process works like this:

❏ When you stop transmitting, the repeater senses the loss of your signal. However, you may not have actually stopped transmitting—you might be traveling through a dead spot where your signal to the repeater is temporarily blocked. So, most repeaters hesitate a bit before resetting. The length of the delay can be changed by the repeater owner, but it's generally about $1/2$ to 1 second.

In addition to allowing time for your signal to "come back," the delay also ensures that there is a slight pause between the time you stop talking and the moment when the next person starts. That pause allows someone else to announce his/her call sign in order to enter the conversation, or to request use of the repeater for an emergency or whatever. Courtesy.

❏ If the delay comes and goes without a signal, the repeater resets. The reset is often (but not always) announced with a beep. That's the courtesy tone.

❏ Finally, after resetting, the repeater continues to transmit for a specified period of time. This transmission period, called the *tail*, can also be adjusted by the repeater owner. Repeater tails can be short or long. The bottom line is that the repeater will stop transmitting entirely if it does not sense a signal during the tail period.

Listening to the Beeps—Or Not!

Usually the repeater generates the courtesy tone to let you know that it has reset and is ready for use by another person. But, not all repeaters use the same courtesy tones—and some tones are more than just simple beeps.

For example, some repeaters can change their courtesy tones to let you know the system status. A repeater courtesy tone might change from a single beep to a Morse code "N" (dah-dit) to let you know that it is in "net" mode with different time-out lengths and tails. Or, it might transmit an "L" (di-dah-di-dit) to let you know that you are using a link frequency—coming in on 222 MHz, for example, instead of the repeater's primary frequency in the 2-meter band. Or, it might just mean that the repeater owner got tired of the old tone and decided to change to a different one!

Some courtesy tones are creative. In fact, they may not be tones at all. Some repeater systems replace the familiar beep with strange sound effects or even digitized human voices. Regardless of what kind of courtesy tone (or other sound) your favorite repeater uses, the important thing is to wait for it before you start transmitting.

Do I hear you saying that your favorite repeater *doesn't* have a courtesy tone? Aha! That's where it gets confusing. There are several repeaters in my area that do not have courtesy tones. For example, one of the major Boston repeaters has no courtesy tone and doesn't reset until *after* the tail drops. This can be very confusing for the first-time user because it means that people using the repeater must wait for it to stop transmitting before the next person begins to talk.

We have another busy repeater that also lacks a courtesy tone, but it's set up in an entirely different manner. In this case, the repeater resets immediately when it senses that a signal is no longer present. In other words, it resets whenever someone stops talking. It also has an extremely long tail—30 seconds—which means that the repeater continues to transmit long after the person has stopped talking. This arrangement encourages lots of short exchanges—much like normal face-to-face conversation among friends.

Tones, tails...does it matter? No, not really. There are many ways in which repeaters can be set up. And different setups encourage different use. Repeaters are meant to be shared, especially during the busy commuting hours. So, spend a bit of time listening before you use a repeater for the first time. And remember that, beep or no beep, *courtesy* is still the key word.

> A single tone is often the only thing standing between us and chaos.

By Chester S. Bowles, AA1EX
RFD 2, Box 335L
Sharon, NH 03458

The Day the Repeater "Broke"

By Larry Wolfgang, WR1B
Senior Assistant Technical Editor

On my way home from work one night I heard several stations on the local repeater. They were having a round-table discussion about TCP/IP (a form of packet-radio networking). I was curious, and wanted to ask a few questions.

During the brief pause between two stations' transmissions, I sent my call once. "WR1B." The next station acknowledged my call and turned it over to me after he finished his transmission. To avoid a possible time-out problem, I waited for the courtesy beep.

I asked a couple of questions, and turned it over to the next station. "WB8IMY to take it, this is WR1B." When I released the mike button, I discovered that Steve was already talking! He made a reference to my "not making it into the machine" and then called me to try it again. "WR1B, try it again Larry. We didn't get anything on that last transmission."

So I tried again. "Am I making it now Steve? WR1B."

"Sorry Larry, nothing heard. Try again if you get into a better location." And the conversation continued without me. I tried calling in once more that evening, but got no answer. I was puzzled, and worried that something had gone wrong with the repeater.

The next morning on my way to work, I heard Jim, KR1S on the repeater. "KR1S listening." I decided to give Jim a call. "Good morning, Jim. This is WR1B." Jim answered immediately, and we had a nice conversation. I described the events of the previous night, but Jim had no idea what may have been wrong.

A few days later I joined another round-table discussion on the way home. Someone mentioned that the repeater had recently been switched to *subaudible tone access*. Ah-hah! Maybe that was the problem!

The Mystery is Solved

At the next club meeting, the topic for discussion just happened to be *tone access*. How convenient! As I listened, I learned that our repeater had recently installed a continuous tone-coded squelch system (*CTCSS*). Despite the complicated-sounding name, CTCSS is easy to understand. It's based on a system that Motorola developed many years ago for business-band radios. In fact, some veteran amateurs still refer to CTCSS by the original Motorola trade name: *Private Line*—or just *PL*.

The original intent of the Private Line system was to allow several business users to share a single channel. For example, the Ace Trucking Company and Mel's Taxi Service might both use the same channel. All the Ace receivers respond to one PL tone and the receivers in Mel's taxis respond to another tone. When the Ace dispatcher calls a truck, their drivers all hear the call, but the taxi receivers remain squelched and no call is heard. As long as both dispatchers don't transmit at the same time, each company enjoys interference-free communications.

Amateurs have several reasons for using this type of system on their repeaters. Preventing *intermod* interference from keying up the repeater is one good application. Intermod can occur when two strong signals mix, producing a signal on the repeater input frequency. For example, a channel-8 TV signal on 181.25 MHz could mix with a business-band radio transmission on 36.4 MHz. The difference frequency is 144.85 MHz (181.25 MHz −36.4 MHz), a popular 2-meter repeater frequency. The result is a repeater that's keyed time and time again, driving everyone crazy and rendering it nearly useless! By using a CTCSS, the repeater will respond *only* to signals carrying the proper tone, *not* the intermod signal.

Another common use occurs when a second repeater is on the same frequency in a neighboring area. Most of the time the repeaters cause little or no interference to each other. But during times of enhanced propagation, or when an amateur increases power considerably to access the repeater from a *fringe* area (beyond the repeater's reliable coverage area), users of one repeater may inadvertently key up the other repeater. In this case, the repeater owners may decide to add a CTCSS function to their machine to prevent hams from the neighboring group from keying it up.

A third application of CTCSS is to create a *closed repeater*. A closed repeater is one intended for use by a specific group of people, such as the members of a particular club, and no one else.

The first two cases are examples of *open repeaters* using CTCSS to solve a particular problem. *The ARRL Repeater Directory* lists the CTCSS tones for many open repeaters that use this system either occasionally, or all the time.

How CTCSS Works

If your transmitter includes a CTCSS tone encoder, it sends a tone along with your transmitted signal. The tone frequency is below the lowest audio frequency that will go to the receiving station's speaker. Since it cannot be heard by other users, it's called a subaudible tone.

The repeater control circuit easily senses the subaudible tone and responds only to signals that include it. This effectively locks out signals that *don't* carry the correct CTCSS tone. Now I understood why I was having so much trouble with the repeater. Without the proper subaudible tone, I was locked out of the system. The problem wasn't the repeater, it was me! I wasn't transmitting the correct tone!

There are 42 standard CTCSS tone frequencies. They range from 67.0 to 254.1 Hz. Table 1 lists the Electronic Industries Association (EIA) standard frequency codes, along with their Motorola alphanumeric designations.

Many VHF/UHF FM radios have a built-in CTCSS tone encoder. If one isn't built into your radio, you can probably add it as an accessory with little trouble. (Check with your radio's manufacturer, or look through the advertising section of *QST*.)

To use the repeater, I simply had to program my radio to transmit the proper tone. The repeater trustee told us to use 88.5-Hz, and the information was printed in the next club newsletter. I had to check my radio's instruction manual to learn how to program a subaudible tone.

After pressing a few buttons, my rig was all set to go. My transceiver includes a **TONE** button, so I can turn the subaudible tone on or off once it is programmed. By programming

---

One day I was in, the next day I was out! What was going on?

the tone first, and then storing the repeater frequency in a memory, I can store a different tone with each memory. Some radios may only select one tone for use with all the memory channels, but that shouldn't be a serious drawback.

The Last Piece of the Puzzle

I asked why the stations on the repeater heard my call that first night, but couldn't hear any later transmissions. As it turns out, I made my initial call *before* the squelch tail dropped from the previous user. The repeater was already keyed, so it received and repeated my call sign. Since I was not transmitting the proper subaudible tone, however, I was unable to key the repeater on my own.

So the next time you think a repeater is "broken," find out if it's using a tone access system. Program your rig for the proper tone and you'll be back in business!

Table 1
CTCSS Tone Frequencies

Frequency (Hz)	Motorola Designator	Frequency (Hz)	Motorola Designator	Frequency (Hz)	Motorola Designator
67.0	XZ	107.2	1B	173.8	6A
69.3	WZ	110.9	2Z	179.9	6B
71.9	XA	114.8	2A	186.2	7Z
74.4	WA	118.8	2B	192.8	7A
77.0	XB	123.0	3Z	203.5	M1
79.7	WB	127.3	3A	206.5	8Z
82.5	YZ	131.8	3B	210.7	M2
85.4	YA	136.5	4Z	218.1	M3
88.5	YB	141.3	4A	225.7	M4
91.5	ZZ	146.2	4B	229.1	9Z
94.8	ZA	151.4	5Z	233.6	M5
97.4	ZB	156.7	5A	241.8	M6
100.0	1Z	162.2	5B	250.3	M7
103.5	1A	167.9	6Z	254.1	OZ

QST

Radio Tips: **Hamfest Shopping Techniques**

If you're a new ham with a tight budget, there's no better place than a hamfest flea market. You'll find excellent bargains on used radios—if you know what to look for! Here are a few hints to sharpen your shopping skills:

❑ Avoid older FM transceivers that require *crystals* to select frequencies. You'll have to buy crystals for all you favorite repeaters—at about $10 each. Pick a more recent rig with a frequency *synthesizer* instead.

❑ When considering a vintage HF transceiver, beware of radios that use a large number of vacuum tubes. Tubes are becoming scarce, and the situation will only get worse with time. If you intend to enjoy the rig for a number of years, ask yourself, "Where will I get replacement tubes?" If you can't afford solid-state rigs, look for *hybrid* transceivers. Hybrids are solid-state with the exception of the driver and final amplifiers. These rigs are reliable, easy to service and their tubes are still available.

❑ Before purchasing any transceiver, find out if the manufacturer is still in business—and if the factory still provides parts and service. Unless you have a solid electronics background and like to tinker, choose a radio that's supported by the manufacturer.

❑ Inspect the rig thoroughly. Twist every knob and press every button! If you're inspecting a VHF or UHF FM transceiver, ask for a live demonstration. This isn't an unreasonable request, especially if the rig is battery powered. Demonstrating an HF radio is more difficult unless the seller has easy access to an electrical outlet.

❑ Carry some small screwdrivers with you. During your inspection, ask the seller if you can open the enclosure and take a peek. Be suspicious if the seller refuses! As you look inside, keep your eyes peeled for burnt components, cracked or cooked circuit boards and melted wires.

❑ Some transceivers require separate power supplies. Ask the seller if the power supply is included. If not, you may have to provide your own.

❑ Ask the seller if the operating manual is included.

The more complex the radio, the more valuable it is to have the operating manual. If you're lucky, the seller may even have the *service manual*. Paying a little extra to get the service manual is well worth it in the long run. You may be able to order operating and service manuals from the manufacturer or other sources.

❑ Buy or borrow a copy of the ARRL's *Radio Buyer's Sourcebook*, a compilation of *QST* product reviews. It's the ideal reference for the used-equipment buyer. Read the book *before* you go to the hamfest. Pick out several rigs that seem right for you and look for them as you walk the aisles.

❑ All used-equipment prices are negotiable. Just because the seller placed a price tag on the radio, it doesn't mean he's unwilling to negotiate. Offer something less than the posted price and see if he accepts. If he says "no," you have three choices: Ask for a smaller discount, pay his price or walk away. Walking away is often an effective strategy. If the seller's bottom-dollar price is too high for the market, he'll have a difficult time selling the radio. Come back in an hour or two and see if he's more flexible. If he really wants to sell the rig, he'll drop his price as the day goes on.

❑ Arrive early. You want to be in the flea market area as soon as the doors open for buyers. The best rigs and the hottest bargains are often snapped up in the first hour.

❑ Be prepared to pay in cash. Many sellers are reluctant to accept checks from someone they don't know.

❑ And remember the ancient rule of the marketplace: *caveat emptor*—let the buyer beware. If you experience problems with the radio after you get it home, it's *your* responsibility. The seller isn't obligated to assist you or to refund your money.—*WB8IMY*

Nobody Talks to Me!

By Steve Ford, WB8IMY
Assistant Technical Editor

NEW HAM COMPANION

All revved up and no place to go. You know the feeling…and so do I. You just unpacked your first 2-meter FM transceiver and you're *dying* to use it. You punch in the frequency of the local repeater and listen. Silence. This is the moment of truth. You key the microphone and, in your most confident voice, announce, "WB8IMY listening."

The repeater transmits for a few seconds, then stops. Surely someone is reaching for their microphone. They'll call you in just a few seconds…won't they? The seconds stretch into minutes. "WB8IMY listening," you announce again, this time with added urgency.

Still nothing.

Again the lonely minutes pass. Maybe you just picked a bad time. You'll try again in an hour or so. As you reach for the **POWER** switch, the repeater suddenly comes to life.

"WB8ISZ this is WB8SVN. You around, Dave?"

"WB8SVN from WB8ISZ. I'm here. Did you just get off work?"

Now you feel a new emotion—anger! It's a safe bet that one of these two guys were listening before. Why didn't they answer you? Is it because you're a new ham?

The Shy Communicators

Hams pride themselves on their ability to communicate, yet there is an odd contradiction: Many hams are painfully shy! If you don't believe this, go to any hamfest. Chances are, you'll see hams whose call signs you recognize—hams who are constantly chattering on the local repeaters. So why are these same hams wandering around so quietly? When you approach them, why do they seem so ill at ease and reluctant to talk?

The answer lies in the nature of Amateur Radio itself. With the exception of visual modes such as ATV, no one can see you when you're on the air. You could be holding a conversation with someone while wearing little more than your underwear. They'd never know! In other words, ham radio allows us to hold the world at arm's length while still maintaining contact. It can act as a filter and a shield for those who are uncomfortable with close, personal communications.

Breaking through the shyness barrier to communicate with a stranger is difficult. Think back to your school days. When the teacher asked for student volunteers for a project, why did you hesitate? Perhaps you wanted to see if anyone else was willing to join you. No one wants to be the first to raise their hand!

A similar situation occurs on repeaters. When you announced that you were listening, a dozen people may have heard you. No one recognized your call sign, though. You're a stranger, an unknown. It's as though the teacher just got on the repeater and asked for volunteers to speak to you. Who will be the first to step forward?

For many hams, the familiar line of reasoning is, "Hmmm…I don't know this guy. What would I say to him? Nah…I'll wait. I'm sure someone else will give him a call." The problem is, when all the hams on the repeater feel this way, no one replies!

And so it goes on repeaters throughout the country. The problem isn't you *per se*, it's the fact that you're a stranger. So how do you make the transition from stranger to friend?

Breaking the Ice

If you keep announcing that you're "listening," someone is bound to come back to you eventually. This could take a long time—especially if you're trying to start a conversation during less popular hours. To really break the ice and shed your "stranger" label, you need to assert yourself on the air. That is, you need to become part of an existing conversation.

Listen to the repeater during the early morning and late afternoon. That's when it's likely to be used the most. As you hear stations talking to each other, listen for an opportunity to contribute something—even if it's just a question. Let's say that you find two hams discussing computers…

"KR1S from WR1B. Well, I'm definitely going to pick up some extra memory at the show tomorrow. I figure I need at least two megabytes."

"I don't know, Larry. I think four megabytes would be a better choice for the kind of software you're running."

Even if you don't own a computer, I bet you can think of a question that will give you an excuse to join the conversation. In the pauses between their transmissions, announce your call sign.

"WB8IMY"

"Well, there's a new voice. Ah…WB8IMY…I think it was…this is KR1S. How can I help you?"

"Hello. My name is Steve and I live in Wallingford. I'm thinking about buying a computer for my Amateur Radio station, but I'm a little confused. You guys seem knowledgeable. Can you give me a recommendation?"

Perfect! Stroking a person's ego is the best way to get them talking. With luck, these fellows will be more than happy to show off their expertise. Just keep the questions and comments coming.

> **You just bought your first 2-meter FM transceiver, but you don't seem to be using it very much. What's wrong?**

If you engage in enough of these conversations on the same repeater, you'll gradually melt through the shyness barrier. In time, your call sign will be as familiar as any other. When you say, "WB8IMY listening," you'll have a much better chance of getting a response. After all, they'll *know* you.

Getting Involved

Another way to establish yourself is to become involved in club activities. Look for a local club that's active in public-service events. Attend the meetings regularly and be prepared to volunteer whenever they ask for help.

Don't worry about your lack of experience in public-service operating. Believe me, it isn't that difficult. You'll be told exactly what to do and, in most cases, an experienced ham will be nearby.

My first public-service activity was a canoe race in my home town of Dayton, Ohio. I was the new face in the club and I was new to ham radio. When they asked for volunteers, it took a great deal of courage to raise my hand. Boy, am I glad I did!

The race organizers needed "checkers" at various points along the river. It was our task to make sure that each canoe passed our checkpoint safely. I was stationed with my FM transceiver at an isolated rural bridge over the Miami river. As each canoe passed beneath me, I checked it off my list and relayed the information to the net-control station. The sun was shining, a gentle breeze was blowing through the trees and I felt terrific! Here I was, an Amateur Radio operator, doing an important job with my fellow team members.

After the race, we all met at a local pizza restaurant and swapped stories. Someone asked if I wanted to be part of the communications team for the March of Dimes walk-a-thon the following weekend. Why not? After participating in several public-service events, everyone knew me by name and call. There was never a shortage of someone to talk to on the repeater.

Some Tips to Try

❑ Try asking for a signal report rather than simply stating that you're "listening." A report request gives an otherwise shy ham an extra incentive to call you.

❑ Join a club that's active in public-service activities. Volunteer for as many events as possible.

❑ Active contest clubs are also good prospects. Offer your time to assist in several major contests at the club station.

Whatever you do, don't let social fears keep you from enjoying Amateur Radio to its fullest. If the locals are too shy to talk to you, reach out and contact them. You'll both benefit from the experience!

DXing with 2-Meter Packet Mail

By Presley Smith, N5VGC
5727 Bent Creek Tr
Dallas, TX 75252-2620

Suddenly, you find yourself with a new license that lets you explore the world above 30 MHz and you say to yourself, "Is there any way I can enjoy some international (DX) contacts up here?" On the VHF and UHF bands, satellites are your best bet for live, *real-time* DXing. But is there an alternative?

Certainly! If you don't mind waiting several days or weeks for a reply from another station, why not try DXing via packet mail? There are hams all over the world waiting to exchange mail with you. Imagine checking into your local packet bulletin board (PBBS) and finding a dozen messages from hams in the UK, Italy, Germany, Japan, Argentina or wherever! All it takes is a basic packet radio station and a little patience.

Getting on the Air

Let's talk about packet radio equipment (see Fig 1). In many cases, you can get started with an old data terminal that you can find for sale at a larger hamfest flea market. Despite its appearance, a terminal is *not* a computer. It's simply a device that allows you to communicate with a computer—whether that computer is a big mainframe system or a tiny microprocessor.

Terminals are popular with some hams because they're inexpensive on the used market. On the other hand, owning a computer has many advantages. With a computer you can use sophisticated software that will make your packet operating more enjoyable. Even a used computer will do the job. If you shop carefully, you can find one for $200 or less—sometimes much less!

The heart of your packet station is the Terminal Node Controller, or *TNC*. The TNC takes data from your computer or terminal and assembles it into packets for transmission over the airwaves. It also accepts signals from your radio and converts them back into information you can read on your screen. There are many types of TNCs available—too many to discuss here. *QST* reviewed several popular models in the December 1993 issue (*QST Compares: Packet TNCs*, page 80).

The radio is the easiest part of your station. Just about any 2-meter FM transceiver will work for 1200 bit/s packet. This includes popular hand-held transceivers. Your TNC connects to the microphone jack and the receive-audio output (external speaker) jack. Your TNC manual will offer advice on how to wire it to your radio and your computer. For additional information on setting up a packet station—and packet operating in general—pick up a copy of the ARRL's *Your Packet Companion*. (Contact your dealer or see the Publications Catalog in this issue.)

I started with a Kantronics KPC-3 TNC, an ICOM IC-2AT hand-held transceiver, and an old terminal that I got for $25 at a sidewalk sale. I ran the radio on a power supply that I paid about $25 for, and I splurged and got a ¼-wavelength ground-plane antenna for $17.50 and mounted it on the roof. I still use this system, but I've made a few upgrades since then.

What's Your Address?

When you get your packet system assembled and ready to operate, you first must select a packet bulletin board system as your *home* PBBS. Ask other packeteers in your area for the call signs and frequencies used by local PBBSs or go exploring with your TNC some evening. A PBBS is a kind of clearinghouse for the bulletins and mail that flows through the global packet network. They're easy to spot by watching for transmissions that contain lists of call signs and "subject" lines.

Choose a PBBS that you can reach without much difficulty. When you check in for the first time, you'll probably need to register as a new user. This usually involves answering a few questions, such as your name, station location and so on. When you're registered with a PBBS, it becomes your home system.

To understand how you go about sending packet mail, you need to know how a *hierarchical* address is created. When you combine your call sign with the call sign of your home PBBS, you produce an address that's unique in the world. If I sign on to the N5AUX PBBS here in Dallas and register with my call sign, N5VGC, N5AUX becomes my home PBBS. Now my hierarchical address is:

N5VGC @ N5AUX.#DFW.TX.USA.NA

Start reading from left to right. You see my call sign followed by an @ (at) sign, followed by the call sign of my home PBBS. There's an optional city/area designator (preceded by a #), the state abbreviation and then the country and area of the world.

The packet addresses of DX stations use the same scheme. Here's an example for Andy, GØPQY, in England. In the UK, they use #nn, where nn is the area of the country where the PBBS is located.

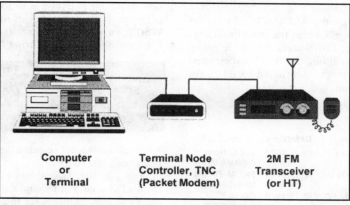

Fig 1—The components of a basic packet station.

Computer or Terminal

Terminal Node Controller, TNC (Packet Modem)

2M FM Transceiver (or HT)

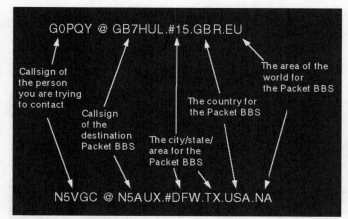

Just as my address is unique, Andy has a unique address, too. I can address a packet message to Andy, send it, and if his address is correct, he should receive it.

Searching for DX Addresses

Check into your PBBS and send the following command:

L> CQ

This tells the PBBS to send you a list of every message on the system that has "CQ" in the "TO:" field. Packet mail DXers often address their messages to "CQ" in the hope of attracting the attention of others. Here's a typical PBBS response:

Message Choice - [*]

Msg #	TSL	Size	To	@ BBS	From	Date/Time	Subject
29102	B$	429	CQ	@WW	VK3USB	0525/1334	CQ.CQ From Australia!
28973	B$	987	CQ	@WW	F6GPM	0523/2011	CQ FROM FRANCE !
28842	B$	895	CQ	@WW	4Z9CHB	0520/1925	* CQ CQ QSL, PSE *
28684	B$	751	CQ	@WW	GU0GWJ	0522/1408	***CQ EVERYONE

In addition to CQs, some hams use the ALL@WW address for messages, although "ALL" isn't a good idea for an address; anything more descriptive helps other PBBS users determine which messages to read. Many times you'll find the "CQ" in their message titles. To see a list of messages addressed to ALL, for example, send the following command:

L> ALL

Here's what you'll probably see:

Msg#	TSL	Size	To	@ BBS	From	Date/Time	Subject
54753	B$	2691	ALL	@WW	DJ8KI	0825/1522	>>CQ from GERMANY<<
54751	B$	1113	ALL	@WW	IK1QLD	0827/2128	FROM TURIN UNIVERSITY
54750	B$	1387	ALL	@WW	EB4AFG	0825/1840	CQ CALIFORNIA
54619	B$	792	ALL	@WW	KD6TKS	0827/2004	WANTED-PACKET FRIENDS
54581	B$	2744	ALL	@WW	ON1BRS	0829/2122	CQ-WW
54568	B$	1070	ALL	@WW	G1VWB	0831/1012	CQ CQ FROM THE UK
54016	B$	1113	ALL	@WW	2E0AAB	0819/2004	CQ DE DAVE

When you find a CQ, you can read it and respond to it.

Don't Wait for a CQ

If you aren't content to wait for someone to send a CQ bulletin, you can start hunting for DX addresses on your own. When you find an address that interests you, try sending a message. You never know what will happen!

Most PBBSs have a command that allows you to see the routing information contained within a particular message or bulletin. On some systems the command is **RH**. On others it might be **V**. Check with your PBBS SysOp if you're unsure. By using this command to read a message, you'll see a display of all the PBBSs that relayed the message. If you were hunting for a contact in a particular country and couldn't find a CQ or other message with an address, you can always try sending a message to the PBBS SysOp listed in the routing information.

```
From   : SV8RV

R:911116/0757Z @:SV1IW.ATH.GRC.EU #:36609 [Euro<>Asia Link - FBB5.13]  Greece
R:911115/1853z @:PA0SCH.NLD.EU Europe Asia Africa Link #:51261
R:911115/1746z @:PI8EAE.PA3EAE.NLD.EU Naaldwijk Westland #36347          Holland
R:911027/2123Z @PI8HWB.NLD.EU #54563 [Breda-FBB5.12b-hf/vhf/uhf/shf]
R:911027/2016Z @ON6AR.#AN.BEL.EU #22239 [<>PWGNET Antwerpen - FBB5.12]
R:911027/1923Z @ON4AWP.#OVN.BEL.EU #13680 [<>PWGNET Gent - FBB5.12]      Belgium
R:911027/1920Z @:ON1CED.#WVO.BEL.EU #25486 [<>PWGNET Zwevezele - FBB5.13]
R:911027/1904Z @:ON1BPW.#WWV.BEL.EU #:23436 [<>PWGNET Poperinge - FBB5.13]
R:911020/1325Z @:FD1NWB.FNPP.FRA.EU #:50831 [Wambrechies - FBB5.13]      France
R:911020/1104z 24682 @GB7ZAA.#34.GBR.EU [Canterbury,] NNA V1.11
R:911020/0958z 5095 @:GB7SEK.#34.GBR.EU [Ashford, Kent JO01JC]           England
R:911018/1643z 64912 @GB7HSN.#32.GBR.EU [Mottingham,London. NNA V1.11]
R:911018/1630z @:WA2NDV.NY.USA.NA [ New York City ] #:11122
R:911018/1117z 30496 @W2JUP.NY.USA.NA [Farmingville] Z:11738            USA
R:911018/0505z @:W5TOO.#DFW.TX.USA.NA Burleson #:60259
R:911017/2221z @:N5LDD.#DFW.TX.USA.NA Dallas 75088 #:28120 O:N5VGC $:28120_N5L
```

For example, if you wanted to make a contact in Belgium, you could send a message to the SysOp addressed as

ON1CED @ ON1CED.#WVO.BEL.EU

Another method of finding an address is by using a *White Pages* server—if one exists on your PBBS. You use the server by making a specific request. For example, to find Israeli addresses on W5IFP, I use the **IH** command (see below). In the example shown, I'm looking for the text string "ISR."

```
N5VGC de W5IFP: at 1159z 920715: B,C,D,H,?,I,J,K,L,M,N,R,S,T,U,V,W >
IH ISR
On 920429 4X1DA @ 4Z4SV.ISR.EU zip ? ? ?
On 900104 4Z4SV @ 4Z4SV.ISR.EU zip ? ? Shoresh , Israel
On 920213 4X1RU @ 4X1RU.ISR.MDLE zip ? ?
5070 calls, 3 deleted, 3 found
```

In this instance, I selected the address shown for 4X1RU. Now I can send him mail.

You can find DX addresses by reading bulletins that come from a DX area. For example, here's a bulletin from France with the Keplerian elements for the Russian *Mir* space station. It includes the sender's packet address:

```
From    : FB1RCI @ FF6KED.FPCA.FRA.EU
To      : KEPLER @ AMSAT
Date    : 920701/1558
Msgid   : B+ 4872@FF6KED, 4618@N5LDD $4872_FF6KED
Subject : MIR 2Line day=183
Path    : XE2XPK!KC9PX!XE1OGH!XE1GGO!W3IWI!WB3FFV!KB2EAR
          !WA2AAR!WA2JVM!F6CDD!FF6KIF!TK0KP!F2XC!FF6KED

MIR
1 16609U 86 17  A 92182.83839957  .00008766 00000-0 12975-3 0  3963
2 16609 51.5960 178.4184 0016708 228.8671 131.0956 15.56007606364407
----- End of message 4618 from FB1RCI @ FF6KED.FPCA.FRA.EU -----
```

Finally, there is the *World Wide Packet Pals Directory* compiled by Ray Harkins, KB6LQV. This directory is sent over the packet network in the form of several bulletin messages:

WORLD WIDE PACKET PALS DIRECTORY
BY RAY HARKINS KB6LQV
kb6lqv @ n6zgy.#nocal.ca.usa.na
PART 5 EUROPE
NAME / QTH / CALL SIGN AND HOME BBS
AGE, HOBBIES, REMARKS
PHILIP VERCRUYSSE / BRUGES / ON1CED @ ON1CED.#WVO.BEL.EU
29 PACKET RADIO

PAOLO / BARI / IW7BNL @ IK7MXD.#BA.ITA.EU
25 2-23-67,TRAVILLING,RADIO,COMPUTERS,MEETING PEOPLE
***** ITA MANAGER *****

PANTELIS / NICOSIA / 5B4ACP @ 5B4TX.CYP.MDLE
RADIO,BASKETBALL,LOOKING FOR GREEK-AMERICAN HAMS

GERD MELCHIOR / MUNICH / DL3MFH @ DK0MUN.DEU.EU
GERMAN,ENGLISH,FRENCH,RUNNING,APLINK MAIL
***** DEU MANAGER *****

JOHN / WEST HANNINGFIELD / G6JPG @ GB7NNA.#31.GBR.EU
32 ELECTRONICS,COMPUTERS,AIDING THE BLIND WITH THESE.
ENGLISH,GERMAN,FRENCH

ANDREW LANGFORD / SCUNTHORPE G0PQY @ GB7WRG.WRG.GBR.EU
27 RADIO, PACKET,HF, 70CM, HOSPITAL RADIO

ROY HULL / ENGLAND / G4CMT @ GB7GBY.#15.GBR.EU
RETIRED PHOTOGRAPHY, SCOUTING, PARACHUTING,
SCOUTING FOR 55 YRS.

Answering a CQ

Let's assume that you've found a CQ bulletin. How do you respond? The first step is to read the message and write down the DX packeteer's address. For example:

```
From       : 4Z9CHB
To         : CQ   @WW
Type/status : B$
Date/time  : 20-May 19:25
Bid        : 9695_4X4HF
Message #  : 28842
Title      : *** CQ CQ QSL, PSE ***
Path       : !W5IFP!4X4HF!
```

Hi !

My name is Ohad and my QTH is Haifa in the northern part of Israel. My QTH locator is KM72MT.
I collect QSL cards from all over the world.
I would like to have yours.
If you don't have one, a postcard with a view of your QTH will be great.
You can send it via the bureau or directly.
My address: Ohad Miller, 4Z9CHB
             12 Ha'ari St
             Haifa 33190
             Israel
73 and shalom de Ohad, 4Z9CHB @ 4X4HF.ISR.MDLE
========== End of message #28842 ==========

If you look carefully, you'll see Ohad's address in the second-to-last line:

4Z9CHB @ 4X4HF.ISR.MDLE

To reply, send the **SP** (send personal) command (or **SR** on some PBBSs). The PBBS will ask you for the subject and text. Enter a brief subject line and then proceed with your message (keep it short). End it with Ctrl-Z or /EX on a line by itself.

SP 4Z9CHB @ 4X4HF.ISR.MDLE
Response to your CQ
Hello, Ohad. This is Presley, N5VGC, from Dallas, Texas, responding to your CQ message. Dallas is a big city in Texas and there are lots of hams in Dallas on packet. I'd like to know more about your family in Israel and will tell you more about my family in Dallas. I'd also be interested in exchanging QSL cards with you. I will look forward to a message from you.
73, Presley, N5VGC @ N5VGC.#DFW.TX.USA.NA
/EX

Always check and recheck the **SP** line. If the address is wrong, your chances of a successful delivery are greatly reduced (just as if your antenna didn't work!). Don't forget to include your return address *in the body of the packet message*. Sometimes addresses on the messages are changed for various reasons by PBBS systems as messages are forwarded to their destinations.

The time it will take for this message to arrive in Israel depends on a number of factors. Packet messages are routed in several ways. Some are relayed to forwarding stations via VHF/UHF packet radio until they eventually get to an HF station that forwards the message to another HF station in a distant place. These HF stations may be running packet or they may forward mail using other digital modes, such as AMTOR, PacTOR or CLOVER. Many international packet messages are also handled by Amateur Radio satellites.

Calling CQ

A word of advice: When you send your CQ bulletin, you must be willing to answer all the responses you get. If you put out a CQ and don't answer all responses, you create a bad impression among your fellow hams. Word travels quickly on the network, so you don't want to cultivate a reputation as a person who sends bulletins and never responds to replies!

To send a CQ, you must send a bulletin targeted to a specific area or for worldwide (WW) distribution. Connect to your PBBS and use the **SB** (Send Bulletin) command. Here are some examples:

SB CQ @ WW
SB CQ @ TEXAS

SB CQ @ GB7ZAA.#34.GBR.EU

When the PBBS asks for a subject, use CQ as part of the title:

CQ from Dallas, Texas

In the body of your message, tell the reader a bit about yourself and include your packet address at the end. Remember that English may not be the first language of many who will read your message, so keep your sentences short and simple.

Just as with live CQs, you may not get the responses you anticipate. And responses may be slower than you expect them to be. Be patient; a CQ may take several weeks to make it around the world. Responses may take several days or more to come back to you. It helps if you make your message interesting. The more interesting you seem to be, the more replies you'll receive.

Happiness is a Full Mailbox!

It won't be long before you have a mailbox full of messages from many places. When you check into your home PBBS, you'll be greeted with something like this:

You have mail waiting:

Msg.#.TS...Size..To..............From.........Date/Time.Subject.................1100z
28329 PN 1771 N5VGC   G7LHQ   0720/0513 Hi Presley
28328 PN 1242 N5VGC   DG2MDJ 0720/0511 Augsbrg again via apcket
28327 PN 3732 N5VGC   G0PQY   0720/0511 HELLO TEXAS
28137 PN 1271 N5VGC   OE1EJA 0717/0604 Vienna here.....
28034 PN 1903 N5VGC   G0PBZ   0716/1516 PART 2!
28033 PN 1544 N5VGC   G0PBZ   0716/1515 GREETINGS FROM BEDFORD!
28032 PN 2089 N5VGC   G0PQY   0716/1514 HELLO PRESLEY
FTWBBS>

There are at least 100 packet-active countries in the world. I've made contact with about 70 of them using the information contained in this article. It's likely that you'll find some frustrations similar to sending a CQ on HF. (In other words, sometimes you get an answer and sometimes you don't!) Even so, packet mail DXing works more often than it doesn't. It's a great way to strike up friendships through Amateur Radio. Enjoy!

Presley Smith, N5VGC, earned a Technician-class license on August 6, 1991. He writes a monthly packet radio column for the Plano Amateur Radio Klub (PARK) newsletter. He owns and maintains the packet hub BBS for Dallas, Texas. He's manager of the Development Software Product department at CONVEX Computer Corp in Richardson, Texas. QST

Radio Tips: An Abbreviated Packet-Speak Glossary

alias: An alternative method of addressing a packet station. For example, the call sign of my personal packet mailbox is WB8IMY-4, but its alias could be STEVEBOX or whatever. Either the call sign or the alias can be used to establish a connection.

download: The act of requesting and receiving information (files or messages) from another packet station.

gateway: A node or packet BBS function that allows packet users on different frequencies to communicate with each other. Gateways also make it possible for some packet users to access nonamateur networks, such as Internet.

node: A junction point in a packet radio network where data is relayed to other stations. A node can support more than one user at a time and can operate on several different frequencies simultaneously.

SSID: An abbreviation for Secondary Station Identifier. It's a number used to differentiate between two or more station functions operating under the same call sign. For example, WB8IMY-2 may be a node while WB8IMY-4 is a mailbox.

terminal node controller (TNC): A device that assembles packets for transmission and decodes received packets for display on a computer or data terminal. The TNC is the nerve center of any packet station.

upload: The act of sending information (files or messages) to another packet station.

For more information on packet operating—including an expanded glossary—see *Your Packet Companion*, available from your dealer or directly from the ARRL—*WB8IMY*

Keeping Up With Hand-Helds

If your hand-held has become more than you can handle, try these clever ideas.

By Joe Simpson, KD4LLV
5910 Crabapple Rd
Durham, NC 27712
Photos by the author

Figure 1—With a key-keeper like this one attached to your belt, it's easy to keep your H-T close at hand. A quick press of the thumb unlocks the ring from the clip when you need to use your radio.

With the tremendous number of hams—particularly new hams—using VHF and UHF, the available range of hand-held transceivers (H-Ts) and accessories has exploded. There's so much stuff on the market and in our shacks that some of us have a hard time dealing with all the pieces. Here are a couple of ideas I use for keeping up with my H-T and its accessories:

Idea Number 1

The first is a cheap way to keep me from losing my H-T when carrying it clipped on my belt. This idea came to me after we had to interrupt a search-and-rescue training exercise because my H-T got knocked off my belt in unfamiliar woods—in the middle of a moonless night! Fortunately for me, one of my team members spotted it on the ground (about a hundred feet from where I was when I noticed it was gone!) after a 10-minute search.

Soon after, I purchased a "key-keeper" at a truck stop for only $4. Hardware stores have them, too. (It's one of those little metal security clips that slips over your belt.) It came with a round split ring intended for keys. I attached this to my H-T handstrap (see Figure 1). When I'm going to have my H-T on my belt for an extended period of time, or in an area where I'm concerned that it might get bumped off or stolen, I slip the clip onto my belt and slide it next to where I hang the radio. If I snap the ring onto the key-keeper when I hang the H-T on my belt, the radio is securely attached—even if it gets bumped or grabbed. The ring unclips easily with one hand. After using it for a short while, securing and freeing the radio becomes second nature. With my H-T securely attached, I'm better able to enjoy what I'm doing since I spend less time worrying about keeping track of my radio.

Idea Number 2

When I bought my first new hand-held, I went hamfest-crazy and bought a full line of accessories: spare battery pack, ear-phone, speaker/mike, an ANLI AL-800 telescoping antenna (which I can't say enough good things about; it makes a rubber duckie seem like a dummy load by comparison!), and a BNC-to-UHF adapter so I could use the radio in the car with a mag-mount antenna.

For a while I carried all this stuff around in various paper and plastic bags. This meant that everything was rattling around loose and scratching everything else—and occasionally falling out of the bag and rolling under the seat. I knew there had to be a better way.

While I was attending a gun show, I realized that indeed there was a better way. I purchased a 12×8.5×2.5-inch foam-lined plastic pistol case. (I've seen them priced anywhere from $4 to $12 at various gun shows and sporting-goods stores.)

It took a few minutes to decide how I would arrange all the items in the case, a couple more moments to mark the outlines of my gear on the foam with ink, and about 20 minutes to *carefully* cut away the marked foam with a single-edged razor blade. The result was a custom-fit slot for each item in the bottom piece of foam. I also cut a small section from the top piece of foam above the radio slot to prevent pressure on the H-T keypad when the case was closed.

As you can see in Figure 2, the radio and spare battery troughs were cut near the hinges of the case. When the case is loaded, closed, and standing up, it has a low center of gravity and doesn't fall over easily. The foam lifts out, so behind the foam in the top half of the case I keep papers such as repeater linking codes, a list of the contents of my H-Ts memories, and a card with my name, address, and phone number on it—and the notation "Reward for Return." A 35-mm film canister holds a coiled-up earphone and a couple of allergy pills. (I never know when I'm going to need those!)

When fully loaded, the case holds an H-T, a spare battery pack, a speaker/mike, three antennas, a coax adapter, various papers, and an earphone. Slight changes in the layout could leave room for a few small tools, too. The case fits neatly under the car seat when I want the gear out of sight. Carrying my H-T and accessories is now more of a pleasure than a chore!

Figure 2—A pistol case like this is ideal for carrying your H-T and its accessories. You can cut out the foam to fit the shape of each item. QST~

Beyond FM

By Jim Kearman, KR1S and **Rus Healy, NJ2L**
Assistant Technical Editor   Senior Assistant Technical Editor

NEW HAM HORIZONS

 FM operating on the VHF bands is fun, but there's even more excitement to be found on SSB and CW. Yes, SSB and CW operation is alive and well on VHF. In addition, you may be surprised to know that SSB and CW equipment usually includes FM—and isn't much more expensive than FM-only gear.

But why bother with SSB and CW? Why not use only FM? For one thing, SSB and CW are more efficient than FM. In other words, the same power level can carry your signal farther on SSB and CW than on FM.

You don't need repeaters to communicate over longer distances with SSB and CW. Except for the amateur satellites, all VHF SSB and CW operation is direct from station to station. FM operators refer to working without repeaters as *operating simplex*. SSB and CW operators wouldn't have it any other way! SSB and CW signals are detectable at levels where FM signals can't even be heard. For this reason, SSB and CW are called *weak-signal* modes. The signals aren't necessarily weak, but you can often copy them even when they are.

The VHF and UHF bands are huge. Fortunately, each band has nationally standardized *calling frequencies*. They save you time when looking for activity or favorable propagation (see Table 1).

The key to enjoyable use of this resource is to know how everyone else is using it, and to follow their lead. Essentially, this means to listen first. Pay attention to the segments of the band already in use, and follow the operating practices the experienced operators are using.

How Are the Bands Organized?

Weak-signal operating is more enjoyable when you know how the bands are organized. By knowing the best frequencies and times, you'll make plenty of contacts.

In most parts of the country, everyone uses the calling frequencies to establish contact. Then the two stations move off the

Sample the excitement of VHF SSB and CW!

calling frequency as quickly as possible to chat. This way, everyone can share the calling frequency without having to listen to each other's conversations. You can easily tell if the band is open by monitoring the call signs of the stations making contact on the calling frequency.

Weak-signal activity on VHF/UHF is concentrated on the two lower VHF bands, 6 and 2 meters (50 and 144 MHz). The number of active stations on these bands is about the same. Above the 2-meter band, there are considerably more active stations on the 70-cm (420 MHz) band than any other.

On 6 meters, a *DX window* has been established to reduce interference to DX stations. Yes, *DX* stations! During years of high solar activity, 6-meter openings to the other side of the world are possible! This window, which extends from 50.100-50.125 MHz, is intended for DX QSOs only. The DX calling frequency is 50.110 MHz. US and Canadian 6-meter operators should call above 50.125 MHz for non-DX work. When contact is established, move off the calling frequency as quickly as possible.

Activity Nights

Although you can scare up a QSO on 50 or 144 MHz almost any evening (especially during the summer), in some areas of the country there isn't always enough activity to make it easy to find someone. Therefore, informal *activity nights* have been established. There's a lot of variation in activity nights from place to place. Check with an active VHFer near you to find out about local activity nights.

Common Activity Nights

Band (MHz)	Day	Local Time
50	Sunday	6 PM
144	Monday	7 PM
222	Tuesday	8 PM
432	Wednesday	9 PM
902	Friday	9 PM
1296 and up	Thursday	10 PM

Contacts *can* be made on non-activity nights as well, especially if the band is open,

but it may take longer to get someone's attention.

Local VHF/UHF nets often meet during activity nights. Two national organizations, SMIRK (Six Meter International Radio Klub) and SWOT (Sidewinders on Two), run nets in many parts of the country. These nets provide a meeting place for active users of the 50- and 144-MHz bands. For information on the meeting times and frequencies of the nets run by SMIRK or SWOT, ask other occupants of the bands in your area or see *Your VHF Companion* for more information.

Propagation

If you're new to the world above 50 MHz, you might wonder what sort of range is considered "normal." To a large extent, your range on VHF is determined by your location and the quality of your station.

For the sake of discussion, consider a more-or-less "typical" station. On 2-meter SSB, a typical rig would be a low-power rig, perhaps a multimode transceiver (SSB/CW/FM), followed by a 100-watt amplifier. The antenna of our typical station might be a 15-element Yagi up about 50 feet, fed with low-loss coax.

Using SSB or CW, how much territory could this station cover on an average evening? Location plays a big role, but it's probably safe to say you could talk to similarly equipped stations about 200 miles away almost all of the time. Naturally, higher-powered stations with high antennas and low-noise receivers have a greater range, up to a practical maximum of about 350-400 miles in the Midwest (less in the hilly West and East).

On 222 MHz, a similar station might expect to cover about the same distance, and somewhat less (perhaps 150 miles) on 432 MHz. This assumes normal propagation conditions and a reasonably unobstructed horizon. This range is a lot greater than you would get for noise-free communication on FM, and it represents the sort of capability the typical station should seek. Increase the height of the antenna to 80 feet and the range might extend to 250 miles, and probably more, depending on your location. That's not bad for reliable communication! Occasionally, the VHF/UHF bands offer special propagation that allows contacts out to 1000 miles or more! We'll cover openings in a future article.

Transceivers

Aside from antennas, the one necessity

Table 1
North American CW/SSB Calling Frequencies

Band (MHz)	Frequency
50	50.110 DX (SSB)
	50.125, 50.200 US, local (SSB)
144	144.100, 144.110 CW
	144.200 SSB
222	222.100 CW/SSB
420	432.100 CW/SSB

of radio communication is a radio! In general, transceivers are the easiest way to get on VHF. *Transverters*— receive and transmit converters designed to go with an HF rig—run second in ease of use, but often first in performance.

Multimode VHF transceivers can be grouped into two distinct classes: home station and mobile/portable. A look at *The ARRL Radio Buyer's Sourcebook* will help you decide what's right for you. It's also a good idea to review recent *QST* product reviews when you're selecting equipment.

Many people just getting into VHF settle on multimode, single-band mobile or portable transceivers (Figs 1 and 2). These rigs are often less expensive, less complex and more flexible (in terms of power sources and size) than home-station rigs. Some home-station rigs include accessories not usually found in portable and mobile rigs.

Although most VHF multimode transceivers are single-band radios, multiband transceivers have been growing in popularity (Figs 3 and 4). Usually aimed at the amateur satellite market, these rigs are also popular among terrestrial operators because of their flexibility. They usually allow you to receive on one band while transmitting on another. These rigs are considerably more expensive than their single-band counterparts, but less expensive than buying separate radios for each band they cover.

Transverters

An alternative to buying one or more VHF transceivers is to buy or build a transverter to go along with your HF rig. Although this equipment sometimes requires some effort to interface with your HF rig (except for those made to go with your particular transceiver), the performance and cost savings can be substantial.

With modern components, you might be surprised at how few parts and how little cost and expertise it takes to get your own gear on the air. A *QST* article by Ed Krome, KA9LNV ("A High-Performance, Easy-to-Build 432-MHz Transverter," *QST*, August and September 1991), is a good example.

Steer clear of anything made before 1980 or so, because equipment performance and reliability have come a long way since then. Older gear may not meet your needs for very long.

Antennas

Almost all SSB and CW activity on the VHF bands is done with horizontally polarized, directional antennas. The Yagi is the most common directive antenna. Yagi antennas are commercially available with three to at least 33 elements. An example of

Fig 1 (top left)—The Kenwood TR-751A is an "all-mode" 2-meter transceiver. In addition to FM (or packet radio), it allows operation on CW, SSB and AM. This 25-watt-output transceiver is no larger than most FM-only transceivers in its power class. The PS-30 13.6-volt power supply on which the transceiver is sitting is suitable for home-station use.

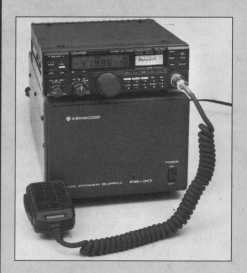

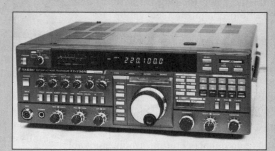

Fig 2 (bottom left)—ICOM's IC-275A transceiver is similar to the Kenwood TR-751A shown in Fig 1. One difference is a built-in power supply for home-station use. The IC-275A can also be used with an external 13.6-V dc supply for mobile or portable operation.

Fig 3 (top right)—Yaesu's FT-736R multimode transceiver allows FM/packet, SSB, CW and AM operation from 144-148 MHz and 430-450 MHz. You can install two additional modules to cover any combination of 50-54 MHz, 222-225 MHz and 1240-1300 MHz. In addition to a built-in ac power supply, the FT-736R includes many features (such as IF shift, notch filter and speech processor) normally found only on HF transceivers. Features attractive to amateur-satellite users are also standard.

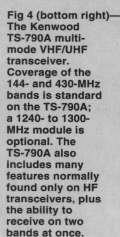

Fig 4 (bottom right)— The Kenwood TS-790A multimode VHF/UHF transceiver. Coverage of the 144- and 430-MHz bands is standard on the TS-790A; a 1240- to 1300-MHz module is optional. The TS-790A also includes many features normally found only on HF transceivers, plus the ability to receive on two bands at once.

a popular commercial Yagi is shown in Fig 5.

Two other kinds of multielement directional antennas are shown in Figs 6 and 7. One is a quad, which uses loop elements instead of wire or rod elements, and the other is a log-periodic dipole array (LPDA), usually referred to simply as a log periodic. In terms of performance on a single band, quads are basically the same as Yagis. LPDAs, on the other hand, cover very wide frequency ranges. The antenna shown covers 50 to 1300 MHz—that's six ham bands and everything in between! The penalty for this frequency coverage is significantly less gain than can be achieved with a single-band Yagi or quad. They're also considerably more complex than Yagis and quads. On the other hand, the convenience of having coverage of so many bands with only one antenna and feed line is attractive, especially for portable operation.

One other antenna that deserves mention is the quagi. A hybrid of Yagi and quad designs, the quagi uses quad-loop elements for the driven element and reflector and Yagi-type directors. Quagis are somewhat easier to build from scratch than long Yagis, yet offer good performance.

Feed Lines: The Weak Link

When you install your antennas, you'll need to connect them to your radios via feed lines. No surprise so far, right? What makes this subject worth discussing here is *loss*. Cable loss is a function of conductor losses. Physically large cables have less loss than smaller cables, because they have more conductor area. That's why you'll hear people talking about feeding VHF antennas with *Hardline* and *Heliax* (types of rigid and semirigid coax).

How does this affect you? Well, in practical terms, you shouldn't use small cables like RG-58 and RG-8X *at all* at VHF. RG-8 and RG-213 are acceptable for short runs (less than 50 feet or so at 432 MHz, less than 100 feet at 6 meters). For longer runs, consider more expensive cables like Belden 9913 or an equivalent—they don't cost much more than RG-213, and the precious decibels you'll save are well worth the extra cost.

There's no sense spending your money on quality equipment and antennas, and then wasting it all in lossy coax. It follows that you should keep all cable runs as short as possible. If you must run very long cables to your VHF antennas, consider moving up to higher-grade cables. You can find more details in *The ARRL Handbook* and *The ARRL Antenna Book*.

The Challenge and the Reward

There's no question that it's easier to get on the air with FM than SSB or CW. With FM, it may be a matter of simply buying a hand-held transceiver and talking through your local repeater. SSB and CW take a little more effort, but the reward is considerable!

As a weak-signal operator, you'll enjoy contacts over distances that FM enthusiasts

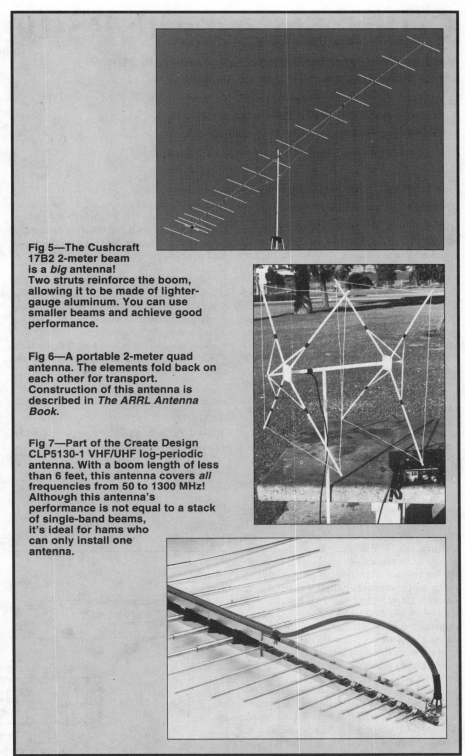

Fig 5—The Cushcraft 17B2 2-meter beam is a *big* antenna! Two struts reinforce the boom, allowing it to be made of lighter-gauge aluminum. You can use smaller beams and achieve good performance.

Fig 6—A portable 2-meter quad antenna. The elements fold back on each other for transport. Construction of this antenna is described in *The ARRL Antenna Book*.

Fig 7—Part of the Create Design CLP5130-1 VHF/UHF log-periodic antenna. With a boom length of less than 6 feet, this antenna covers *all* frequencies from 50 to 1300 MHz! Although this antenna's performance is not equal to a stack of single-band beams, it's ideal for hams who can only install one antenna.

can only achieve through complex linked-repeater systems. Best of all, you'll experience the true magic of VHF operating. As you sharpen your skills, you'll be able to predict when band openings are about to take place.

Weak-signal VHF operating will challenge you every day. DX stations sometimes appear when you least expect them—and disappear just as suddenly. Wait until the day when you turn on your equipment and hear a flood of distant CW and SSB signals. The excitement will be electrifying and you'll know in that moment what you've guessed all along: There is much more to VHF than FM!

Getting Started with RS-10

**You say you've never tried satellite operating?
Meet RS-10, a satellite anyone can use!**

By Walter Daniel, KE3HP
PO Box 1686
Bowie, MD 20717

NEW HAM COMPANION

You don't need expensive gear and large antennas to use a satellite. While they're slightly more involved than HF contacts, satellite conversations are not difficult. In fact, they're easier than you think!

Radio Sputnik 10, or RS-10, is one in a series of Amateur Radio payloads launched by Russia. RS-10, and its inactive companion, RS-11, are electronics modules attached to the Russian COSMOS 1861 navigation satellite. RS-10 is active at all times and available for you to use whenever it's in view of your home. The satellite is in a low Earth orbit at an altitude of about 1000 km. This means that it's available for only about 15 minutes as it passes near your station. Even so, you can chat with hams over a huge area during that 15-minute window (see Fig 1).

Repeaters in Space

Amateur satellites that support phone and CW conversations do so with *linear transponders*. A transponder is much like your local 2-meter repeater. It receives RF signals and retransmits them on different frequencies. While your local repeater is designed to retransmit one signal, a satellite transponder retransmits all signals in a range of frequencies called the *passband*. The RS-10 passband is 40 kHz wide. Signals from 145.860 to 145.900 MHz are retransmitted at 29.360 to 29.400 MHz. Because a satellite receiver has to be sensitive to work effectively, a satellite transponder is designed to transmit in another amateur band to avoid *desensitizing* its receiver. Think of amateur satellites with linear transponders as crossband repeaters in space.

Although RS-10 has several operating modes, the transponder usually operates in a configuration called *Mode A* by satellite users. A satellite mode simply refers to which bands contain the uplink (ground to satellite) and downlink (satellite to ground) frequencies. Mode A indicates a 2-meter uplink with a 10-meter downlink. The RS-10 Mode A transponder frequencies and band plan are shown in Table 1.[1] For example, a 145.880-MHz uplink signal will be translated to a 29.380-MHz downlink signal by the transponder if no Doppler shift is present (more about Doppler later).

With 40 kHz of passband available, many conversations can take place on the

trans-ponder at the same time. To squeeze as many signals into the passband as possible, CW and SSB are used. Note that the band plan calls for CW QSOs in the lower half and phone QSOs in the upper half of the passband.

Satellite transponder operation is *full duplex*. To operate full duplex, you tune your receiver to a different band than your transmitter. By receiving and transmitting *simultaneously*, you're able to listen to *your own signal* as it is relayed by the satellite! (This is always a big thrill for new satellite users.)

Table 1
RS-10 Transponder Frequency Plan

Uplink	Downlink	
	29.357	Beacon
145.860	29.360	Passband lower limit
	CW	◊
145.880	29.380	Passband center
	USB	◊
145.900	29.400	Passband upper limit
	29.403	Beacon

An advantage of full-duplex operation is that you can immediately hear if you have a problem, such as hum or distortion in your transmissions. When operating full duplex voice, be sure to use headphones to prevent receiver audio from getting into the transmitter microphone.

RS-10 Ground Station Equipment

To receive RS-10 signals, any multiband HF transceiver, 10-meter rig or shortwave receiver with SSB and CW will suffice. As solar activity nears minimum in the mid-1990s, the 10-meter band will be less populated. You'll find lots of used 10-meter transceivers at bargain prices now, and the bargains should be even better by 1995. A simple antenna such as a vertical or dipole for 10 meters is fine. Beam antennas are not necessary because the downlink signals are robust.

A 10-meter preamp is sometimes helpful. Some receivers may not be designed to hear relatively weak satellite signals, so a preamp gives much better performance. Losses in coaxial cable are small at 29 MHz, so the preamp can be installed in the shack for convenience. (At higher frequen-

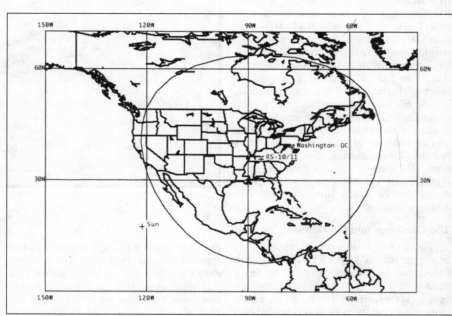

Fig 1—Typical RS-10 coverage over North America. Most of the stations within this circle will be able to talk to each other through the satellite. Imagine a repeater with this kind of coverage!

Table 2
Typical Satellite-Tracking Program Output

| | | *RS-10/11* | | | |
| | | Time EDT | Az | El | Range | Doppler |
DOW	MM/DD/YY	HH:MM:SS	Deg	Deg	km	Hz
Sun	05/09/93	14:06:40	4.5	0.0	3699	3258 Rise
Sun	05/09/93	14:14:50	73.0	26.3	1828	4 Max
Sun	05/09/93	14:22:58	140.9	0.0	3693	−3286 Set
Sun	05/09/93	15:52:11	345.6	0.0	3699	3597 Rise
Sun	05/09/93	16:00:43	270.2	44.4	1332	5 Max
Sun	05/09/93	16:09:15	194.2	0.0	3692	−3579 Set

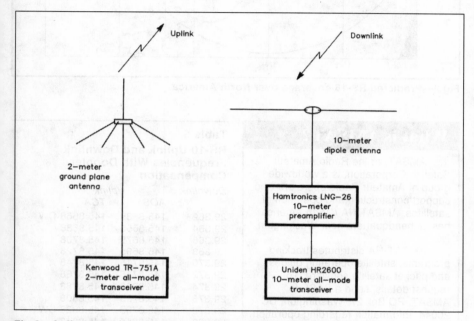

Fig 2—A diagram of the Mode A satellite station at KE3HP.

cies it's sometimes advantageous to mount the preamp at the antenna.) A preamp is a good home-brew project, so consult the *ARRL Handbook* for details.[2]

To transmit to RS-10 using Mode A, you need a 2-meter multimode radio that's capable of SSB and/or CW.[3] These rigs don't cost much more than FM-only units. If you're going to buy a 2-meter radio, why not spend a little more and get full CW/SSB/FM capability? Believe me, you'll be glad you did.

In a pinch, you can even key an FM-only rig to produce chirpy CW, but few stations will answer since the signals are difficult to decode. Another problem is that FM-only rigs usually tune in 5-kHz increments, far too coarse to compensate for Doppler shift.

The RS-10 receiver is rather sensitive, so you need only about 25 watts output for voice, or 10 watts for CW. As with the downlink, an omnidirectional antenna is best for the uplink. Verticals and ground-planes for 2 meters work well.

Fig 2 is a diagram of my Mode-A station. I use a Uniden HR-2600 10-meter rig as the receiver with a Kenwood TR-751A as the transmitter. I have a Hamtronics LNG-28 10-meter preamp in the shack. My 2-meter antenna is a home-brew ground plane made from coat hangers and an SO-239 connector! The 10-meter antenna is a home-brew wire dipole. Both of these antennas are in my attic since I live in a neighborhood with antenna restrictions. If you were to buy all these items new, the cost would be about $900, with the TR-751A making up two-thirds of the total. With some careful shopping, and with an emphasis on used equipment, you can set up your RS-10 station for much less money.

Satellite Tracking

You have to know when the satellite is in view to use it. While satellite tracking may seem difficult to newcomers, it is really straightforward and interesting. Tracking is usually done with a computer, but older graphical methods such as the OSCAR Satellite Locator are still perfectly functional.[4] RS-10 is in a near-circular orbit that passes over the polar regions of the Earth; the period is about 105 minutes. While the satellite moves through the orbit, the Earth rotates underneath it and makes the ground track appear to drift to the west. Typically, two useful RS-10 passes separated by about 105 minutes occur, then two more passes take place about 12 hours later.

Computer tracking programs require user-supplied data about satellite orbits. This data is usually referred to as *Keplerian elements*. These elements are named for Johannes Kepler, an astronomer who first described satellite orbits mathematically in the early 1600s. The elements represent a snapshot in time of the satellite position and velocity and are generated by the ground-based radars of NORAD, a joint Canadian-American monitoring effort. Once the elements are loaded into the computer, a tracking program can predict when a satellite will be in view of a particular location (see Table 2).

You might not even need a tracking program since some packet BBS operators make available a file of satellite predictions for downloading. If you don't know of a BBS in your area that carries such predictions, ask around. A local satellite user will probably step forward and generate such a file.

Doppler Shift

You are probably familiar with Doppler shift from everyday experience. The classic example is a train horn near a road crossing. At first, the train horn sounds as if it has a constant pitch, although the pitch is actually dropping slightly. As the train nears, the pitch drops noticeably. After the train passes, the pitch seems to settle at a lower value than at the beginning. Doppler shift affects the apparent frequency of the sound of the horn to those who are waiting at the intersection.

Because satellites move very fast (several kilometers per second!), Doppler shift affects even radio frequencies. For a high-elevation RS-10 pass, the total shift is almost 7 kHz, about twice the bandwidth of an SSB phone signal. For reliable communications through RS-10, users have to compensate for Doppler shift. Calculating the appropriate uplink and downlink frequencies involves using the Doppler shift in a *translation equation* that reflects the properties of the transponder.[5]

When I first began working RS-10, I found that juggling the translation equation while trying to read the Doppler shift from a computer screen was too much activity during a fast-moving pass. I also found that the RS-10 translation equation to be 4.8 kHz different from what is implied in Table 1. After much calculation and experimentation, I developed the operating aid shown in Table 3.

Two uplink frequencies are provided for a given downlink frequency. The first is AOS (Acquisition of Signal, the beginning of the pass); the second is TCA (Time of Closest Approach, or the middle of the pass). This table combines the effects of Doppler shift and the observed translation equation in one place. By using Table 3, you can avoid the hassle of calculating the proper uplink frequency for RS-10. I'll show you how in a moment.

BENEDICTINE UNIVERSITY AT MESA LIBRAR

Operating Procedure

To operate RS-10, remember the most important rule of Amateur Radio: listen first! Start with the CW beacon on 29.357 MHz (the 29.403 MHz beacon is not active continuously). Listen to the beacon to verify that the satellite is in view at the time your tracking program has predicted. Once you find the beacon, listen to some QSOs in the passband. Hearing other contacts will prepare you for your own operations.

When you are ready to operate, select a pass that will come at least 30° above the horizon. After listening for the CW beacon, wait for a couple of minutes until the satellite is at least 10° above the horizon. Select a downlink frequency and tune your receiver. Listen to the frequency and check one or two kHz on either side to make sure you won't interfere with another conversation. Because the satellite has just popped over the horizon, you need to use the AOS column of Table 3 to find the approximate uplink frequency. For example, if you want to use a downlink of 29.390 MHz for phone operation, you would select an uplink of 145.8915 MHz from the table.

To find yourself on the satellite, send a few dits (CW) or speak your call sign (USB). The table should get you within 2 kHz, so tune your uplink frequency slightly until you hear your own signals. Don't "swish" your transmitter frequency through the passband while searching for signals. Holding down the key or whistling uses much of the limited transponder power, disrupts other conversations, and inflicts severe pain upon the ears of users listening to the satellite!

Remember to keep your downlink (receive) frequency *constant* and compensate for Doppler shift by changing your uplink (transmit) frequency. As you hear your own signal drifting on the 10-meter downlink, gently adjust your 2-meter transmitter *while you're transmitting* to compensate for the drift. If you're operating SSB, for example, keep one hand on your 2-meter dial and tweak it slightly to keep your voice sounding "normal" in your headphones. Resist the temptation to compensate by simply tuning your 10-meter receiver. (You may be forced to tune your receiver, however, if the other station is not following this procedure.)

By using your uplink signal to compensate for Doppler shift, you'll avoid drifting into other conversations on the satellite. You'll find that you need to gradually increase your uplink frequency throughout a pass; the rate of increase is fast in the middle and slower at the beginning and end of a pass. You might wish to practice tracking Doppler for an entire pass until you are ready for your first QSO.

At first, call CQ and let a more experienced user find you. Say something like, "CQ RS Ten, CQ RS Ten, this is KE3HP calling CQ RS Ten and standing by." Pause for a few seconds between calls so you can

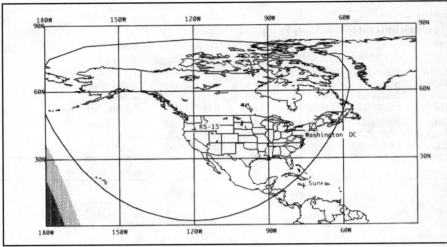

Fig 3—Predicted RS-15 coverage over North America.

What is AMSAT?

AMSAT, or the Radio Amateur Satellite Corporation, is a worldwide group of Amateur Radio operators who support construction and operation of satellites. AMSAT-NA (North America) has its headquarters near Washington, DC.

AMSAT-NA distributes tracking programs, satellite operating guides, and packet satellite software. To request details, send a SASE to AMSAT, PO Box 27, Washington, DC 20044. Information regarding operation of amateur satellites is disseminated through the AMSAT News Service bulletins that are distributed by packet radio and read over several weekly HF and VHF nets. Members of AMSAT-NA receive *The AMSAT Journal*, a bimonthly newsletter that contains detailed articles on satellites, equipment and operating procedures.

Table 3
RS-10 Uplink and Downlink Frequencies With Doppler Compensation

Downlink	Uplink	
	AOS	TCA
29.362	145.8635	145.8668 CW
29.364	145.8655	145.8688
29.366	145.8675	145.8708
29.368	145.8695	145.8728
29.370	145.8715	145.8748
29.372	145.8735	145.8768
29.374	145.8755	145.8788
29.376	145.8775	145.8808
29.378	145.8795	145.8828 CW
29.380	145.8815	145.8848 ——
29.382	145.8835	145.8868 USB
29.384	145.8855	145.8888
29.386	145.8875	145.8908
29.388	145.8895	145.8928
29.390	145.8915	145.8948
29.392	145.8935	145.8968
29.394	145.8955	145.8988
29.396	145.8975	145.9008
29.398	145.8995	145.9028 USB

hear when someone is setting up on the frequency. Keep calling CQ to give the other station a target. Once contact is established, keep each transmission short so your uplink won't drift very far while you listen. Some hams like to make quick contest-like contacts to work as many stations as possible. (I once worked stations in Kentucky, New York, Utah, Michigan and Nebraska within 10 minutes!) Others prefer to have conversations for as long as the pass permits. Perhaps my most pleasurable contact was with a station in Arizona that lasted the entire pass, during which we talked about every amateur satellite then in orbit.

If you want to start a new QSO in the middle of a pass, use an uplink frequency from the TCA column of Table 3. At TCA, the Doppler shift is zero, but is changing at the fastest rate. For example, if your chosen downlink is 29.390 MHz, the corresponding uplink is 145.8948 MHz.

You may be enjoying a QSO when the signal fades unexpectedly. This fading is usually due to cross-polarization. The antennas on RS-10 are linearly polarized and most Mode A ground station antennas are also linearly polarized. It is possible for RS-10 to move through an orientation in which the satellite downlink antenna is horizontal while your 10-meter antenna is vertical. The result is a temporary reduction in received signal strength. While it is possible to build circularly polarized antennas to reduce or eliminate cross-polarization, a 10-meter version would be large and unwieldy.

After you gain some Mode A experience, *answering* another station will be much easier. Tune your receiver through the passband until you find a station you wish to answer. Set your downlink frequency and leave it there for the duration of the contact. Find the appropriate uplink frequency from Table 3 and set your transmitter accordingly. Wait for a pause between calls by the other station before attempting to find your signal on the downlink. Call the other station by saying something like, "W1AW, this is Kilo Echo Three Hotel Papa, go ahead." When contact is established, the QSO proceeds like any other. I end each transmission with "go ahead" or "over" (phone) or "KN" (CW). Satellite time is precious, so I don't want the other station to have to wonder if I have finished my transmission.

Once you have made your first contact, you are eligible for the AMSAT *Satellite Communicators' Club* award. AMSAT offers several other awards for making satellite contacts.[6] The ARRL has satellite endorsements to familiar awards such as *Worked All States*.[7]

The Future of Mode A

There will be more Mode A satellites in the future. Russian hams are preparing to launch RS-15 in late 1993. While the RS-15 hardware will be similar to that of RS-10, the carrier satellite will be in a 2300 kilometer-high orbit, more than twice as high as RS-10. The coverage of the RS-15 transponder will be much broader than that of RS-10 (see Fig 3). Another amateur satellite that will offer Mode A capability is the US-built SEDSAT-1. In addition to a 64-kHz passband Mode A transponder, SEDSAT will have other capabilities.

Only the Beginning

I hope that getting on RS-10 is only the beginning for you. If you started with voice operation, you might want to give CW a try. Perhaps you'll read about the CW Robot aboard RS-10. It answers your precisely formatted CW transmission with a response and contact number. Of course, there are several other satellites available for your use.[8] Good luck getting started and I hope to work you on RS-10 soon!

Walter Daniel, KE3HP, is an Advanced-class amateur who is active on RS-10 phone. He works on scientific satellite programs for a NASA contractor.

Notes

[1]G. G. Smith, "The RS Satellites Operating Guide" (Washington: AMSAT, 1992), p 9.
[2]R. Schetgen, ed, *The ARRL Handbook for Radio Amateurs*, 1993 ed (Newington: ARRL, 1993), pp 31-1 through 31-2.
[3]J. Kearman and R. Healy, "Beyond FM," *QST*, Feb 1993, pp 61-63.
[4]M. Davidoff, *The Satellite Experimenter's Handbook*, 2nd ed (Newington: ARRL, 1990), pp 6-4 through 6-8.
[5]M. Davidoff, *The Satellite Experimenter's Handbook*, 2nd ed (Newington: ARRL, 1990), pp 10-1 through 10-3.
[6]A. MacAllister, "The AMSAT Awards Program," *The AMSAT Journal*, Mar/Apr 1993, pp 10 through 12.
[7]S. Ford, "The Paper Chase," *QST*, Mar 1993, pp 54 through 55.
[8]S. Ford, "The EasySats," *QST*, Sep 1992, pp 30 through 34.

`QST`

Radio Tips:

VHF/UHF Propagation Beacons

Propagation on the VHF and UHF bands can change rapidly. If you're trying your hand at long-distance (DX) work, you need to know when the bands are open—and where they're open to!

You can gain a lot of information about band conditions by listening for *propagation beacons*. These are automated Amateur Radio stations that transmit continuous signals, 24 hours a day, on specific frequencies. Propagation beacons usually send their call signs repeatedly using Morse code. Many beacon stations send additional information such as the type of antennas they're using, where they are located, how much power they are running and so on.

So how do you use propagation beacons? Well, let's say you live in central Kentucky and you like to chase 2-meter DX. You're exploring the band one day and you suddenly hear Morse code from a beacon station. After pausing to copy the information, you learn that the beacon is located in Atlanta, Georgia. Hmmm…you've never heard a 2-meter beacon from Georgia before. As you tune further, you stumble onto strong beacon signals from Alabama, South Carolina and even Florida. Sound the alarm! The 2-meter band is open to the southeast!

Chances are, the hams in the states we've just mentioned are hearing beacons from your area, too. Like you, they'll be heading for the 2-meter SSB and CW calling frequencies in the hope of making some contacts before the band closes. If you think this situation is uncommon, think again. On occasion, the VHF and UHF bands have burst wide open with spectacular propagation to many areas of the country. If you keep an ear to the beacons, you'll know when a major propagation event is taking place.

You'll find VHF and UHF propagation beacons in the following subbands:

    50.060-50.080 MHz
    144.275-144.300 MHz
    222.050-222.060 MHz
    432.300-432.400 MHz

There are also beacons on many microwave bands. For a complete list of propagation beacon call signs and frequencies, see the *ARRL Repeater Directory* or the *ARRL Operating Manual* (Chapter 2).—WB8IMY

Radio Tips:

Secrecy and You

On January 19, 1987, the Electronics Communications Privacy Act of 1986 (the ECPA) went into effect as Public Law 99-508. The ECPA sought to revise the Wiretap Act of 1968 to purportedly protect certain electronic communications by making it illegal to monitor communications defined as not "readily accessible" such as cellular telephones, electronic mail, various video/data communications and scrambled/encrypted transmissions. Perhaps as an unintended side effect, the ECPA creates a new set of rules governing the interception of radio communications additional to those already found in Section 705 of the Communications Act of 1934, as amended.

Secrecy of communications is the subject of 705. The message in this section is that it's not forbidden merely to *receive* a radio signal not intended for you; you also must not divulge or publish "the existence, contents, substance, purport, effect or meaning thereof." Additionally, you are not to use what you hear to your own benefit. Not to worry, though. The signals of several radio services transmitted for the use of the general public are *exempt* from Section 705 protection, and may be received and discussed freely: Broadcasting, Amateur Radio, CB or transmissions relating to ships, aircraft, vehicles or persons in distress. See *The FCC Rule Book*, published by ARRL, for more information.

As to Public Law 99-508, it seems to parallel Section 705 to the extent that under its provisions, you can *legally* monitor, among other things, any amateur, CB or General Mobile Radio Service transmission, any marine or aeronautical mobile communication, any communication for the general use of the public or relating to ships, aircraft, vehicles or persons in distress, the radio portion of cordless telephone conversations, any public safety (including police/fire) radio communications system readily accessible to the general public, and satellite transmissions of network feeds (which are governed exclusively by Section 705), and more. For further details, see December 1986 *QST*, page 51.—*from the* ARRL Operating Manual, 4th edition

RS-12
Worked All States

If you're looking for a challenge, tune your operating skills with this easy satellite—and have fun doing it!

By R. A. Peschka, K7QXG
2580 SW 195
Aloha, OR 97006

There was a time when I thought satellite operations were reserved for the technically elite. That misguided perception prevailed until April 1993 when I overheard an interesting conversation on 15 meters between Roger, N4ZC, and a station in Puerto Rico. N4ZC was encouraging the KP4 to try a contact on the next pass of the RS-12 satellite using mode K (mode K means you transmit on 21 MHz and listen on 29 MHz). Their conversation intrigued me so much I decided to give it a try myself. A short time later I had made contact with N4ZC via the RS-12 satellite and my space odyssey began.

Sharpening My Skills for WAS

N4ZC proved to be a great help. He sent me a list of the times when I could expect the "bird" to pass within my range. It wasn't long before it became clear that the use of a good computer program would go a long way towards making these operations even more fun and rewarding. I joined AMSAT; acquired a good program for my PC; and now—charged with excitement—became active on the satellite. After a month or so, it became apparent that the challenge of chasing my Worked All States (WAS) award on RS-12 would be an excellent way to tune up my operating skills, which had become quite rusty.

At first I evaluated each projected pass of the satellite. I designed a precise strategy; but I threw all my good intentions to the wind when the thrill of the hunt took over. I'm sure I missed many golden opportunities to contact some of those hard-to-reach stations.

I began making progress when I took my methods seriously. After every pass I evaluated the results to see what worked—and what didn't. Part of the trick was becoming intimately familiar with every little knob and dial on my transceiver. I began to spend far more time listening than transmitting, and learned how to compensate for noise, Doppler shift, and all the other nuances encountered when working the "bird." I honed my skills with practice and the states fell one by one.

Down to the Last States

After nearly a year, I needed only five states to reach my goal: South Dakota, Wyoming, Montana, Delaware and Maine. A good friend and fellow satellite hunter suggested Clarence, N7RPC, in Wyoming. I fired off a letter to Clarence, seeking a schedule on RS-12. The letter resulted in a telephone call, a bit of preparation and a QSO attempt. After some momentary confusion, followed by another quick telephone call, we made contact. Meanwhile, by pure luck, I managed to find WØIT in South Dakota.

Clarence, in turn, suggested Ken, WG7G, in Montana as a possibility to move up one more notch. A letter was sent to Ken, but before his reply arrived he found *me* on the satellite! With Montana in the bag I had a total of 48 states! Only Delaware and Maine remained elusive.

As I chased the states I renewed operating skills long forgotten, not the least of which was patience and courtesy. I once again became familiar with the frustrations of having pens run out of ink at the precisely wrong moment; of having two too many thumbs, and of drinking too much coffee before the "window" opened to the usual flurry of activity.

The search for Delaware and Maine continued. Finally, I heard Gene, NY3C, in Delaware, but the satellite sank below the horizon before I could make contact. It was letter-writing time again. Gene had the true ham spirit. He called me by telephone and we arranged a list of possible schedules. We made contact on the very first try. That left only Maine.

I had sent letters to a couple of stations in Maine, but never received a response. NY3C stepped into the breach again and spread the word of my quest on various nets. Two days later, on my favorite RS-12 CW frequency, I was called by W1OO in Maine!

Conclusion

While on this space journey to WAS, I discovered the warm camaraderie that exists among satellite operators. It was the kind of attitude I remember from more than 33 years ago when I was first licensed. With that in mind, I owe a sincere debt of gratitude to Clarence, N7RPC, and to Gene, NY3C, for helping me over the final hurdle.

One disappointing note: I encountered only *one* female ham during my quest to Work All States on RS-12, and that was VP5JM. Satellite operating is for everyone! We need to see more women participating in this area of our hobby.

What's next? Well, there are still a host of other satellites out there and many new skills to learn. And the exciting Phase 3D is only 18 months from launch. See you on the birds!

About RS-12

This amateur satellite is actually part of a large Russian *Cosmos* navigational satellite launched in 1988. It was assembled at the Tsiolkovskiy Museum for the History of Cosmonautics in Kaluga (about 180 km southwest of Moscow).

Although it is capable of operating in a number of modes, RS-12 only functions in mode K at this time. The frequencies are:

Uplink passband: 21.210 to 21.250 MHz
Downlink passband: 29.410 to 29.450 MHz
Operating modes are CW or SSB *only*.

Elaborate antennas and high output power are *not* required to work RS-12. Your 100-W transceiver and dipole antennas are more than adequate. You will need a radio that can operate split frequency on separate bands (most modern rigs can do this), or separate radios for 15 and 10 meters. You'll also need an Extra or Advanced class license to operate in the uplink passband. For more information about RS-12 and how to use it, read "Working RS-12—The Ultimate Satellite Primer" by Robert Capon, WA3ULH, in the February 1994 *QST.—WB8IMY*

By Kirk Kleinschmidt, NTØZ

On-Air Conversations: Go Beyond the Basics

If you're tired of "cookie cutter" contacts, why not jump out of your rut and say what you really mean? Here are some tips on turning boring, "by the book" QSOs into interesting—even educational—on-air *conversations*.

Ham Radio is extremely technical. Just ask anyone, and they'll tell you straightaway that our hobby has a lot to do with complicated doohickeys and thingamabobs. There are wires galore, and transistors, integrated circuits, the occasional big amplifier and digitally enhanced circuits of every type, to name just a few . . .

And don't forget the tests we're all required to pass to get our licenses! Although beginning hams no longer need to learn Morse code, we do need to bone up on radio and electronics theory—it's not a total walk in the park.

With all of the study, brainpower and red tape involved, you'd think that the whole mess is about technology, right? About knowing when 10 meters will be open to the Pacific, how grounded-grid linear amplifiers are tuned, or how digital signal processing helps dig out those weak DX signals.

Wrong!

That's the great irony about many technology-based hobbies (ham radio, computers, cruising the Internet, BBSing, etc). For the majority, the technology is simply a vehicle for an underlying, deeper reason for participating: Communicating with other people who share similar interests (people who often live outside the local area). After all, if they lived down the street, you could talk to them over coffee, during barbecues or while playing canasta!

To effectively participate, we need to learn about the technology involved—and certainly about operating procedures and protocols (that is, how to correctly communicate with others using whatever technology is involved). But once that's learned, we're still faced with simply talking to someone else. Having a conversation. Sharing something of ourselves. Learning something about the person on the other end of the mike, key or keyboard.

Sure, some of us become hams for primarily "technical" reasons. Some might love to build radios, or study the intricacies of VHF propagation from a scientific standpoint. But even "specialty hams" love to talk to other hams who *share* their particular interest. Just listen to two "homebrew-ing" hams talk about building *anything* and you'll be convinced.

So, despite the trappings of technology, it's all really about communicating. And to maximize your enjoyment of Amateur Radio, you need to be a good communicator. It's not difficult, but a refresher course can often help get the ball rolling!

Much like seeing a light at the end of a tunnel, every now and then you'll tune across a really interesting QSO. The participants are so caught up in whatever they're discussing, and the exchanges are so lively and natural, that the "mechanics" of ham radio are transcended ("back to you," "W9XYZ for ID," " QTH is . . .," etc). Why, it's almost as if they're having a *conversation!*

Most hams—whether they'll admit it or not—don't really care what kind of rig you have (they're talking to you, so it must be doing okay), what your weather is like (unless you're in a hurricane or something interesting), what brand of antenna you have, and so forth. Sure, they may find these things interesting, but what they really want to know is something about *you*. What makes you different, interesting or unique.

With only a little effort and a slight change in approach, interesting on-air conversations can be your norm. But before we discuss ways to have more fun talking with and learning about our fellow hams, let's review several (unfortunately) typical exchanges you could hear on the bands almost anywhere . . . and discuss what you can do to jazz them up.

Boring QSOs You've Heard . . . and What to do About Them!

❏ *Robot DXing*. When it comes to wasting wonderful opportunities to exchange meaningful communication, the rapid-fire exchanges between "Robot DXers" immediately come to mind: Call sign, signal report, adios. QSL 100%. Look me up in the *Callbook*, buddy. Next . . . Over and over.

Amazingly, it took me 12 years to become bored with this. How

HE DRAGS 'EM IN PRETTY GOOD AS LONG AS I DON'T FORGET TO WIND HIM UP

long will it take you? (I'm not picking on "country hunters" and contesters, just hams who *never stop* contesting!)

Talking—and I mean really *talking*—with people in faraway lands is one of the most powerful incentives to become a ham operator. Why trade meaningful exchanges for QSL cards on the wall? When you're old and gray will you look lovingly through your QSL card collection and fondly say to yourself, "Yep, I remember when I talked to this particular guy in England . . . it was in the summer of 1985, and we talked for eight seconds. I think my signal report was five by nine."

It's not *always* possible to chat with DX operators. Band conditions can be poor, interference can be atrocious, your station may not have enough oomph, your respective Morse code speeds may be too far apart—or the ham on the other end may not even want to chat with you! Don't be offended—he may not feel that his English language skills are adequate for a ragchew, or he may not want to disappoint others who are waiting for a QSO. DXers the world over are afflicted with "Robot DX-itis," and if that's the case, forget chatting.

But what if the DX operator is interested in communicating beyond the basics—even if it's just for a minute or two to personalize each contact? Many DX ops leave telltale signs that they're interested

Tips for Better Communicating

Here are a few tips to "break the ice." Remember: Don't be shy! If necessary, just blurt something out. If your QSOs are stuck in a boring rut, dare to do something different. You'll enjoy Amateur Radio in an exciting new way.

❑ **Families.** If you can figure out whether your QSO partner has kids and/or grandkids, an invitation to talk about them often will be warmly received. Don't push too hard, though; some cultures regard family questions as more private than others.

❑ **The Map/Atlas Gambit.** There's no doubt about it: The handiest tool for budding ham radio conversationalists is a good map or atlas.

When you figure out where the other guy lives, check out his QTH on the map. That little blue squiggle might seem insignificant on your end, but your new friend might have been trout fishing there since he was a kid.

By simply asking about the local geography, at least two things will happen: (1) you'll learn a lot more about that little blue squiggle (or whatever it is), (2) you'll wake the ham on the other end to the fact that a real conversation is about to take place. Both are big steps in the right direction.

❑ **Famous Places.** If you or your QSO partner live in a "famous place," feel free to get a little conversational mileage out of it. If you're chatting with someone in Winterset, Iowa, try out your best John Wayne accent. It couldn't hurt, could it?

I've started many an interesting QSO by mentioning that I live in Little Falls, Minnesota, the boyhood home of Charles Lindbergh (and the stomping ground of Paul Bunyan and his blue ox Babe). You can, too.

❑ **The Big Question.** Asking people questions—on almost any topic—can often spice up an otherwise routine exchange. Be tactful, but ask away. Examples: "What do you do for a living?" "How about those Minnesota Vikings?" "Have you ever been to Japan?" You get the idea. To narrow down the range of possibilities, tailor your Big Question to what you already know about your QSO partner—or what you intuit or suspect.

❑ **Hobbies.** As hams, the one hobby we have in common is ham radio. But that's not all we have in common, and discovering other mutual hobbies will turn a by-the-numbers QSO into a real conversation.

❑ **Nets.** If you're shy about conversing with strangers, why not check into one or more of the many specialty nets out there? If everyone on frequency is crazy about ultralight airplanes—and you are, too—they're no longer strangers (and you're suddenly "one of the guys").

❑ **Say Cheese!** One of the most interesting and potentially rewarding ways to visually liven things up—usually with a "more established" QSO partner—is the Film Exchange. You each shoot a roll of film, choosing subjects that have meaning to your ham radio and personal lives, and then you exchange the undeveloped film or the printed pictures. When the exchange is complete, you hook up on the air to discuss the photos. This adds a visual element to the mix in a very personal way.

❑ **IDs.** As long as it's within reason, feel free to let other hams know a little bit about what you're up to. Instead of keying the repeater with "This is W9XYZ, listening," try "This is W9XYZ, on a round-the-world motorcycle trip, listening." Which do you think would garner more responses on a typical sleepy repeater?

Maybe the old-timer's CQ—"This is Bill, W9XYZ, calling CQ from the Louisiana bayou town of Swampy Creek"—heard regularly in decades past, has some merit. Don't use it while checking into an emergency net, and don't use it all the time, but you might give it a try on an uncrowded HF band just to see what happens.

❑ **Delicate Subjects:** One last word of advice: Be careful when discussing potentially controversial subjects such as politics, religion, sex, light beer, left-handed pitchers, etc. I'm not trying to step on your First Amendment rights, I'm merely suggesting that you be respectful and use common courtesy when bringing up certain topics. Amateur Radio is diverse, but it's also tolerant and accepting, and the best ham radio discussions build on a common ground of shared interests.

Regardless of which techniques you use (there are many more than those listed here), taking steps to make ham radio friends through better conversation will only increase your enjoyment of our hobby. You never know when you'll make a lifelong friend you would have otherwise overlooked because of a "cut and dried" QSO!

---

in (or might be coaxed into) conversing. If the pace of their QSOs is strictly rapid fire, you're probably out of luck, but if interesting tidbits creep in every so often, that op may be a talk-your-ear-off ham in disguise! When it's your turn to transmit, throw out a tidbit of your own to see if he takes the bait! If he's speaking English but you know something in his native language, slip in a greeting in that tongue—you may be suprised at the response!

If the DX station isn't interested in conversing, he'll acknowledge your tidbit and quickly move on—before you can blurt out some other interesting item that will only slow down his QSO rate. If this happens, it's no big deal. You simply have one more quick DX contact to put in your log. You'll likely have many more to keep it company.

If you have a "big signal," you can set the conversational tone of your DX QSOs. The rule of thumb for CQers is, if you're chatty, they'll be chatty. This works amazingly well, but you have to have the signal to back it up.

US hams can actually be at a disadvantage when it comes to blabbing with DX ops. There are so many American hams on the bands, DX stations are often deluged by waves of US ops calling them or replying to their QSOs. In fact, many DX ops think US hams only want a quick contact and a prize QSL card!

Don't get caught up in the details, though. Go ahead and see if the other op is interested in chatting. They're out there, and when you find one, you'll certainly have a more interesting contact—and you may even make a new friend you'll talk to regularly. That's how friendships are started.

❑ **The Domestic Robot.** The domestic variant of "Robot DX-itis" is just as boring (and, in fact, may stem from boredom itself!): Name, location, signal report, rig, antenna type, best wishes to you and your family, see-ya-later. Over and over. Painfully boring! Why bother turning on the rig? Are we taking a survey, or are we communicating?

❑ **Repeaters.** When it comes to being stuck in a rut, many repeater conversations aren't much better than their HF cousins, although some greater communication takes place occasionally—if only to convey street directions to inquisitive hams who are passing through town!

❑ **Mode Considerations.** Chatting on Morse code can be difficult—especially if you're used to "cookie cutter" QSOs. With a little practice, however, your code speed will increase, as will your appreciation and enjoyment of ham radio. Think about it. Conversing in Japanese would be challenging, too, unless you practiced a bit! Morse can help when language might otherwise be a barrier.

If your typing speed is slow, chatting on the digital modes may seem tough. Solution: *practice*! Every mode has its challenges and benefits, and it's possible to have meaningful comms on every one (certain moonbounce and weak-signal modes excepted). Don't get stuck in a rut.

Instead of propagating (and perpetrating!) limiting, unfulfilling conversations, why not enhance your communicating skills and expand your ham radio horizons? There are millions of interesting individuals out there disguised as ham operators! Dig deeper—you won't be disappointed!

Kirk Kleinschmidt, NTØZ
1010 Grove St
Little Falls, MN 56345

QST

I Passed My Code! Now What?

By Chester S. Bowles, AA1EX
RFD 2, Box 335 L
Sharon, NH 03458

 "Hey, I just passed my five-word-per-minute code!"

"Congratulations! When will you be getting on the air?"

"Well…I'm not sure. I'm eager to start using my HF privileges, but something's bothering me."

"What?"

"I've been listening around the bands, but the CW contacts are like Greek to me. I don't have a clue about what's going on. I studied the books and learned some of the abbreviations, but a lot of what I hear still doesn't make any sense. None of this stuff was in the book! I'm kind of intimidated about getting on the air and making a fool of myself."

Does This Sound Familiar?

Maybe you've had a similar conversation with a new ham or perhaps you've felt the same way yourself. In any event, it's real. Much of what goes on in the CW portion of the bands sounds strange indeed!

So I led my young friend into the shack to listen to some CW contacts in the Novice/Technician subbands. As we listened, I pointed out techniques and offered helpful hints to make these initial forays into the world of CW more enjoyable.

The Basics

"The first rule," I told my friend as we tuned up the rig, "is that none of the rules matter! As long as you properly identify your station, almost anything is acceptable. The point is to get on the air and practice. You'll be amazed at the tolerance and understanding of most people. After all, they were once newcomers, too."

The first station we heard was calling CQ.

"CQ," I pointed out, "means, 'calling anyone.' The derivation of the term is lost in history, but it's understood almost everywhere in the world. Maybe it got started by somebody who figured it sounds like 'seek you.'

"Listen to this guy. He's sending CQ correctly. Some people run the characters together, like 'CQ.' This guy's sending them as separate characters, 'C Q.' He's making a mistake, though. He's been calling for quite a while, but have you heard him give his call sign?"

"No," answered my friend.

"You'll hear people sending groups of 12 to 15 or even 20 CQs before they identify themselves and wait for a call. That's boring and impolite. You should follow the '3 by 3' rule: Send CQ three times, then send your call sign three times. That gives someone time to find you and copy your call sign correctly, and it keeps you from cluttering up the bands with useless interference."

"That's logical," my friend replied.

"Sure. Now let's find a QSO and see what else we can learn."

So we tuned up the band a bit and found two stations in a QSO. One station was just in the process of sending it back to the other station:

WA1FEU DE AA1EX KN

The other station responded with:

R R R DE WA1FEU

"There's a couple of things to learn from that little exchange. First, notice that AA1EX used 'KN' at the end of his transmission. That's an indication that he only wants a specific station to respond. He would have sent 'K' if he'd been calling CQ or if he didn't mind other stations joining the conversation. You sometimes hear KN sent as two separate characters, like 'K N.' That's correct for CQ, but it's not right for this prosign. It should be sent as one character, 'KN.'

"The second thing about this exchange is that WA1FEU sent several 'Rs' at the beginning of his transmission. He was saying 'Roger' or 'all received okay' to let the other station know that the entire message had been received. It's great shorthand and saves a lot of time. Oh, and 'R' is also used to represent a decimal point when sending numbers. For example, the frequency 7.135 would be sent as '7R135.'

"Finally, you heard each station send the characters 'DE' before they sent their call signs. That's like saying 'from' if you're using voice. In fact, that's the literal translation of the French word *de*."

"This is great. It's starting to make sense already!"

"There's a lot more to learn—like punctuation."

"Oh, yeah" sighed my friend. "I get confused between the comma and the question mark."

"No big deal," I said. "Here's why: The comma is one of the longest characters to send, so it's almost never used, except to separate the city and state when you send a QTH, mainly in traffic handling. The question mark, on the other hand, is used a lot. Any time you ask a question, send a question mark. It lets the other station know you're asking a question instead of making a statement. You'll also hear people send two question marks. It's not necessary, but I guess they want to make sure the other person knows it's a question."

"That's easy. But what about periods?"

"Periods are great. For some reason, though, periods have fallen out of favor. I'm not sure why, but people now send the prosign 'BT' instead. I suspect 'BT' is easier to send on an electronic keyer. 'BT' means 'Stand by. More to follow.' Besides going where you'd expect a period, it's sort of like saying 'ummm…,' or 'Wait while I collect my thoughts.'"

"Makes sense. Anything else I need to know?"

More Advanced Tips

"You can sound like an old pro if you understand and use the signs and characters we've talked about. A few other hints can make CW even easier and more fun.

"First is 'QRS,' which means, 'slow down.' Hey, if you want to be super polite, you can even send, 'pse QRS.' Don't worry about asking people to slow down. They'll almost always be glad to help. It's a lot more fun to have solid copy on someone, rather than be frustrated and have to guess at what's being said.

"While we're talking about asking people to send more slowly, never send a CQ at a rate faster than you can copy comfortably. If you send your CQ at 13 words per minute, people will naturally assume that you can copy that fast and they'll respond at that rate. So even though you can get proficient at sending CQ and your call sign fast, avoid the temptation to go faster than your ability to copy."

"Okay, but what if I hear someone sending CQ at a rate faster than I can copy? Should I answer them?"

"Sure! As long as they're sending at a speed relatively close to your ability to copy, don't be afraid to answer. Just answer them at a speed that's comfortable for you. Most people respond to your speed and slow down to accommodate you. But be realistic—if you hear someone sending at 20 or 25 words per minute and you can only copy a solid eight, keep moving the dial. That's too big a difference and it's a lot to ask for someone to slow down that much. On the other hand, if you hear someone sending at 12 or 13 words per minute, go ahead and answer them at eight words per minute. I can almost guarantee that

You've got the ticket— now it's time to get on the air!

they'll be happy to have the contact with you."

"That sounds easy. Hey, listen to these guys. I know that RST is a signal report, but what are they saying?"

UR RST 5NN. I AM RUNNING 1TT WTS.

"It's not as strange as it sounds," I answered. "Those are just what I call 'clipped numbers.' For example, you heard the station giving an RST of '5NN.' The 'Ns' are just a short way of sending the number '9.' You also heard the station giving his power as '1TT.' The 'Ts' are a shortened way of sending zeros. Don't feel that you have to use shortened numbers. Sending '9' or '0' is perfectly acceptable.

"While we're at it, there are lots of abbreviations you'll hear. Many books, like the *ARRL Handbook*, show long lists of abbreviations. Use them as you see fit. Just remember that it's better to spell things out than to confuse someone. I have a good friend who's a mega-CW operator, and he says, 'If it's important enough to send, spell it out.' Maybe that's extreme, but he makes a good point. Besides, I feel that the amount of time you save by using abbreviations is minimal."

Contests

The next station we listened to was sending:

CQ CQ CQ NR DE KB1AER/T K

"Hey, I forgot it was time for the Novice Roundup."

"What's that?" asked my friend.

"It's an ARRL contest for Novices and Technicians to contact and exchange information with as many stations as possible. It runs a week and it's lots of fun. The rules are published in *QST*."

"I'm not sure I'd want to get in a contest."

"Contests are a way of life on the ham bands. Some people like 'em, other people can't tolerate 'em. In many ways, though, CW contests are often more friendly and less intimidating than contests in the phone portions of the bands. Two contests you might want to try are the ARRL Sweepstakes and the Novice Roundup. Both are low-key and you'll find tons of operators in the Novice portions of the bands. They're fun and I've been pleasantly impressed with how tolerant the operators are when they need to ask for repeats of information or when they can't understand your transmission."

QTH? Name? RST?

We continued tuning up the band and listened in on several typical QSOs:

NAME IS BRIAN ES QTH IS MIDDLETOWN, CT. UR RST 599. RIG HR IS KNWD 520S RUNNING 100 WATTS. TNX FER QSO. 73.

Morse Code Abbreviations

Here's a quick rundown on the Morse Code abbreviations used in this article that are not explained in the text:

AGN	again
CU	see you
DN	down
ES	and
FER	for
GE	good evening
HPE	hope
HR	here
KNWD	Kenwood
MNI	many
TNX	thanks
U	you
UR	your
URS	yours (as in "you and yours")
WRK	work
WTS	watts (W is also used)

"Hear that?" I asked. "Doesn't sound like much fun, does it? But you'll hear lots of QSOs just like that—nothing more than exchanging location, name and signal report. Sometimes you hear about the other person's rig and how much power they're running, and if they're long-winded, they might even talk about the weather. But then they say good-bye. It's as if that's all they know how to send! Don't get caught in that trap. It's not that hard to get the other person to talk. Try asking questions like these:

'Where do you work?'

'Do you like it?'

'Good news about your son. Where does he go to school?'

'How do you like your 520?'

"It takes longer on CW than on phone, but the effort's worth it. You'll be amazed at what you'll learn. An added benefit is that your CW skills improve rapidly as you branch away from the standard phrases and characters. Besides, it's more fun."

Shave and a Haircut

Next we heard two people ending a QSO with one station sending:

DIT DI-DI-DIT DIT

The other station sent:

DIT DIT

"Shave and a haircut," I said.

"What?" said my friend.

"I guess no one knows how it started, but you often hear people end a QSO by sending the old 'shave and a haircut' pattern—you know, 'Dah di di dah dah.' The other operator responds with, 'Dit dit.'

"It's just a silly little routine to end a friendly chat. Nobody official recommends it, but it just sorta turns up. Another thing that's just done for fun."

"Kinda cute, I guess."

"Much more common, though, and probably related, is the custom of sending two 'dits' at the end of a transmission. For example, if the other station has already signed off, I might end my transmission by sending, '73 WA1FEU DE AA1EX SK E E.' The other station would respond with his own 'E E.' It's the final good-bye to the conversation. A nice tradition that's commonly used throughout the world."

"Quicker, too. Besides, how can you know if a ham in Lesotho has any idea what 'shave and a haircut' means!"

Wrapping it Up

...ES MNI TNX FER QSO BILL BT HPE TO WRK U AGN BT CU FERTHER DN THE LOG BT 73 73 BEST DX ES GE TO U ES URS BT HPE CUAGN BILL...

"After hearing this guy, I'll give you one more hint, and then I'll turn you loose on your own.

"Saying good-bye on CW is, for some reason, often a long, drawn-out affair—especially during ragchews. I guess it's because saying good-bye is easy to do and because there are so many ways to say it. I've heard good-byes that lasted longer than the QSO!

"CW isn't as quick as speech. A long good-bye only makes it worse, so get to the point and end the conversation. The other ham won't be offended."

Have Fun

"That's about it," I said. "Now, don't panic when you hear other new things, like people who use the letter 'C' for 'yes' or 'N' for 'no.' These 'conventions' are just refinements of the basic principles and procedures. Sort of like the icing on the cake. If you're sure you copied right, but you can't figure out a CW abbreviation or shorthand procedure, just ask in plain text. Don't worry about them, just screw up your courage, wipe off those sweaty palms and pick a nice, clear frequency in the Novice subbands to send or answer a CQ. You'll have a great time and meet many other people just like you who are learning a new language."

"Great! Thanks for the help. Meet me on 3.715?"

"Sure. No problem. Glad I could help."

"Dit dit!"

"Dit dit, yourself," I chuckled.

Chet Bowles, AA1EX, was licensed in 1967, but only recently discovered the fun and challenge of CW. Chet has had several articles published in QST *and other amateur magazines. He is Public Information Coordinator for the New Hampshire section and president of the Souhegan Valley Amateur Radio Club. His son David is N1MZZ. This article is dedicated to Peter Büttner, WA1FEU, a champion CW operator who became a Silent Key on January 16, 1993.*

You *Can* Copy 30 Words Per Minute!

By Lee Aurick, W1SE
1043 Deer Run
Winter Springs, FL 32708

I qualified for an ARRL 30 word-per-minute code proficiency certificate in 1954. In the nearly 40 years that have passed since then, it's been my pleasure to help more than a thousand people pass their code tests. After so many years of teaching, I've managed to accumulate a small collection of helpful tips. I've also observed a few things that, in my opinion, you should avoid.

Let's start abolishing the notion it's only necessary to practice 15- or 20- minutes at a time, a couple of times a week. I have one word for that idea: *nonsense!* By the time you get around to your next practice session, you may slip back to where you were before. At this pace, progress is slow—tantalizingly slow.

Code instructors should be honest with their students. They should tell them that it's going to require some effort and dedication. A coach doesn't tell his basketball hopefuls that the road to the NBA is lined with velvet. He tells them that there are tough times ahead. Why are we less truthful with aspiring hams?

The Farnsworth Method

Should a code student begin at five words per minute and work upward from there? How about starting at 50 words per minute instead? (I can hear the gasps now.) No, I'm not suggesting that we bombard them with CW conversations at that speed—just characters!

This technique is put to good use in what has come to be known as the "Farnsworth Method." The letters are *formed* at anywhere from 15 to 18 words per minute, but are sent with *5 word-per-minute spacing*. It may seem like an unusual method, but it works.

You begin by learning each character. As soon as you're confident that you know each letter, number and punctuation mark, start decreasing the spacing between them. The sounds of the characters *remain the same,* only the spacing changes. Within a short time, you'll reduce the spacing from the 5 WPM level to 18 WPM. During this process you don't need to relearn the characters—you already know them at 18 WPM! In other words, they're the same characters you learned the first time around. They're just coming at you faster.

Why don't we take this idea farther? Why not start by forming the letters at 20 words per minute? Moving from 5 to a solid 20 words per minute would be a snap. As an experiment, I taught my 9 year-old grandson the code in less than a day with the letters formed at twenty words per minute. Upon returning to his home in Wisconsin, he entered a class and qualified for his Novice license before the class was half-over. He is now KA9SNP. His mother had her Novice ticket at age nine and was, for a time, one of the youngest female hams in the country. This was in the late 50s, before the era of club-sponsored schools. Her elder sister qualified at age ten. All of them profited by means of code-teaching techniques that are

sound and easy to apply.

Code Practice Tapes

Some of the worst tapes in existence are those which purport to send code as though you are listening to two stations having a conversation. Many use very poor procedures, and that's reason enough not to use them. As a new ham, the last things you need to learn are bad habits. In addition, these tapes are easily memorized, making them nearly worthless for instruction. On the other hand, tapes that use the Farnsworth Method are fine learning tools for new hams and I encourage you to use them. (ARRL practice tapes employ the Farnsworth Method.)

Are you finding it difficult to increase your code speed? Use these techniques to go as high as 30 words per minute— or beyond!

Tapes not withstanding, if you already have a Novice or Technician ticket, I have four very important words for you: GET ON THE AIR. Seek out stations working just a bit faster than you can copy. Who cares if you have to ask the other station to repeat his or her name? The code practice available from W1AW is an excellent way in which to determine just how fast you're capable of copying. Use W1AW to measure your progress as you practice.

Copying Behind

When you copy at slow speeds, there is a great deal of *lost time* available. The sending operator must observe the proper spacing between parts of characters, between the characters themselves, and between words. A space equal to a *dit* is required between character components. A space equal to a *dah* is required between each character and a space equal to three dahs is required between each word. Now that's a lot of time that you can use to your advantage.

At speeds above 15 words per minute, you can watch the receiving operator writing down the text in a very jerky fashion. Why? He's trying to follow the sending operator *exactly as he is sending*. This makes for erratic copy and a lot of stop-and-go writing.

Instead of trying to maintain such a frantic pace, slow down and relax a little. At 15 words per minute, let the first letter go by. Don't

write it down the instant you hear it. Jot the first letter as the operator starts to send the second. Don't rush it! You have all the time in the world.

At 20 words per minute, you can afford to let two letters slip by before putting pen to paper. Why did I say pen? You should copy with some variation of a ball-point or fiber pen. The best pencils have a habit of breaking, especially when you're a little nervous! Try to master long-hand writing rather than printing. It may seem strange at first, but you can copy code much faster in long-hand than you can by printing each letter.

At 30 words per minute, experienced operators can copy at least three or four letters behind; many copy a full-word behind. However, this requires some practice. If you want to reach the 30 word-per-minute goal, you must learn to copy behind. There's no way you can keep up with the operator, letter-for-letter, at that speed.

Many years ago I had the privilege of standing at the side of the legendary T. R. McElroy, as he was typing code at 55 words per minute. He was talking to me at the same time. I could hear snatches of words coming from the headphones. I soon realized that he was copying *a full sentence behind*! Ted, though he is no longer with us, claimed the world's record of 78.5-words per minute. A few years ago I met a young man at the Dayton HamVention who came there with the avowed intention of breaking Ted's record. He claimed to be able to copy code at 80-words per minute. I learned later that he didn't make it, but people are out there trying.

I strongly recommend headphones for any CW enthusiast. The degree of concentration you can achieve with headphones is perhaps 10 times that of copying from a speaker. In addition, when copying from a speaker, the reverberation from walls can make it difficult to hear the code accurately.

Some Final Advice

Here are 10 valuable tips for learning to copy code at any speed you wish:

1) Relax
2) Learn to copy behind
3) Use long-hand (Don't print)
4) Use a ball-point or fiber pen
5) Write slowly
6) Get on the air (The world's best practice!)
7) Use headphones
8) Practice
9) Practice
10) Practice

During World War II, Lee Aurick was an Army Signal Corps High-Speed Operator and Communications Chief. Interested in Amateur Radio since 1933, he was finally licensed in 1946. He attained one of the first Amateur Extra Class licenses in 1952. Lee served two hitches at ARRL Headquarters and retired in 1987 after more than a decade of service as QST Advertising Manager.

QST-

Remedial Radio

**Are more hams in the mood to be rude these days?
Or is it just a lapse of manners and good operating practice?**

By Kirk Kleinschmidt, NTØZ
Assistant Managing Editor

NEW HAM COMPANION

The latest wave of FCC crackdowns on illegal HF operations, recent DXpedition problems and a ham from the south who told me an incredible story of Amateur Radio rudeness have all prompted me to discuss this: on-air behavior and good operating practices!

In the grand cycle of ham radio evolution, bad manners never really go away. Hams exhibit them, talk about them and write about them—to Amateur Radio magazines, the ARRL and even the FCC.

Veteran hams will tell you that there have always been crackpots on the airwaves. This is true. There is a rogue's gallery of terrible hams who enjoyed their 15 minutes of infamy and then faded—thankfully—into the mists of history. Such amateurs are, and always have been, a tiny minority. Like the proverbial sore thumbs, however, they tend to get more than their fair share of attention!

Misplaced Priorities

The other day, a fellow ham told me of an experience in Florida. He had gone there to join some friends in a short bicycle tour. A short distance out, he came upon an injured cyclist who had broken or dislocated her hip in a fall to the pavement. Because she couldn't be moved, an ambulance was needed. Enter ham radio.

After failing to raise any of the 2-meter repeaters within a 50-mile radius, the ham sprinted back to his car and turned on his HF rig. He quickly found an active net on 40 meters, checked in and asked to pass emergency traffic. Several hams who were on frequency offered to call the Florida Highway Department, so the two slipped off frequency a few kilohertz to exchange information. So far so good.

As the two started their exchange on what sounded like a clear frequency, they were rudely interrupted by a ham who demanded to know the nature of the emergency and who belligerently disrupted their communications. He had been ragchewing with a friend when the emergency came up. This self-appointed "policeman" didn't think that a woman with a potentially broken hip, painfully lying on a Florida roadside, was anything to get worked up about, much less relinquish "his" frequency for.

After trying to reason with the guy, the two moved elsewhere and passed the traffic. The ambulance came (several minutes later than it could have) and the woman was saved. Folks, in my opinion, this is unacceptable behavior. It's just as childish as tuning up on someone, running a vacuum cleaner next to your microphone or shouting obscenities on the repeater. If there had been a heart attack victim lying beside that Florida road, the "frequency hog" could have cost the victim her life!

Finding a Clear HF Frequency

In light of the previous story, let's take a look at how the considerate operator finds a clear frequency. It's really quite simple.

First, tune up your rig or antenna tuner with a dummy load or as little power as possible. Throwing a loud carrier on someone else's frequency definitely falls into the "rude behavior" category. Besides, your antenna tuner will probably tune up just fine on 10 watts instead of 100.

Before you call CQ, tune around the part of the band you want to operate on and listen. Then listen some more. This will give you a good idea of propagation and the general activity level. There's a big difference between an evening on 75 meters and an evening on 10 meters during a sunspot cycle minimum. One's wall-to-wall, the other's virtually dead.

After you've found what sounds like an unoccupied frequency, say (on phone): "Is this frequency in use? This is NTØZ." (Remember to use your own call sign....)

On CW you'd send: "QRL? de NTØZ." (Again, with your call sign.) Regardless of its meaning in the early days, QRL? is now accepted to mean "Is this frequency in use?"

If the frequency you're inquiring about is in use, you should be rewarded with a polite "Yes it is, thanks for asking," or something similar.

On CW you might hear "QRL." Without the question mark, QRL means "Yes, this frequency is in use. Thanks for asking." You may also hear the Morse letter "C," short for "Yes," or (incorrect, although heard occasionally) the Morse letter "R," short for "Roger." Even if you don't get an immediate reply, the frequency may still be in use. This occurs frequently on 10 and 15 meters, where two stations are conversing, but you can only hear one of them.

Considerate operating practices should be the rule, not the exception. Strive to accommodate. Strive to set the best possible example for others. When that DX station says "listening for sixes," don't transmit unless you have a six in your call sign, even if a half-a-dozen other ops do. When the DX station says "listening up five," transmit only where he's listening for calls, not on the DX station's transmit frequency. You get the idea!

Repeater Manners

Always *listen first* before you attempt to use a repeater. If a conversation is in progress and you need to make a call, just say your call sign between their transmissions. When one of the stations acknowledges you, say, "This is NTØZ. I'd like to make a quick call."

Wait for the station to give you the go-ahead, and then make your call.

"WB8IMY from NTØZ."

If your friend responds, ask him to go to another repeater or a simplex frequency where you can talk. Thank the courteous hams for allowing you to call your friend and then leave the repeater quickly. If your buddy *doesn't* reply, clear off the repeater and, once again, thank the stations for letting you break in.

Emergencies are a different matter. Interrupt the conversation by saying, "Break," or "Break—emergency." Emergency situations always take priority, so don't worry about seizing control of the repeater. The stations will have to take their conversation elsewhere, or stay on the frequency to assist you.

Whenever you use a repeater, make sure to pause between your transmissions so other hams can break in if necessary. And be mindful of long conversations during "prime time"—early morning and late afternoon. Try to keep your discussions short so that other hams can enjoy the repeater, too.

When You're the Victim of Intentional Interference

The question of why one ham intentionally interferes with another would make a fascinating study topic for psychologists. The answer usually involves anger of some sort—either anger at you personally, or anger at the world in general. Amateur Radio is the ideal medium for those who want to act on their frustrations with little fear of suffering the consequences. A ham who wouldn't dare insult you to your face has no problem anonymously garbling your transmissions.

This type of ham gains pleasure from his actions *only* when you acknowledge them. He craves attention and your angry response gives him exactly what he needs. The trick is to do everything possible to ignore him. Try to continue your conversation as best you can, working around his interruptions without comment. If the interference is so bad that you cannot continue, move to another frequency.

I know it's difficult to hold your tongue in the face of such rude behavior. By ignoring his antics, however, you'll rob him of the pleasure he seeks. Eventually, he'll become bored and move on. That's the worst punishment you can inflict!—*WB8IMY*

QST

A *Cheap* Way to Hunt Transmitters

By Glen Rickerd, KC6TNF
221 S Catamaran Cir
Pittsburg, CA 94565-3613

Now that I have your attention (what ham can resist the word "cheap" in a headline?), here is a new twist to an old technique for hunting the wily hidden transmitter. Not only is it cheap, it works very well. This method has caught on with a number of us in the San Francisco Bay Area (Pacific Division, East Bay), and many are now using it to sniff out the "fox" once we are in close. It also works at substantial distances from the transmitter. Some hunters who use this method exclusively are turning in mileage scores as low as those using Doppler units or directional antennas.

The origin of this idea is a good example of serendipity. Don Pass and his son Brad, KD6ERV, were having trouble using *body-fade* techniques to home in on strong signals during local transmitter hunts. They built the device described below in an effort to find a better means of shielding their H-Ts. By shielding the transceiver, you reduce the received signal strength. This makes it possible to obtain an accurate fix, as you'll see in a moment.

The next time they went on a hunt with Frank Vervoort, WA6BZP, the device proved to be surprisingly effective. Frank looked it over and said, "I know why that works so well; what a great idea!"

Construction

Start with a pasteboard mailing tube that has sufficient inside diameter to accommodate your H-T. Cover the tube completely with aluminum foil. Some of us seal the bottom end with foil, too. It doesn't seem to matter whether the end is sealed if the tube is long enough. The foil tends to be quite fragile if left unprotected, so for durability, most of us wrap the aluminum foil in packing tape. You will also need a short, stout cord attached to the H-T, like a wrist strap. That's all there is to it!

A Little Theory

Many have heard of using body fade for direction finding with a 2-meter H-T. The idea is simple. You stand, holding the H-T to your chest, and slowly turn around, looking for a fade in signal strength as your body intervenes between the *fox* transmitter and the H-T. Your body provides a shield that gives the H-T a *cardioid* sensitivity pattern, with a sharp decrease in sensitivity to the rear (otherwise known as a *null*) that indicates the direction of the transmitter.

This simple device gives precise directional readings when used with an H-T.
You probably have the materials to build it right now— and it only takes a few minutes!

The difficulty with body fade is that it has always been subject to variables that change that ideal cardioid pattern. Anything that affects signal strength—including transmitter power, distance, receiver sensitivity, or the size and shape of your body—can work to smear or obliterate the null. The body fade null, which is rather shallow to begin with, can be obscured by reflections.

This is where the tube comes in. At the frequencies commonly used in transmitter hunts, it functions as a so-called *wave guide beyond cutoff*. Don't let the terminology spook you. In microwave parlance, a signal that is too low in frequency to be

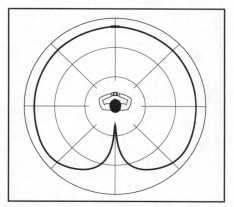

Fig 1—Hand-held receive sensitivity pattern when using body fade for direction finding.

propagated in a waveguide is attenuated at a predictable logarithmic rate.[1] In other words, the farther inside the tube, the weaker the signal gets. In-line devices that use this principle to reduce signal strength are commonly known as *air attenuators*. They are commercially available, and there are plans in the transmitter-hunting literature detailing how to build one.[2] In this body-fade application, we use the foil-wrapped tube to reduce the received signal level until the cardioid sensitivity pattern is reestablished.

On with the Hunt!

Hold the tube to your chest (vertically), and lower your H-T into it until the signal begins to weaken. Holding the H-T in place, turn around slowly and listen for a sudden decrease in signal strength. If you don't get a good null, vary the depth of the H-T in the tube and try again. Repeat until you get the null that you need to determine the direction. You do not need to watch the S meter; in fact it will likely be out of sight in the tube. Keep adjusting the depth until you get a sharp null.

This method of direction finding is highly dependent on your body's particular shielding characteristics. The depth of suspension that works for another person will not necessarily work for you. Experiment with it until you get a feel for what works best. It will take a little persistence to find your most effective technique.

A word of warning about reflections: they can and will obscure or shift the null in unpredictable ways. If you are hunting in a car, step well away from the vehicle before trying to get a bearing. Avoid large buildings, cyclone fences, metal signposts and the like. Hunting in a crowd of people is nearly useless because many of us are tall enough to be good reflectors at 146 MHz! Make sure that anyone standing nearby is at least 10 to 15 feet away when you are taking a bearing.

With this setup you can obtain an impressive amount of useful attenuation. I've been able to get a good null while standing less than five feet from a 30-watt transmitter. I simply extended the wrist strap with a shoelace to get sufficient depth in the tube. On another occasion, I nearly stumbled over a transmitter hidden in tall grass when I took a step backward in the indicated direction. It's dynamite for close-in work!

Fig 2—Using the attenuator tube. The H-T is suspended by the wrist strap inside the tube. For very strong signals, such as those encountered close to a hidden transmitter, remove the rubber duck antenna and suspend the H-T deeper within the tube, adjusting depth for optimum signal strength. (*photo by Don Pass*)

The best thing about it is the cost: next to nothing if you scrounge the tube and scavenge some foil from the kitchen. Construction time is less than five minutes. This is an ideal group project, too. Think what it would mean if everyone in your club had one of these tubes in their car and knew how to use it, ready to help locate a jammer, a "stuck" transmitter, or a rescue beacon!

Notes

[1] E. Jordan, Ed., *Reference Data for Engineers: Radio, Electronics, Computer and Communications*, seventh edition, Howard W. Sams Inc, 1986. Page 30-3, "Propagation of Electromagnetic Waves in Hollow Waveguides." Page 30-8, "Attenuation in a Waveguide Beyond Cutoff."

[2] Joseph D. Moell, KØOV, and Thomas N. Curlee, WB6UZZ, *Transmitter Hunting: Radio Direction Finding Simplified* (TAB books, 1987), p 61, "The Waveguide Attenuator."

Glen, KC6TNF, is a technical writer with Systron Donner, Safety Systems Division in Concord, California. In his boyhood he accompanied his dad, W8BQD, on many transmitter hunts in Michigan. Licensed in March 1991, Glen's major interests are packet radio, satellite communications, and transmitter hunting.

Radio Tips:

Those Versatile Hand-Helds

Hams call them HTs, handie-talkies, walkie-talkies and bricks. And countless amateurs select pocket-sized hand-held VHF/UHF FM transceivers as their first rigs. Hand-held transceivers save money over buying separate mobile and base units, and they work fine for FM simplex, repeater or packet operation. That's a lot of versatility for such a small package!

In the US there are more than 6000 repeaters on 2 meters, 1600 on 220 MHz, 4100 on 440 MHz and 200 on 1.2 GHz. There are even FM repeaters that are linked to 10 meters, opening up the possibility of long-distance contacts (yes, codeless Technicians can legally use repeater links to the 10-meter FM subband).

It's great to keep your radio nearby, whether you're in the living room, in your backyard or out for a walk. Hand-held transceivers can be used to talk to the ground crew while you're working atop a 100-foot tower or to keep in touch with friends as you browse at a flea market.

To get the most from portable operating, be sure your battery's charged and keep a spare on hand. The "rubber duckie" antennas supplied with hand-held transceivers are adequate, but you can substitute a telescoping whip for increased performance.

A hand-held rig can become a mobile unit if you have a cigarette-lighter power adapter and a magnetic-mount or trunk-lip mount antenna. Using VHF/UHF FM, you can ask for directions, call for help (for yourself or another stranded motorist), exchange information on road conditions or enjoy a pleasant chat during your daily commute. A lonesome road through unfamiliar terrain is safer if you can contact other hams.

If you use a hand-held rig in your car, it's worthwhile to invest in a remote speaker/mike to avoid having to hold the transceiver up to your face when you transmit. In noisy vehicles, hand-held transceivers may not put out enough audio to be heard clearly. This can be remedied by connecting an extension speaker with a built-in 12-V audio amplifier to boost the sound level.

If you use your hand-held transceiver in your car, be sure both sides of the power cable are fused. The manufacturer may offer a power adapter with this feature or you can make the cable yourself. Secure the radio so it doesn't fly off the console during quick maneuvers or conk you in the head if you have to stop quickly. Keep it shielded from direct sunlight, but mount it near your line of sight. Better yet, get to know your rig well enough so you don't need to look at it to make adjustments while driving. Don't leave your rig inside your car on a hot summer day.

Do you enjoy traffic-handling? Do you like to chat with friends while burning dinner or watching *The Simpsons*? Bring your hand-held into the house, connect it to a 12-V power supply and you're all set. You can mount a good antenna on your roof, tower or inside the attic. In a pinch, plop a mobile mag-mount antenna on top of the refrigerator or a cookie sheet. In urban areas, almost anything will get you on the air!

Standard AX.25 or TCP/IP packet radio operation on FM works fine with your hand-held transceiver. You can use it in the field or in your car with a laptop computer, or in your shack with a desktop PC or terminal. All you need is a source of power (a battery or a power supply) and a cable to connect your rig to your TNC. Almost every type of hand-held radio has been used for packet, so it shouldn't be difficult to get information on how to wire the mike and speaker connections.

You can invest between $75 and $600 in a hand-held VHF/UHF FM ham transceiver. It all depends on features, whether you buy new or used, single-band or multiband, and other variables. Older models cost less and are easy to find at hamfests and flea markets, but may be crystal-controlled, put out less power and lack fancier features. It's also difficult to find battery packs and accessories for older rigs.

Modern units are computer-controlled with dozens of features, put out plenty of power and may include more than one band. It will take you a while to learn how to use all their buttons and knobs!

The best strategy in selecting a rig is to talk to other hams, ask to try out their radios, browse through used-equipment classified ads and haunt local hamfests. Sooner or later, you'll locate the perfect all-purpose hand-held rig.—*NTØZ*

Do I Need a Linear Amplifier?

By Lee Aurick, W1SE
1043 Deer Run Rd
Winter Springs, FL 32708

Have you been putting off buying a linear amplifier because you weren't certain about what it would do for you? Many new amateurs, and a few old-timers too, aren't sure if the cost is really worth the benefit. They also wonder if an amplifier might infringe on some of the other equipment in the station, and where it would fit in the normal chain of components leading to the antenna. Well, wonder no longer. Here are answers to some questions you may have been afraid to ask!

"Joe Ham"

Pretend for a moment that you're the typical "Joe Ham." Your station includes a modern HF transceiver, an SWR/power meter and an antenna tuner. It's a modest, but complete station. The reason you need the antenna tuner is because you've erected the "standard" 135-foot center-fed wire antenna used by thousands of hams. You're feeding it with low-loss coaxial cable or ladder line and you're using it on nearly all bands. Because of the action of the antenna tuner, your radio "sees" a 50-Ω impedance on all bands and generates its full output power as measured by the power meter.

For some reason, you decide that it might be nice if you could operate with just a bit more *authority*. Perhaps you've been frustrated trying to work some difficult DX. Maybe your friend, whom you meet on the air each week, keeps telling you that your signal is "in the mud." Will a linear amplifier solve your problems?

Adding Up the dBs and Dollars

It's a case of "how far do you want to go?" as well as, "how much money do you have to spend?" First, let's see what you get for each increase in power. Then we can take a look at what it might cost to achieve the increase.

If we ignore the amplifiers that use TV sweep tubes (never designed, intended, or tested for RF-amplifier service), you might be looking at an amplifier with a single 3-500Z, or two or three 811A tubes. These amplifiers can provide a marginal, but worthwhile step-up in power with an output in the range of 500 to 600 W. How will it affect your signal strength at the other station?

The amount of received-signal improvement follows an immutable law: Each time you double your power output, your friend, or that distant DX station, is likely to see no more than a 3-dB increase on his or her S meter. In other words, their meters will only move up about one-half of an S unit—a paltry increase at best! To move their meters a full S unit, you must *quadruple* your output power: a 6-dB increase.

> *A linear amplifier may be one of the most overrated pieces of equipment in any ham station.*
>
> *Before you shell out the big bucks, make sure the pain is worth the gain!*

Look at it this way: You are presently running 100 W output. To move the S meter of the other station one unit, you must increase your power output to at least 400 W. Reaching the next 3-dB level, for a total of 9 dB, requires an output power of approximately 800 W—beyond the range of the amplifiers described above. This is a significant jump, but not the "booming" improvement you probably expected. It may be sufficient, however, to bring you out of the noise on some occasions.

Ten-Tec advertises its solid-state Hercules II amplifier. With a rated output of 550 W, it's roughly equivalent to the amplifiers we've been talking about. Its price is $1295, plus shipping and handling.

Of course, you could go shopping for a used amplifier and pay much less, but you never know what you're buying. Is it a gem or a dud? There is seldom an opportunity to test the equipment under such circumstances, and these used amps usually do not come with warranties. What you see is what you get!

Okay. You say you want more power. Going from 500 W to a kilowatt will give you another 3-dB increase. With a kilowatt, you're 10 dB above your non-amplified power output of 100 W. Now your buddy and the DX station will see slightly less than a two S-unit increase on their meters. They'll hear the improvement, but it won't be astounding.

How much will you shell out for this nearly two S-unit benefit? According to the same Ten-Tec advertisement, you'll pay $1395 for a Centurion amplifier *without tubes*. It will give you the necessary 1300 W PEP (for SSB) and 1000 W CW. The amplifier uses two 3-500Z tubes, which cost about $125 each. Finding the tubes, as well as the cost justification, is up to you.

Now for the big one. Hams are permitted to run 1500 W output. The FCC no longer specifies the maximum input power, as was done for more than 60 years. Ten-Tec has an amplifier to meet this majestic power level, if you feel you need it. The Titan delivers 1500 W on all modes with a pair of 3CX800 tubes. If you can afford the amplifier (at $2995), you can probably afford the cost of a new pair of tubes at replacement time. Henry Radio Company, ETO, Command Technologies, and other *QST* advertisers offer excellent, "legal-limit" amplifiers. Once again, however, the prices are considerable.

Even with a 1500-W monster, you're only running about 11 or 12 dB above the 100 W you had before you started. If the other stations look very closely at their S meters, they will notice that your signal has increased in strength by about two full S units. In other words, the needle will move about one-quarter inch to the right. If your former signal strength was an S7, you would now appear on their meters at about S9. The cost to achieve this improvement was "only" $3000. Add the cost of a 1500-W antenna tuner and you're up to almost $3500.

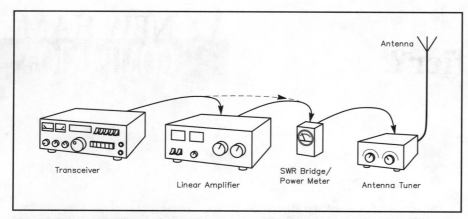

Figure 1—Block diagram of a station layout employing a linear amplifier. The dotted line above the amplifier indicates that when the amplifier is OFF, or in STANDBY, power from the transceiver goes directly through the linear without amplification. In the ON, or OPERATE positions, the unit will amplify the signal from the transceiver. The option is controlled automatically by the selection of a switch, or switches, on the linear amplifier.

Throughout this article we've been talking about improving a so-so signal, but you're not always weak. Let's say that your signal isn't down in the mud at all. Instead, it's 13 dB over S9 on your friend's meter. By switching on the monster amplifier, you'll pop up to 25 dB over S9. If the position of a needle on a meter is your only concern, that's a major improvement. But what about the effect on the *sound* of your signal? You'll sound just as loud and clear as you were before you reached for the amplifier **ON** switch.

If You *Really* Need One...

So, do you *need* an amplifier? Perhaps the better question is, do you *want* an amplifier? Ah, that's a different story! To some, it may be a status symbol, and may have absolutely nothing to do with improving their signal.

Look at it this way: Sometimes an amplifier will help you to be heard a bit better than you are now. It will do nothing for you as far as you hearing other stations is concerned.

You may want to consider a much smaller investment—such as a better antenna. It is an accepted axiom that one should improve the antenna to the max, before buying a linear amplifier.

But you want a linear amplifier, no matter what the cost or benefits, right? How do you install it in your station—and how does it affect the operation of the rest of your equipment?

It's really very simple. All linear amplifiers are built the same way in one respect. In **OFF** or **STANDBY** mode, the power from the transceiver is fed directly *through* the amplifier, as if the amp wasn't even there. It is only when the amplifier is switched to **ON**, or to **OPERATE**, that the unit comes to life. It accepts the power supplied to it by the transceiver, amplifies that power, and passes it on to the antenna.

It doesn't require any special skills on

your part to use an amplifier. Just read the manual and follow the directions. In most cases, using a linear amplifier is as easy, if not easier, than adjusting an antenna tuner.

Oh yes, did I mention that you will likely need a 240-V ac line in the shack to power your new amp? Many hams buy an amplifier without giving this consideration. Even a "small" amplifier may require 10 A at 240 V. That's 2400 W of electrical power. Many high-power transmitting tubes require at least 100 W just to light the filaments! Some amplifiers may be customer-wired to operate from 120 V, but now you're looking at pulling 20 A, or more, through your house wiring. The voltage drop may be more than you would consider acceptable. In addition, it isn't very safe. Your clothes dryer uses this much current and it's operated on 240 volts. Unlike your amplifier, the dryer is usually located in the same room with the circuit breakers or fuse box, and is connected with a short, heavy-duty, ac line.

I recommend that you hire a licensed electrician to run a 240-V line to your amplifier. Be sure to tell the electrician how much current the amplifier will be drawing. (And prepare yourself for a $200 to $300 bill.) If you're thinking of doing the wiring yourself consider this: If something goes wrong and your home is damaged, your insurance company could refuse to pay.

Linear amplifiers have their place. Depending on your operating goals, those times when it will make a difference may be important to you. In handing traffic when conditions are poor, it may spell the difference between success and failure. If you're a contester or a serious DX hunter, an amplifier combined with a superior antenna often makes a *big* difference. But if casual operating is your goal, spend your money on renovating your antenna instead. Only when you've improved your antenna system as much as possible should you even *consider* buying a linear amplifier. **QST**

Q Can you offer some advice on waterproofing coaxial connectors?

A It's my pleasure. Apply clear silicone grease to the threads and other parts of the connectors before you put them together. This will help keep out moisture. (It also makes it easier to get them apart after years of exposure.)

Wrap a layer self-vulcanizing splicing tape around the assembled connection. You'll find this type of tape at electrical-supply stores. Cover this layer with several wraps of Scotch 33 or 88, then Scotchkote. Be sure to overlap the edges of adjacent turns of tape to ensure watertightness. The combination of all these steps should protect your coaxial connectors for years to come.

Q I have a light dimmer in my living room. It's generating severe RF noise. How can I fix it?

A For the most part, the only way to fix a noisy dimmer is to replace it. There is usually not enough room inside the junction box to install a commercially available filter and the ac line is *not* the place for home-brew noise filters.

Some dimmers have a positive-on position at the top of their travel that switches the light directly to the line, bypassing the dimmer circuitry. When the control is fully on, therefore, there will be no interference from the dimmer. A line of toggle dimmers (the Dynapak line) with the positive-on position is made by Power Controls Corp, 1067 Bandera Rd, San Antonio, TX 78228.

One of our members recently discovered a dimmer that seems to be less noisy than most. It is model N-600 manufactured by Lutron Electronics Company, Suter Rd, Box 205, Coopersburg, PA 18036; tel 215-282-3800. Contact them to find the location of your nearest distributor.

Q I have three simple questions concerning the use of ladder line:
(1) Should it be twisted? If so, how many twists per foot?
(2) How close should it come to other metallic objects?
(3) Any guidelines for the radius of curves? In other words, how drastically can I bend it?

A Okay, three simple questions nets you three simple answers:
(1) Twisting isn't critical. Some hams believe that a 180° twist every 2 feet provides better stability in windy environments.
(2) Try to keep your ladder line a minimum of *twice* the line width from metallic objects. In the case of commonly used 450-Ω ladder line, that's about two inches.
(3) Make any bends and turns as gradual as possible. A one-foot minimum radius is a good rule of thumb for 450-Ω line.

Getting Started on the
Magic Band

NEW HAM COMPANION

By Ken Neubeck, WB2AMU
1 Valley Rd
Patchogue, NY 11772

Six meters (50 to 54 MHz) is commonly called the *magic band* by hams who operate it on a regular basis. This band has been misunderstood since its incorporation into the Amateur Radio spectrum in 1945. It has many nicknames besides the *magic band,* including the unfortunate misnomer, the *TVI band.*

Sadly, 6 meters seems to be known more as the "forgotten band" because it is often so empty. (According to an ARRL survey, there are twice as many active hams on 222 MHz than 6 meters.—*Ed.*) It enjoyed a golden age during the 1960s and, with all the new hams flooding into the VHF bands, it may rise to glory once again! All it takes is the proper equipment and, most important, the right *information.*

I've been a ham for more than 23 years with much of my first two decades spent on HF. During this time, I've gone through two sunspot minimums where the HF bands lost much of their utility for easy long-distance work. Even through the lean years I continued to prowl the bands and managed to achieve HF-oriented operating awards such as 5-Band DXCC. I viewed 6 meters as a kind of oddball band. Oh, I had some exposure to 6 meters during a couple of Field Day operations, but the spark never flared into full-fledged activity.

A little over three years ago, I found a complete 6-meter station at a local flea market. It included a Swan 250 transceiver, microphone and power supply—all for under $100. Once I figured out the rig and the various 6-meter calling frequencies, I finally made some contacts with a few locals. I worked even more stations during the September VHF QSO Party. Still, there was nothing to convince me that long-range contacts were commonplace. The band seemed quiet better than 90% of the time.

Sporadic E

When I finally heard my first *sporadic-E* opening in June of the following year, my whole perspective changed! Sporadic E is one of the most dominant long-distance modes you'll find on 6 meters. When

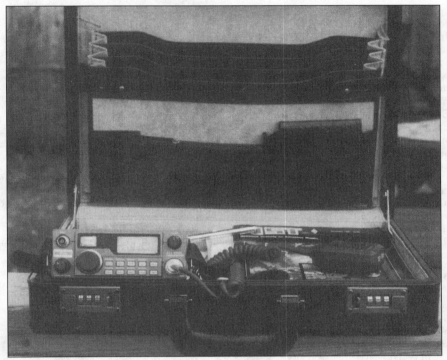

Figure 1—The Yaesu FT-690 Mark II transceiver is small enough to be carried in an attaché case during a business or vacation trip.

sporadic E is active, you can make contacts of over 1000 miles with low power.

Sporadic-E propagation has held the curiosity of hams and scientists for decades. What is known about sporadic E is that it follows a seasonal pattern and that it is caused by the formation of ion clouds in the E layer of the ionosphere. These ions are metallic in composition and are suspected to originate from meteors and other sources. The resulting clouds act like huge floating mirrors for radio signals, refract-

ing (bending) them back to Earth great distances from their point of origin. The clouds come and go depending on various conditions. Their erratic behavior is why we call the propagation they provide *sporadic* E.

I'm often annoyed by hams who assume 6 meters is worthless when the sunspot cycle declines toward its low ebb—as it is now. Yes, global *F2* propagation disappears, but sporadic E is strong *throughout the entire solar cycle*! During the summer

> *If you're looking for a good VHF band that offers both local and long-distance communication, 6 meters may be right for you!*

of 1993, I saw a number of double-hop sporadic E openings from my home on Long Island into the West Coast and even Europe. I worked CU1AZ from the Azores with just 10 W and a dipole! Sporadic E is especially good for low-power work. There is less signal loss because of the efficiency of sporadic-E refraction.

I counted over 70 days of sporadic-E openings during the four summer months of May, June, July and August 1993. Certainly, there is an optimal time for sporadic E depending on your location. As a rule, the summer months are the best for stations in the mid-latitude areas of the Earth. There are occasional openings in the winter, too. Most sporadic-E openings take place at midday and during the early evening hours.

After spending most of the last three years on 6 meters, I find it difficult to get back into the swing of things on the HF bands. It's no longer business as usual for me on HF now that I'm active on six!

A Great *Local* Band, Too

Six meters is greatly underutilized as a local communication band. There is over 2 MHz of FM repeater space available and yet you'll be lucky to hear one or two repeaters in use at any given time (unless you live in Southern California). Even the weak-signal modes such as CW and SSB should see more activity than they do. The sad part about this lack of local activity is that 6 meters has excellent *groundwave* capability. You can work stations up to 100 miles away using about 50 W of power. I once worked a station 45 miles away using just 2.5 W and a mobile whip antenna! It goes without saying that 6 meters is an excellent band for mobile and portable work, regardless of what mode you choose.

Equipment Options

If you want HF coverage in addition to 6 meters, you have plenty of choices. ICOM's IC-729 is an HF rig that includes 6 meters. In addition, the ICOM IC-575H is a 100-W transceiver that covers 6 and 10 meters exclusively. By the time you read this, ICOM will also be introducing their new IC-736. The IC-736 is a 100-W all-mode HF transceiver that features 6-meter coverage. Another radio worth considering is the Kenwood TS-690. This is an HF rig with a 6-meter option. Not to be left out, Yaesu offers their FT-650 and FT-690 transceivers, both of which include 6 meters.

Figure 2—The author with his portable 2-element 6-meter Yagi antenna in its retracted position. The antenna is made of telescoping elements normally used for automobile antennas. The antenna dimensions follow the standard formulas for Yagi antennas found in the *ARRL Antenna Book.*

FRAN NEUBECK

Further Reading...

Books

Six Meters—A Guide to the Magic Band by Ken Neubeck, WB2AMU. Published by WorldRadio, PO BOX 189490, Sacramento, CA 95818. $10 plus $2 shipping and handling.

This new book is a labor of love by the author and it provides comprehensive information on all of the equipment and modes that can be found on this band. In addition, a little history of the golden age of 6 meters is provided along with some explanations for the causes of various forms of propagation.

The ARRL Handbook and the *ARRL Operating Manual.* See your dealer or the Publications Catalog elsewhere in this issue.

Articles

E. Pocock, "Sporadic-E Propagation at VHF: A Review of Progress," *QST*, April 1988.

K. Neubeck, "The Mysterious 6-Meter Band," *QST*, December 1992

The Yaesu FT 690 Mark II and the new Kenwood TS-60S are currently the only *single-band* 6-meter all-mode transceivers on the market. The Yaesu FT-690 (see Figure 1) is in the $700 price range with 10-W output, and the TS-60S is about $1000, with 90-W output. Both are small enough to pack in a suitcase for portable or mobile work.

If you're particularly interested in 6-meter FM work, Azden has two radios that are right up your alley. The PCS-7500H is a 50-W mobile transceiver that lists for $389. The ultimate in 6-meter FM convenience may be the Azden AZ-61 *hand-held* transceiver! This 5-W rig lists for $379 and gives you the capability to operate 6-meter FM anywhere. FM enthusiasts may also want to consider the ICOM IC-901, a 2-meter/70-cm transceiver has a 6-meter option.

VHF/UHF operators will want to look closely at multiband all-mode radios such as the Yaesu FT-736. With the addition of a single module, the FT-736 will operate on 6 meters.

Of course, if you can't afford new radios, try the used market. Used gear is not too common despite the large number of rigs built in the 1960s. As a newcomer, however, be aware that older rigs may require fixing—and may be more prone to TVI complaints.

Antennas for 6 meters are very easy to construct. A half-wave dipole cut to 50.1 MHz is only 112 inches long. A quarter-wave vertical is just 56 inches in height. The small wavelength of the band is ideal for all types of antenna experimentation. My friend Tom Glaze, KC4SUS, built a high-performance, 7-element cubical quad for 6 meters. You don't have to get this elaborate, however. Yagi beams with two or three elements are fairly easy to build and work quite well (see Figure 2).

Don't be fooled by all the photos of 6-meter beam antennas that you see in books and magazines. You don't really need a beam to become active on 6 meters! Simple wire dipoles and verticals are effective antennas on this band, particularly if you have a space problem.

Getting the *Feel* of 6 Meters

One part of the 6-meter problem is education. New hams have a difficult time learning about the excitement this band has to offer. The only solution is to take matters into your own hands. If you have a receiver with 6-meter capability, tune to 50.110 or 50.125 MHz and listen for SSB activity. You'll also find that

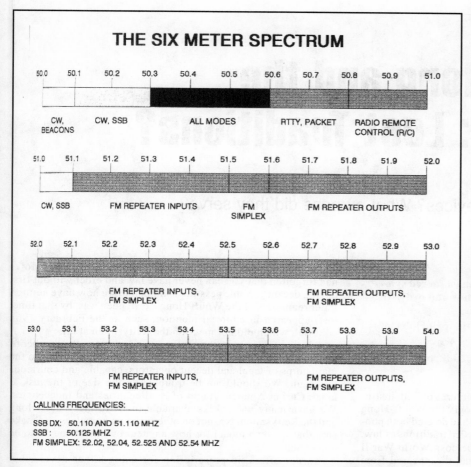

THE SIX METER SPECTRUM

| 50.0 | 50.1 | 50.2 | 50.3 | 50.4 | 50.5 | 50.6 | 50.7 | 50.8 | 50.9 | 51.0 |

| CW, BEACONS | CW, SSB | ALL MODES | RTTY, PACKET | RADIO REMOTE CONTROL (R/C) |

| 51.0 | 51.1 | 51.2 | 51.3 | 51.4 | 51.5 | 51.6 | 51.7 | 51.8 | 51.9 | 52.0 |

| CW, SSB | FM REPEATER INPUTS | FM SIMPLEX | FM REPEATER OUTPUTS |

| 52.0 | 52.1 | 52.2 | 52.3 | 52.4 | 52.5 | 52.6 | 52.7 | 52.8 | 52.9 | 53.0 |

| FM REPEATER INPUTS, FM SIMPLEX | FM REPEATER OUTPUTS, FM SIMPLEX |

| 53.0 | 53.1 | 53.2 | 53.3 | 53.4 | 53.5 | 53.6 | 53.7 | 53.8 | 53.9 | 54.0 |

| FM REPEATER INPUTS, FM SIMPLEX | FM REPEATER OUTPUTS, FM SIMPLEX |

CALLING FREQUENCIES:

SSB DX: 50.110 AND 51.110 MHZ
SSB: 50.125 MHZ
FM SIMPLEX: 52.02, 52.04, 52.525 AND 52.54 MHZ

Figure 3—As you can see from this chart, 4 MHz of spectrum awaits you on 6 meters. The chart is organized to show the frequencies for various modes and activities.

52.525 MHz is an active FM simplex frequency (see Figure 3). Try monitoring during the late afternoon and early evening hours.

Some new hams are negatively influenced by what they hear from veterans concerning television interference on 6 meters—particularly in areas where Channel 2 is active. It's true that TVI was a serious problem in the past, but things have changed. Transceivers have much better output filtering to reduce the potential for interference. In addition, well over half the homes in the United States are wired for cable TV. A cable system that's working properly is much less susceptible to 6-meter interference than over-the-air TV reception.

I don't want to oversell the long-range capability of 6 meters. Sporadic E or F2 propagation is not an everyday occurrence as it can be on the HF bands. It's not a *given* that you can routinely contact any part of the world on 6 meters since the band is open for skip communication less than 10% of the time. The challenge is to be there when an opening occurs!

Listening to 6 meters sharpens your radio sense and your monitoring skills. Not only should you monitor the SSB calling frequencies, you should also hunt for bea-

con signals in the 50.0- to 50.1-MHz range. Beacons are the navigational buoys of the ham bands. They're typically low-power CW stations that transmit repeatedly on one frequency. On 6 meters, they are particularly valuable because you can use them to spot band openings. Beacon lists can be found in both the *ARRL Repeater Directory* and the *ARRL Operating Manual*.

A Band is a Terrible Thing to Waste

In all likelihood, we will retain our privileges to operate on 6 meters because no commercial or military groups are interested in this block of radio spectrum—yet! Why should we let these frequencies go to waste? Six meters is becoming popular in several countries in Europe because their amateurs were recently granted privileges to use the band. Activity there and in Japan actually *exceeds* activity levels in the US.

What's our excuse? Here is a band that can be accessed by all Amateur Radio license classes other than Novice, yet it is the least-used spectrum in the VHF range. Aside from casual operating, experimental work is being done on this band. Not only are there the many interesting phenomena such as sporadic E, meteor scatter and auroral propagation, but other activities such as moonbounce and radio control

have carved out niches on 6 meters.

If more amateurs knew how much fun 6 meters can be, and how easy it is to construct decent antennas, I think they would be pleasantly surprised. As the sunspot count declines over the next few years, HF band conditions will deteriorate. Why not give 6 meters a try and see how much fun you can have?

Ken Neubeck, WB2AMU, is a Long Island native who was first licensed in 1971 as WN2AMU. He upgraded to General the following year and earned his Extra Class in 1988. He is an avid VHF and 10-meter contester. Ken works as a reliability engineer with the Parker Gull Company in Smithtown, New York. QST-

---

Radio Tips: *Activity Nights*

Unless there is a contest or band opening going on, scaring up an SSB or CW conversation on the VHF and UHF bands isn't always easy. To encourage more so-called *weak signal* operation, informal *activity nights* have been established in many parts of the country. Each band has its own night.

There is a lot of variation in activity nights from place to place, so don't trust the following chart to be entirely accurate. Check with someone in your area to find out about local activity nights.

Band (MHz)	Day	Local Time
50	Sunday	6:00 PM
144	Monday	7:00 PM
222	Tuesday	8:00 PM
420	Wednesday	9:00 PM
902	Friday	9:00 PM
1296	Thursday	10:00 PM

Activity nights are especially important for 222 MHz and above. If you've just finished a new transverter or antenna for one of these bands, you'll have a much better chance to test them during one of the activity nights. This doesn't mean that there is no activity on the other nights. It may just take longer to get someone's attention.

On activity nights your best bet is to check around the established calling frequencies. Most hams will make their initial contacts on these frequencies, then move off to other frequencies nearby. The following list of calling frequencies applies to domestic SSB or CW only—*Mike Owen, W9IP*

Band (MHz)	Calling Frequency
50	50.125 (SSB)
144	144.100, 144.110 (CW) 144.200 (SSB)
222	222.1 (SSB/CW)
432	432.1 (SSB/CW)
902	903.1 (SSB)
1296	1296.1 (SSB/CW)

By L. B. Cebik, W4RNL

The Wouff-Hong and the Rettysnitch: Lost Traditions?

Who made these dreaded devices? What purpose did they serve?

> "The Wouff-Hong is Amateur Radio's most sacred symbol and stands for the enforcement of law and order in amateur operation."
>
> "The Rettysnitch...is used to enforce the principles of decency in operating work."
>
> —from *The Radio Amateur's Handbook,* 1930, page 11

In 1930, *The ARRL Handbook* had pictures of both instruments of enforcement. By 1936, only the Wouff-Hong appeared. By 1947 the *Handbook* had deleted both photos. Just when Amateur Radio needed traditions of law, order and decency to guide its growth in the post–World War II explosion of technology, these symbols had disappeared from view.

Many of today's hams have never seen a Wouff-Hong or a Rettysnitch. To rectify that gap in hamdom's essential history, I present two examples for your inspection. The Wouff-Hong appears in Figure 1. The two main pieces are constructed of wood banded by metal strapping and by heavy wire. Some hams say that a true Wouff Hong is marked by a dark area at the upper end of the longer wood piece, as if stained by blood or purified for its grave duties in the fires of purgatory—or both.

The Rettysnitch, an all-metal tool, is shown in Figure 2. Of the five teeth around the disk near the pointed end, only three remain. According to tradition, the other two have done their work and perished in the effort.

The Story

The story of the Wouff-Hong and the Rettysnitch was retold in 1934. Thanks to Ed Guilford in Bothell, Washington, I have the May 1934 *QST,* in which Rufus P. Turner—famous in the annals of electronics writing—recounted "Hamdom's Traditions: A Bedtime Story for Young Squirts." But even by Turner's time, the Rettysnitch was relegated to a paragraph on the story's continuation page in the back of the magazine. Somehow, even then, folks had forgotten that you can never have law and order without first having decency. Some pessimists think that we now have neither. Later reminders of the Wouff Hong (its hyphen was, by that time, lost) appeared in editorial mention, such as the February 1961 editorial, which did not mention the Rettysnitch at all.

I do not subscribe to the pessimist's view. Sure, the number of rotten operators has skyrocketed, but not their proportion to the main corps of legal and decent operators, capable and courteous to a fault. We should not be troubled by the size of the task at hand: Curing Amateur Radio of its illegalities and indecencies. We have many more folks available to wield the Wouff-Hong and the Rettysnitch. No, not on others, but on *ourselves*—to make sure that we set a model for how amateur operations ought to be conducted.

Turner offers no prescription for using either device, but thought the Wouff-Hong was capable of beating out King Kong's brains or plowing up acres of Manhattan bedrock. That will tell you something of the power of these machines. But it won't tell you how they came to be.

We must revisit T.O.M.—The Old Man—who wrote, in the earliest days, of "Rotten QRM." His very first article in 1917 blasted the concocted Morse abbreviations coming into use. From among the almost unintelligible gibberish in his headphones came the words "wouff hong" and "rettysnitch," which he guessed must surely be instruments of terrifying punishment. By mid-1917, the ARRL was besieged by orders for these contraptions, orders that could not be filled because the Headquarters staff had never seen either device.

In 1919, after World War I (then called simply the Great War, since no one could imagine doing all that destruction and killing all over again), the League once more took up its work in earnest. At this critical time, the directors received from The Old Man a package containing an authoritative and well-preserved specimen of the Wouff-Hong. Turner described the contents of the package as "the gruesome instrument of torture." By order of the directors, it was hung in the office of the secretary-editor, within easy reach.

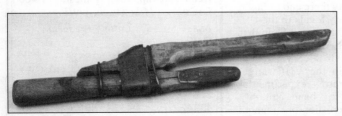

Figure 1—The original Wouff-Hong designed and built by "The Old Man" himself, Hiram Percy Maxim, W1AW. You can see it on display in the ARRL museum.

Figure 2—The Rettysnitch was truly a device of excruciating torture. Note the missing teeth! This is the *original* model, also enshrined in the ARRL museum.

Its first portrait appeared in the July 1919 issue of *QST*. At each Board meeting, the Wouff-Hong stood on display, to the blanched looks of the humbled directors.

The Old Man also presented the world with its first glimpse of the Rettysnitch. In 1921, the monstrous machine was presented to the League's traffic manager by the Washington, DC, Radio Club, ostensibly after receiving it from T.O.M. Even at its first public appearance, two of its teeth were missing, suggesting a long history of necessary and effective use. However, to this day, the Rettysnitch has lost no further teeth. It was ordered to be displayed by its mate.

In the 1920s and '30s, many reproductions of both instruments—but especially of the Wouff-Hong—materialized across the country. A group of hams in Flint, Michigan, created a mystic society known as the Royal Order of the Wouff-Hong. The society endures to this day, according to legend (I have, so far, not been privy to complete information). And The Old Man has been given a name: Hiram Percy Maxim, W1AW. According to legend, T.O.M. glared at "Kitty" while reflecting on the "rottenness" of everything. Maxim did have a cat. However, true to feline nature, Maxim's cat never spilled the beans.

We Need Them *Now*

But what has become of the Wouff-Hong and the Rettysnitch? More importantly, what has become of their power to enforce decency and order on the ham bands? Hams used to cringe at the thought, let alone the sight, of these dreadful tools of enforcement. But, we do not hear of them much anymore. Oh, a tremor of curiosity every now and again brings out a ripple of questions and speculation. But not much more than a ripple.

You see, today, we have much more terrifying weapons, things like Uzis and H-bombs and the like. They scare us in ways that seem to make the Wouff-Hong and the Rettysnitch tame and toothless. However, even in Maxim's day, objectively more powerful weapons were used in France—tanks, and gas more poisonous than that made by Texas chili. Why were the Wouff-Hong and the Rettysnitch so powerful to those early hams?

Because those hams cared about Amateur Radio in their hearts. They desired that which they knew they could never have: A perfectly law-abiding, decent radio service that would inspire young and old alike to become hams or, lacking the inclination to electronics, to become admirers of hams. Every minute of on-the-air time was a chance to show how noble a pursuit Amateur Radio was and should always be. They feared the Wouff-Hong and the Rettysnitch as instruments of their own consciences, as they strove to meet the standards they set for themselves.

And that is where you will find the Wouff-Hong and the Rettysnitch today—deep in your own conscience. If they seem to hold no power, then you know it's time once more to elevate your standards a notch higher, and then to strive to achieve them perfectly. Each of us has a secret and private office where no one else may go. Above the door, facing our individual operating tables, hang two instruments, one of law and order, the other of decency. However much the outside world may neglect the traditions of these terrible reminders of responsibility, each of us possesses our own Wouff-Hong and Rettysnitch. May you never deserve their sting.

Like all legends, this one, too, must end with special words: *Pass it on.*

This article originally appeared in the New England QRP Newsletter *edited by Dennis Marandos, K1LGQ.*—Ed.

1434 High Mesa Dr
Knoxville, TN 37938-4443
e-mail cebik@utk.edu

QST

Q Ken Holden, KB2SFS, asks, "What are the differences between RTTY and packet? Do these modes require special radios? Can you operate RTTY or packet over telephone lines?"

A There are a number of differences between radioteletype (RTTY) and packet. The principal ones are:

❏ RTTY sends information in a continuous stream of data. Packet sends information in bits and pieces (no pun intended!) known as *frames*.

❏ Packet has the ability to detect errors and request retransmissions of damaged frames. Generally speaking, you see only error-free text on your monitor. RTTY has no error-detection scheme. Whatever makes it through the noise and interference, plus whatever the noise and interference fools your demodulator into thinking it has received, is what you get.

❏ Packet supports the complete ASCII character set, including upper- and lower-case letters. RTTY uses a truncated character set that allows only upper-case letters and limited punctuation.

❏ To converse in packet you must establish a *connection* with another station according to the AX.25 packet protocol. This involves certain timing parameters, the exchange of particular data frames and so on. Your packet terminal node controller (TNC) does this for you automatically. RTTY doesn't require such an elaborate connection. You simply key the transmitter and start typing.

❏ Packet requires reasonably strong, stable signals to maintain connections. RTTY is useable under all conditions—as long as you don't mind some very fragmented copy when the going gets rough.

RTTY is favored among HF digital contest operators because of the ease with which quick contacts can be made. You'll also see it used frequently by DX operators for similar reasons. Although packet is used on HF, it is best on VHF and UHF where noise, fading and interference are not as common.

Just about any transceiver can be used for RTTY or packet. RTTY is a 100% duty-cycle mode (continuous full-power transmissions). If the radio you're using for RTTY is not rated for 100% duty cycle operating, you'll need to reduce the output, perhaps by as much as 50%, to avoid damage.

Power isn't a consideration for packet, but the radio must be able to switch rapidly from transmit to receive. When your radio transmits a packet frame, for example, it must jump to receive immediately to hear the response from the other station.

Because both RTTY and packet rely on audio tones to send information, you could certainly operate over telephone lines, but it wouldn't be nearly as much fun!

Q Myles Myers, W4OMC, asks, "I own a Kenwood TS-520SE transceiver. My problem is that when I key the mike, the rig will not return to the receive mode. I have to switch the radio off completely, then turn it on again. I've checked the transmit/receive relay, but it seems to be operating normally."

A Let's assume that the relay is okay. If this is the case, I suspect the transistor that switches the relay could be defective, or abnormally biased. A biasing resistor could have shifted in value, or a dc-blocking capacitor could be leaky.

If all is well with the switching circuit, you need to inspect the previous stages with a similar idea in mind. Measure the PTT line with a voltmeter and see if something is keeping it "shorted out." A faulty PTT switch isn't the most likely culprit, however. It wouldn't be "fixed" by turning the radio off.

NEW HAM HORIZONS

W1AW at the Flick of a Switch

If you don't already have a shortwave receiver capable of receiving code practice and news from W1AW, this little build-it-yourself gadget can do the job for under $35!

By Lee Richey, WA3FIY
RD #4 Box 220 Miller Rd
Franklin, PA 16323

O ur radio club's Novice training program director needed a simple, low-cost receiver that could be built in quantity by club members and loaned to students in our classes. Here's the result: a two-IC, fixed-tuned direct-conversion receiver you can build to hear W1AW code practice and news bulletins at 80, 40 or 20 meters. It's simple to use: You just turn it on and listen! It can produce useful W1AW audio even with 15 to 20 feet of wire as an antenna. Best of all, building it is easy because a complete kit is available.[1]

The Receiver Circuit

Fig 1 shows the circuit. An NE602A mixer/oscillator IC serves as the detector. Two sections of an MC33078 low-noise opera-

[1]Complete kits (including crystal, but less battery, antenna and headphones) are available for $29.95 (plus $3.25 UPS shipping to the 48 contiguous states; PA residents, add $1.80 sales tax); specify the R1-80 (80 meters), R1-40 (40 meters) or R1-20 (20 meters). Crystals for the 40- and 20-meter W1AW frequencies are available separately for $5 postpaid; specify 060-0130 (40 meters) or 062-0129 (20 meters). PC boards, less parts, are available for $6.50 postpaid; specify 090-0035. To order, or for information on quantity discounts and the availability of wired and tested units, contact Matric Limited, RD #4 Box 240, Franklin, PA 16323, telephone 814-432-3647, fax 814-432-8434.

tional amplifier filter the detector's audio and amplify it to headphone level. The MC33078 provides adequate drive for most low to medium impedance headsets.

Construction Notes

Building the receiver from the available kit (which includes a printed-circuit board and punched metal panel/base as shown in the photos) is probably the quickest, easiest and most sure-fire way of getting this receiver going. You can also build it from scratch, of course.

The values of the input tuning components (coils L1-L3, capacitors C1-C6, and the crystal) depend on the band you choose (80, 40

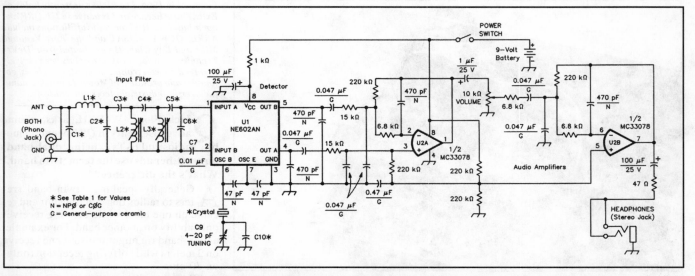

Fig 1—You can build this simple circuit to pull in W1AW code practice at 80, 40 or 20 meters—either from scratch, or from the kit available from Matric Limited. Info for scratch-builders: All of the receiver's resistors are 5%-tolerance, ¼-W carbon film units. The **VOLUME** control is an audio-taper potentiometer that includes a switch. The circuit's polarized capacitors (those with one lead marked +) can be rated anywhere from 10 to 50 WVDC.

Which Band Should You Choose?

Should you build your receiver for 80, 40 or 20 meters? These two maps give a rough idea of which of the receiver's three bands often provides the best daytime and nighttime reception of W1AW in the 48 contiguous states. First, think about whether you'll listen to W1AW in the morning or afternoon/evening. Use the "Day" map shown below for sessions before your local sunset. Then check the corresponding map for an idea of which band to listen on at that time. Finally, check with local hams to learn what bands *they* prefer for W1AW reception at the times you'll listen. Your choice of 80, 40 or 20 meters should be pretty clear by then.—*David Newkirk, WJ1Z*

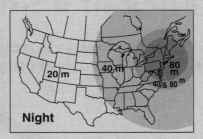

Table 1
Band-Specific Parts for the W1AW Receiver

	80 Meters	40 Meters	20 Meters
C1	1000 pF	470 pF	180 pF
C2	2200 pF	1200 pF	390 pF
C3	270 pF	150 pF	39 pF
C4	22 pF	8.2 pF	2.7 pF
C5	2200 pF	560 pF	82 pF
C6	270 pF	180 pF	68 pF
C10	not used	8.2 pF	2.7 pF
L1	2.2 µH	1.2 µH	0.82 µH
	(Mouser 43LS226 or Ocean State 70F226AI)	(Mouser 43LS126 or Ocean State 70F126AI)	(Mouser 43LQ827 or Ocean State 70F827AP)
L2/L3	6-8.2 µH	2.9-3.9 µH	2.9-3.9 µH
	(Digi-Key TK1416)	(Digi-Key TK1414)	(Digi-Key TK1414)
Crystal	3579.545 kHz	7047.5 kHz	14047.5 kHz
	(Digi-Key X-049)	(Matric 062-0130)	(Matric 062-0129)

Use ceramic C0G or NP0 units for all capacitors listed. See the main text's kit-ordering footnote for how to order Matric Limited parts.

For the addresses of Digi-Key, Mouser and Ocean State Electronics, see Table 42, the ARRL Parts Suppliers List, in Chapter 35 of the 1993 *ARRL Handbook*.

Yes, this is all there is to it: Put a handful of parts together, and you're receiving W1AW. The spaces you see for uninstalled components allow you to expand the receiver for use as part of a low-power (QRP) Morse code *transceiver!* *(photos by Kirk Kleinschmidt, NT0Z)*

or 20 meters). Table 1 lists the component values you need for each band. See the "Which Band Should You Choose?" sidebar for help in deciding between 80, 40 and 20.

The chassis consists of a 4¾- × 5-inch piece of aluminum bent into an **L** shape and equipped with stick-on rubber feet. If you want, you can label the front panel with W1AW's operating schedule.

Checkout and Alignment

To align the receiver, you need a strong test signal at or near your frequency of interest. To obtain one, connect a transmitter capable of producing a signal at your frequency of interest to a dummy antenna capable of handling its power. Connect a short wire to the receiver antenna terminal and lay this wire across the cable between the transmitter and the dummy antenna. Set the **TUNING** capacitor to midrange. Turn the **VOLUME** control up about ¼ of its travel, key the transmitter, and tune the transmitter slowly around your frequency of interest until you hear its signal in your headphones. Once you hear the test signal, adjust L2 and L3 for maximum volume, keeping the **VOLUME** control setting as low as possible for comfortable listening.

Connect an antenna to the receiver—a regular ham antenna, or almost any wire longer than 15 or 20 feet, should work—and wait until W1AW is on the air. Adjust the **TUNING** capacitor until you hear W1AW's code at a pleasant pitch. Now you can put your radio to work!

On the Air

This receiver provides good selectivity against interference, but sometimes other stations may operate very close to W1AW. Under these conditions, it's normal to hear more than one signal at a time. Don't be discouraged—copying W1AW with interference present builds your listening skill. Good luck, good practice, have fun improving your CW, and I hope to meet you on the air soon.

Licensed in 1966, Lee Richey presently holds an Extra Class license and is active in HF QRP and home building. His ham radio affiliations include ARRL, QCWA, AMSAT and the Fort Venango Mike and Key Club. He graduated from DeVry Technical Institute in 1962 and has been actively involved in electronics ever since. He is co-founder and president of Matric Limited, a manufacturer of industrial electronic controls.

Q **Jack Flory, W4RXH, asks, "Some advertisements in** *QST* **promote mobile radios and H-Ts as being 'dual-band' units. Other ads use the term 'twin band.' What's the difference?"**

A Generally speaking, "twin band" refers to radios that can transmit and receive on one band while offering receive-only ability on another band. For example, a twin-band rig might transmit and receive on 2 meters while offering reception (only) on 70-cm.

"Dual-band" transceivers can receive *and* transmit on two separate bands. A dual-band 2-meter/70-cm transceiver can transmit and receive on 2 meters *or* 70 cm.

Speaker-Mikes and Replacement Microphones

If you need an extra microphone, adapt a used commercial model.

By Robert B. Whitaker, KI5PG
121 S Main St, Suite 205
Victoria, TX 77901
Photos by the author

C ould you use an inexpensive speaker-microphone for your hand-held radio? Maybe you occasionally need a spare or back-up microphone for a mobile or base station radio. This article will show how easy it is for you to adapt a surplus microphone or speaker-mike for your specific requirements.

In the true spirit of hamming, I love to adapt or recycle radio gear. I hate to throw out anything that's still useful. Swapfests are great sources for cheap surplus commercial gear that performs quite well in amateur service. I've found that many commercial speaker-mikes and microphones work perfectly with amateur hand-held, base station, and mobile radios.

Roll Your Own Speaker-Mike for Hand-Helds

There are a lot of older commercial speaker-mikes finding their

A GE *Portamobile* speaker-microphone is ideal for use with H-Ts. It's durable and sounds great!

It takes a steady hand to solder microphone connectors. A small grip vise is a big help!

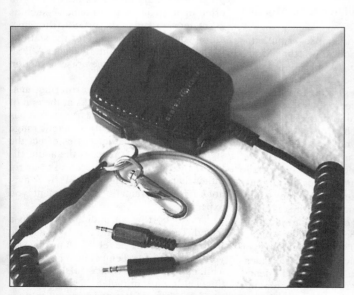

A belt clip can be added for strain relief by taking a larger gauge wire and wrapping a short loop around the cable.

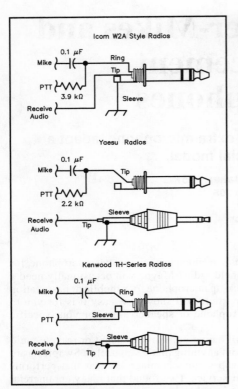

Figure 1—Speaker/microphone wiring diagrams for popular ICOM, Yaesu and Kenwood hand-held transceivers.

Connector Sources

Radio Shack

3-conductor, $1/8$-inch miniature plugs—274-1547 or 274-284
2-conductor, $3/32$-inch subminiature plugs—274-289
4-pin plug—274-001
8-pin plug—274-025

Mouser Electronics

2401 Highway 287 North
Mansfield, TX 76063-4827
tel 800-346-6873
3-conductor, $1/8$-inch miniature plugs—17PP004
2-conductor, $3/32$-inch subminiature plugs—17PP095
3-conductor, $3/32$-inch subminiature plugs—171-3305

way into swapfests and flea markets. They may be bulky compared to newer models, but they're still useful. Recently I picked up five GE *Portamobile* speaker-mikes at a swapfest for only $2 each. This model features a well-designed speaker and an electret microphone with a small built-in preamp. It works superbly with my Alinco DJ-580 H-T. I've also used this model with Kenwood and ICOM hand-held radios.

Of course, other models would probably work just as well. All you need to do is take the time to test them. Open the case and make written notes or draw a schematic diagram of the internal wiring. Identify the ground wire, the speaker wire, the microphone wire and the PTT (push-to-talk) wire.

The main concern in speaker-mike design is the keying circuitry. Most modern hand-helds fall into either of two categories. Kenwood TH-series radios key by completing a circuit between the PTT line and chassis ground. ICOM, Yaesu, Alinco and Radio Shack radios generally key by completing a circuit between the microphone lead and *PTT ground*. (Note that this is not electrically the same as chassis ground.) In these models a dropping resistor is often used in series with the microphone line. Different manufacturers may use different dropping resistor values. Check your owner's manual for specific information on your radio's external mike and speaker connections. If the manual does not include the information you need, try the H-T diagrams shown in Figure 1, or

call your manufacturer and ask for assistance from the service department.

Soldering H-T Speaker-Mike Connectors

I use small shielded audio cable to fabricate my connections. The cable is flexible and relatively easy to solder. It takes a steady hand to solder the subminiature connectors used with modern hand-held radios, though. Having a bright light and a mounting vise helps. Use a low-wattage, lightweight soldering iron with a sharp tip for best results.

Some H-T connector plugs may be difficult to locate. I grabbed a handful of hard-to-find $3/32$-inch three-conductor plugs at a recent swapfest. Radio Shack carries the $1/8$-inch three-conductor plugs and the smaller $3/32$-inch two-conductor plugs. (See the sidebar "Connector Sources.")

Replacement Microphones for Mobile and Base Radios

Quite frequently I see packet bulletins asking for microphones for the Alinco DR-1200 data radio. (Alinco doesn't include a mike with the DR-1200.) It's also common to see notices asking for other base and mobile replacement microphones. Many commercial microphones will operate with amateur mobile or base radios.

Most commercial radios, like most modern amateur radios, use amplified electret microphones. Commercial two-way radio shops usually have junk boxes full of these salvaged from broken rigs. Many times these high-quality commercial mikes can be garnered *free for the asking*—or for a modest contribution to the office coffee fund.

As with the H-T speaker-mikes, you must first open the microphone case to identify the ground wire, mike and PTT leads. Don't be afraid to rewire the microphone leads to suit your purposes. Your investment of modest and empirical (trial and error) ex-

perimentation often gives the greatest enjoyment! For example, I discovered that the GE *Portamobile* speaker-mikes do a super job with Kenwood TM-series mobile radios and the Alinco DR-1200.

Mike connectors for many base and mobile radios are different than those used for H-Ts. They often require a separate pin for supplying power to the microphone preamplifier. Fortunately, the GE *Porta-mobile* speaker-mike is already set up for this requirement with the addition of a dropping resistor and a coupling capacitor on the microphone lead. It's a tight squeeze to fit the additional components under the hood of the eight-pin connector, but it can be done!

QST.

Q **Robert Lockridge, KQ4NU, asks, "I'm using an older transceiver and a vertical antenna on the HF digital modes. My performance is disappointing and I'm debating whether I should invest in a DSP audio filter or a new radio. Any advice?"**

A Because you're using a vertical antenna, you're picking up signals from virtually every direction. Not only are you receiving the signals you want, you're also picking up a lot of signals you don't want. A digital signal processing (DSP) audio filter may improve your performance, especially in the digital modes and CW. If you often operate on crowded bands—such as 20 meters—a super-sharp DSP filter may allow you to separate some of the stations from the surrounding interference. A DSP filter may also offer some noise reduction for SSB work.

The problem with audio filtering, analog or digital, is that it works at the end of the pipeline, so to speak. If a transceiver has poor sensitivity, selectivity, dynamic range and so on, these characteristics effect the signal long before it reaches the audio filter. If the problem is centered in your rig rather than your antenna, a DSP filter may not offer the dramatic improvement you expect.

Try to borrow an audio filter from a friend. Test it with your transceiver and see if it provides the level of improvement you're looking for. Temper your expectations a bit. DSP filters are wonderful devices, but they can't work miracles. If you like what you hear, buy a filter and hang on to your transceiver for a few more years.

An Over-the-Dash H-T Mount

By Herbert Leyson, AA7XP
670 Wood Crest Dr
Springfield, OR 97477

Take your hand-held transceiver on the road. All you need is a coat hanger and some plastic tubing.

NEW HAM COMPANION

When I purchased my Radio Shack HTX-202 hand-held transceiver (H-T), operating 2-meter FM from a fixed location became a thing of the past. The portability of my H-T was wonderful and its *rubber duck* antenna was easy to manage on my patio! When I decided to try mobile operating, I quickly learned that I had nowhere to put the H-T when I wasn't using it—except in my lap!

My search for a suitable mounting position began. The radio had to be in front of me so I could easily change frequencies without taking my eyes off the road for more than a few seconds. The radio had to be within the length of my speaker/microphone cable. The H-T could not block my view of the instruments and it had to be mounted securely, yet easily released for out-of-vehicle action.

I located a good position on my dashboard. The radio would fit nicely just to the right of the instruments. The problem was how to mount it. I considered a handle secured to the dash with screws. The H-T's belt attachment could slip right over it. Not a bad idea, but I wasn't keen on drilling holes in the dashboard. I kept searching.

I soon discovered that I could hang my H-T in the desired position by using a rectangular wire loop covered with plastic tubing (see Figure 1). But how would I anchor the loop? Then I saw the air vents behind the windshield and my problem was solved. I hooked the loop into the air-vent slots and the H-T's belt clip attached to the end of the mount. The weight of the H-T held the entire mount in place (see Figure 2).

Construction

All you need is about three feet of stiff wire (I used a coat hanger) and two feet of 1/4-inch plastic tubing. The total cost is about a dollar and it will take you 20 to 30 minutes to assemble the mount once you find a suitable location.

The dimensions of the loop will vary according to the depth of your dashboard and the size of the belt clip on your H-T. I found that the fin hooks had to be long enough to prevent vibrations from bouncing the mount from the vents. In my case, the dashboard *saddle* was 8 1/2 inches long. I used a *drop* length of 3 inches for eye-level height on the dash. The *hanger* portion of my mount is 2 inches in length.

With the H-T attached to the mount, I can use the rubber duck antenna, or attach a coaxial cable to my 5/8-wavelength magmount antenna on the roof. My cigarette lighter is close by for power and the cables provide a "bounce guard" to protect the dash. If you can't prevent bouncing in this manner, add a trapeze onto the hanger bar and use a small piece of foam rubber to act as a cushion between the H-T and the dash. If you encounter too much left-to-right sway, spread the fin hooks for a firmer grip. Remember: Thread the plastic tubing onto the loop *before* you form the fin hooks! **QST.**

Q W. Andrew Houston, KD4MGE, asks, "A friend of mine and I own commercial radios as well as our ham transceivers. Rather than carry two transceivers on our belts, could we simply modify our ham rigs to work for both Amateur Radio *and* commercial applications?"

A You can't use your ham transceivers on commercial frequencies because they're not *type accepted* by the FCC. Type acceptance is granted only if a transceiver meets certain standards according to how it will be used. To gain type acceptance, a manufacturer must submit measurement data and other information to prove that the radio meets these standards. It's a long, expensive process.

On the bright side, it's a blessing that most Amateur Radio gear doesn't require type acceptance. As long as we operate within our privileges according to Part 97, we can build (or modify) our equipment without having to get clearance from the FCC.

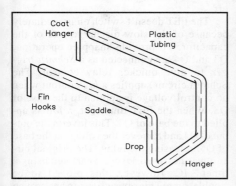

Figure 1—The over-the-dash H-T mount is made from a coat hanger covered with plastic tubing. The dimensions of the fin hooks, saddle, drop and hanger must be determined by measuring your dashboard and the belt clip on your H-T (see text).

Coat Hanger
Plastic Tubing
Fin Hooks
Saddle
Drop
Hanger

Figure 2—My HTX-202 hand-held transceiver is secure in its over-the-dash mount. Its own weight holds it in place. I can remove the radio in seconds, however, when I leave the car.

HERBERT LEYSON, AA7XP

I Wonder If...

Don't take chances with your mobile radio. Here's a circuit that protects your transceiver from power surges whenever you start your car.

By Jack Huston, WØJAW
PO Box 151
Woodland Park, CO 80866

When you climb into your car and turn the key in the ignition, do you find yourself thinking, "I wonder if the radio is on?" I bet some of you are saying, "Who cares? What difference does it make?" Believe me, it can make a world of difference when you consider the possible damage to your equipment!

Many hams follow auto industry recommendations and connect their radios directly to their automobile batteries. The battery and its charging system offer a stable source of high-current dc power. There is one disadvantage, however. When the engine is started, the radio is subjected to *inductive pulses* from the starter motor. The amplitudes of the pulses are directly dependent on such things as ambient temperature, age and charge state of the battery and the condition of the vehicle electrical system.

For example, if the battery is low and the engine is cranked with the radio on, these powerful pulses can wipe out your microprocessor memories. In some instances, the microprocessor must be reset (usually requiring removal and disassembly of the radio). And this is just the beginning. Depending on the strength of the pulse, even more serious damage may result.

In the good old days (when gas was 25 cents-per-gallon), American cars had a provision on the starter switch that temporarily disconnected power from the broadcast radio whenever the engine was started. Most hams used this function to activate a relay that switched power to their equipment *after* the car was up and running.

In those cheap-gas days, I operated 10-meter mobile using homemade AM equipment. This type of operation was similar to what hams enjoy today on 2-meter FM. As an FM user myself, I wanted to power my

2-meter rig just like my old 10-meter equipment. That is, when I started my car, I wanted the rig to come on automatically—*after* the engine was running. When I parked the car, I wanted the radio to shut off automatically. Unfortunately, many of the autos we drive today lack this capability. The only solution was to design a special circuit to do the job.

The project I'm about to describe restores this convenient, rig-saving feature to any vehicle in which the battery is used to power the transceiver directly. If you're like me, you probably forget to turn your rig off before you start your car. I forget to turn off my radio lots of times—and I've had to reprogram my transceiver a few times, too! Even when you do remember, you're not completely safe. A transceiver can still lose memory if it has an internal circuit that bypasses the main power switch.

The circuit shown in Fig 1 controls power to the radio, switching it on when the ignition is turned on, off when the starter is operating and back on when the engine is running. It also features a shut-down time delay. Whenever you turn off your car, the power to your radio is switched off automatically a couple of minutes later. This allows you to make (or hear) a few final comments even after your car has stopped running. When this circuit is in the idle mode, it draws only five milliamperes from the battery (many rigs draw the same amount of current or more when switched off).

The length of the shut-down time delay is set according to your preference. The values shown in Fig 1 provide about a five-minute delay. This may vary slightly depending on the quality and tolerance of the timing capacitor C1 and resistor R5. Increasing the values will result in a longer timing cycle. The circuit uses a Field-Effect Transistor (Q2) to generate the delay cycle and a power transistor (Q5) to switch a relay (K1). The relay is a 30-amp SPST type commonly used for switching fog lights. A small signal transistor (Q1) is used to switch off power when the engine is starting. Voltage from the ignition circuit keeps the relay closed whenever the ignition is on.

One factor that cannot be overlooked is the memory-backup battery inside the radio. **Do not use this circuit if your radio does not include a battery-backup feature.** This switching circuit completely disconnects the radio from its power source. If your rig does not have a backup battery to retain the microprocessor memories—or if the backup battery is dead—you'll lose them each time the circuit shuts off power to your radio.

How the Circuit Works

Power to the radio is controlled by relay K1. Twelve volts is applied to the common relay terminal and coil. When the ignition switch is turned on, voltage is applied to the base of Q5 through R3, saturating Q5 and providing a ground path for the cold end of the relay coil. The relay then closes, providing power to the radio.

When the starter is engaged, power is applied to Q1 through R1, saturating Q1 and presenting a *low* voltage at the base of Q5. This releases the relay and opens the power circuit. When the starter circuit shuts off (when the car is finally running), the power circuit path is restored.

When the ignition is turned off, C1, which has been receiving voltage through D2, begins to discharge through R5. The FET (Q2) remains off until the voltage at its gate discharges to approximately –2 volts. At this point, the FET conducts. This creates our timing cycle. The timing period can be reset by switching the ignition on and back off.

The FET doesn't switch on immediately because of the slow discharge rate of the capacitor. To provide snappier operation, Q3 and Q4 are connected as a *Schmitt trigger* to give quicker relay control. The Schmitt circuit supplies a *high* output when no control voltage is applied to the base of Q3. When the FET times out, a *low* is applied to the base of Q3. This inverts the output of Q4 and removes the voltage at the base of Q5, releasing the relay. The original circuit was designed several years ago using a timer IC. However, this proved to be troublesome. This revised design has proven itself to be rugged and reliable.

Construction, Testing and Installation

Construction is straightforward. There is nothing critical about parts placement. You can use perforated board to mount and wire the

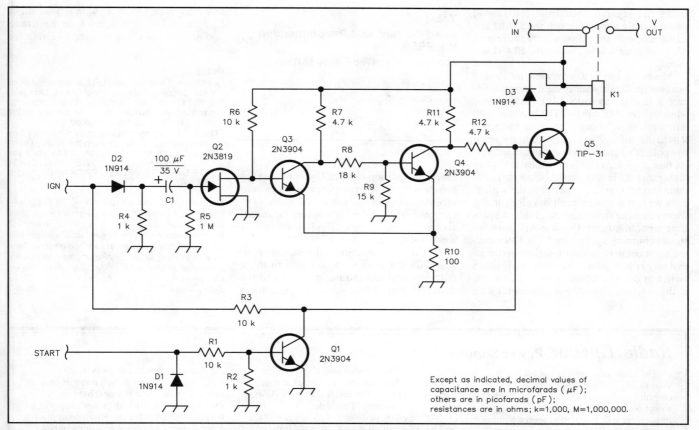

Fig 1—Schematic diagram for the power-switching circuit. Resistors are ¼-watt, 5%-tolerance carbon-composition or film except as noted below. All resistors are available from Radio Shack. Diode D3 is mounted at the base of relay K1.

C1—100 µf, 35-volt electrolytic
    capacitor (Radio Shack 272-1028)
D1, D2, D3—1N914/4148 switching
    diode (Radio Shack 276-1122)
Q1, Q3, Q4—MPS3904 or 2N3904
    transistors (Radio Shack 276-2016)
Q2—2N3819 field-effect transistor
    (FET) (Radio Shack 276-2035)

Q5—TIP-31 power transistor (Radio
    Shack 276-2017)
K1—30-amp auto relay (Radio Shack
    275-226)
R1, R3, R6—10 kΩ
R2, R4—1 kΩ
R5—1 MΩ

R7, R11, R12—4.7 kΩ
R8—18 kΩ
R9—15 kΩ
R10—100 Ω
Feedthrough Barrier Strip (Radio Shack
    274-653)
Box with cover (Radio Shack 270-231)

Fig 2—The author mounted his components on perforated board, but a circuit board is also available. Note the neat, uncluttered layout. (photos by Kirk Kleinschmidt, NT0Z)

components (see Fig 2), or purchase a circuit board from FAR Circuits.[1] If you want to make your own circuit board, you can get the etching template from the ARRL free of charge.[2]

I installed my circuit in a small box and mounted a terminal strip (with labels) along the top. This makes it easy to connect and disconnect wires when you install the circuit in your car. All parts (including the box and terminal strip) are available at your nearest Radio Shack, making this a perfect club project!

Once you've wired everything into place, the circuit is ready to test. Connect a 12-volt light bulb between the **V OUT** and **GND** (ground) connections on the terminal strip. Using a dc power supply (or a battery), apply +12 volts to the **V IN** terminal and connect the **GND** terminal to the power supply ground (– terminal). Using a separate wire attached to the +12-volt output of your power supply, touch the **IGN** terminal. The bulb should glow. When you remove the wire from the **IGN** terminal, the bulb should switch off after the delay cycle is complete. (If you use my design, the delay could last as long as five minutes.) You can check the start-interrupt function by connecting a jumper wire between the **V IN** and **IGN** terminals.

Using the separate lead from the 12-volt power-supply terminal, touch the **START** terminal. The bulb should switch off and remain off as long as the lead touches the **START** terminal.

Mount the box in a convenient location in your car, preferably under the dashboard. Secure it in place so it doesn't bounce around when the car is in motion. The **V IN** and **GND** terminals must connect to your battery—**V IN** to the positive pole and **GND** to the negative pole. It's a good idea to install an appropriate fuse *at the battery*. Use one rated at slightly higher than the radio fuse, but below the maximum current-carrying capacity of the wiring. This way, if a short circuit develops in the wiring running from the battery into the passenger compartment, the fuse will blow instead of burning up the wires. The **IGN** terminal must connect to your ignition switch so that power is applied whenever the ignition switch is on. The **START** terminal connects to the junction where the starter-motor wire

Table 1
Load Current and Recommended Wire Size

Load (amps)	Wire Gauge (AWG)
5	16
15	14
20	12
25	10
35	8
50	6

meets the ignition system. If you're not sure how to wire these terminals, consult an auto mechanic. If your car is under warranty, contact your dealer *before* attempting the installation. Installing this circuit may violate some warranties.

The radio connection is the easiest of all. Just wire the positive power lead to the **V OUT** terminal and the negative lead to the **GND** terminal. While we are on the subject

of wiring, take a look at Table 1. You might find the information helpful the next time you need to know the correct wire size for different loads.

Notes
[1]A PC board and part overlay are available from FAR Circuits, 18N640 Field Court, Dundee, IL 60118; price $4.25 plus $1.50 shipping and handling per order. Check or money order only; credit cards not accepted.
[2]The PC-board template and part overlay are available free of charge from the ARRL Technical Department Secretary. With your request for the HUSTON POWER SWITCHER PC BOARD TEMPLATE PACKAGE, send a #10 SASE.

Jack, WØJAW, and his wife Carol, NØGYQ, obtained their amateur licenses together more than 40 years ago. They have three children who all became amateurs. Two (now adults) are still active. Prior to retirement three years ago, Jack was employed as an engineer and electronics technical writer and editor for three major corporations: Cessna Aircraft, Litton Data Systems and TRW.

QST

Radio Tips: DC Power Supplies

DC (*direct current*) is the lifeblood of your radio. If you multiply voltage by current you get *power*—the ability to do work! None of the components in your transceiver will function properly without a source of dc electric power.

Batteries are one source of dc. They're especially useful to H-T owners and mobile enthusiasts. Another power source is as close as your nearest wall socket, but you can't use it straight from the tap, so to speak. The electricity in your house is *ac*, not dc. If you intend to run your radio from your house power, you must first convert the ac to dc at the voltage your rig requires. That's the function of the *dc power supply*.

A typical dc power supply diagram is shown in Fig 1. Examining the figure from left to right, the first thing you notice is the *transformer*. Transformers are made of coils of wire wound around an iron core. Depending on how the coils are wound, a transformer can convert (*transform*) a high voltage to a low voltage, or vice versa. Since most modern radios require 12 volts, our power supply transformer takes the 120 volt ac and converts it accordingly.

We've reduced the voltage, but we're not done yet. The ac must still be converted to dc. This is the job of the *rectifier*. Most rectifiers are composed of one or more *diodes*. If you remember your radio theory, you'll recall that diodes conduct in one direction only. Alternating current, however, flows in one direction, then reverses. What do you think will happen when the ac from the transformer reaches

the diode(s)? The diodes will allow current to flow in one direction, but will block it when the flow reverses. The result is current flowing in one direction *only*. That's dc!

We've converted the ac to a lower voltage and we've rectified it to dc. Are we finished? Not quite. The output of a rectifier is *pulsating* dc, unsuitable for radio use. So the next task is to filter and purify the dc, removing any of the ac characteristics—pulsations—that remain. Finally, we add a *regulator* circuit to keep our power-supply voltage as stable as possible. The result is stable, pure dc that we can use to power our radios and other electronic equipment.

Almost every electronic device in your home has a dc power supply similar to the one we've just discussed (unless it is battery operated, of course). You may see an ac cord snaking into the back of the cabinet, but rest assured that there is a power supply nearby. It may be simpler than the one we've described, or more complex. It all depends on the requirements of the equipment.

Buying a Power Supply

When you're shopping for a dc power supply, pay careful attention to the voltage ratings. Most power supplies for Amateur Radio service are 12-volt (or 13.8-volt) units. Check your equipment manuals and determine which voltage level you need.

Current is also critical. Once again, check your manual and find out the *maximum* current required. Your power supply must at least be capable of providing the maximum current. When it comes to current capacity, however,

the more the better! Let's say you've just purchased a 25-watt 2-meter amplifier. It needs 12 volts dc at 6 amps, but you've found a 12-volt, 30-amp power supply at a bargain price. Go for the 30-amp supply. Your 2-meter amplifier will draw only as much current as it needs, and a 30-amp power supply can satisfy it easily. Better yet, there's plenty of current capacity to spare. This will allow you to run other devices, including your amplifier, off the same supply. Just remember to use heavy-gauge wire between the supply and devices that draw large amounts of current (over 5 amps).

You'll often see the current capacity shown with two values—continuous and intermittent. Use the continuous figure as your yardstick. That's how much current the supply can deliver without pauses. The intermittent, or *surge*, rating only tells you how much current the supply can provide for a brief period of time.

Another key feature is filtering and regulation. The power supply diagram shown in Fig 1 includes a regulator, but not all commercial power supplies incorporate this feature. Good filtering and regulation are very important for Amateur Radio applications. Poor filtering will manifest itself as hum in audio circuits and erratic behavior in microprocessor-based systems. A power supply with shoddy regulation—or none at all—may vary its output voltage wildly as current demand fluctuates. You'll pay extra for a properly designed supply with robust filtering and regulation, but it's worth it.

You'll also find power supplies that offer meters or variable-voltage capability. These are nice items to have, but they're not necessary and they add significantly to the cost of the power supply. If your budget is tight, choose a basic, fixed-voltage supply without metering.
—*WB8IMY*

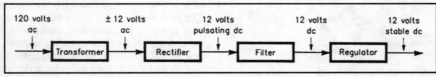

Fig 1—A block diagram of a typical 12-volt dc power supply.

Build a 12-V Junction Box

Power all your 12-V equipment from a single power supply with this easy project!

Robert S. Capon, WA3ULH
322 Burlage Circle
Chapel Hill, NC 27514

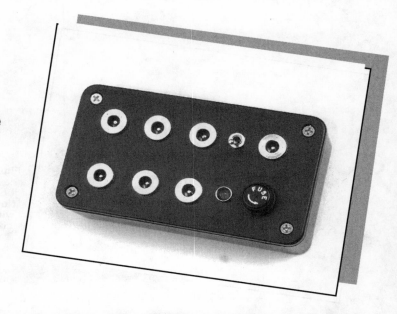

I've been frustrated for years with the proliferation of 12-V power cords to the many accessories in my shack. Whenever I add or change an accessory, I have to remove numerous frayed wires from my power supply, carefully twist the many wires together, and then meticulously wrap them around power posts designed for a *single* accessory.

One day I removed the power cord from my QRP rig and carelessly tossed it aside. The frayed wires shorted and smoked my power supply. Needless to say, I was not a happy camper.

This event prompted me to design and build a 12-V junction box to organize my accessories. The box is equipped with an on/off switch, an LED lamp, and a panel-mounted fuse. You can build the junction box in one evening for about $25, less if you have some of the parts in your junk box.

Parts List

Here's a list of the parts necessary to build the junction box. All of the parts are available at Radio Shack.

Item	Radio Shack part number
D1—LED in panel-mount holder	276-068A
F1—1.5 A, 250-V fuse and holder	270-362
J1-J7—5.5 mm/2.1 mm dc power jacks (7)	274-1563
R1—470-Ω resistor	271-1317
S1—SPST microminiature switch	275-624
#20 stranded hook-up wire	278-1225
5.5 mm/2.1 mm dc power plugs (7)	274-1569A
Plastic project box	270-221

Construction

I suggest you begin building the junction box by preparing the case. A template for drilling the needed ten holes is shown in Figure 1. Photocopy and cut-out the template, then tape it to the flat cover of the case. Drill ten small, $^1/_{16}$-inch guide holes. Then remove the template, and use larger bits to drill the remaining holes. I used wood drill bits to create the larger holes. The bits cut very easily through the soft plastic.

Next, install all of the panel-mounted components: seven jacks, the LED lamp, the

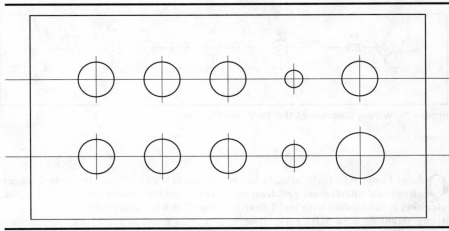

Figure 1—Drilling template. Photocopy this page, cut out the template and tape it to your box.

SPST switch, and the fuse holder. Be sure to orient the jacks so that the ground lugs are facing the center line of the project (see Figure 2).

Bend the ground lugs 90° toward the project center line, so that the lugs are almost touching. Interconnect all the ground connections with stranded bare wire and solder the wire to the lugs.

Use short pieces of red stranded wire to connect all of the power connections from the center conductor of J1, to the fuse, and finally to the switch (see Figure 3).

From the switch, use one long piece of red stranded wire, nipping away the red insulation and pulling the insulation back to expose a series of half-inch sections of bare wire. Solder the end of this length of wire to the other side of the SPST switch. Wrap the exposed half-inch sections around the center posts of the panel jacks, and solder each of the jacks in turn.

Finally, wire the LED lamp and resistor, as shown in Figure 3. (The long lead of the diode goes to the resistor, the short lead to ground.)

Prepare Your Accessories and Power Supply

Next, you'll need to round up all of your accessories and standardize your shack on the mating male dc plugs. Remove the odd assortment of plugs from these devices, and solder the new plugs to each. The positive lead goes to the center conductor, and the negative or grounded lead goes to the shield of the plug. Do not automatically assume that the red or the striped wire from your accessory is the positive lead. Carefully check each device with a volt-ohm-milliammeter and check the documentation to determine the correct polarity of each lead.

When you solder the leads to the plugs, be sure to avoid a short circuit between the positive and negative posts. If they're at all close, you can wrap the center post with a small piece of electrical tape to insulate the connection.

I standardized all of my accessories on the 5.5 mm/2.1 mm plug, including QRP rigs, keyers, SWR meters and so on. I also standardized my Field Day equipment in the same way, including my solar panels, bat-

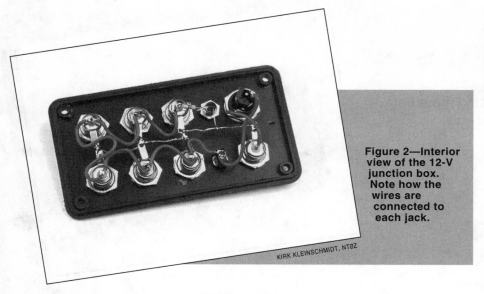

Figure 2—Interior view of the 12-V junction box. Note how the wires are connected to each jack.

KIRK KLEINSCHMIDT, NTØZ

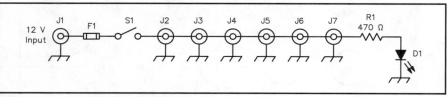

Figure 3—Wiring diagram of the 12-V junction box.

teries, charge controller and memory keyer.

Attach another male plug to a length of two-conductor, heavy-gauge wire. Strip the insulation from the opposite end and secure it to the terminals of your power supply. Once again, make sure to observe the polarity of the plug. The positive lead goes to the center conductor, and the negative or grounded lead goes to the shield of the plug. This is the cable that supplies power to your junction box. Plug it into J1 and turn on your power supply. When you move switch S1 on the junction box to the **ON** position, the LED should glow. This means you're ready to put your box to work!

Conclusion

I've really enjoyed using my one-evening 12-V junction box, and my shack has never looked neater! The device is especially handy for taking my solar powered QRP rig and accessories out for Field Day. It would have been a lot cheaper to build this junction box *before* I smoked my power supply! **QST**

Q Scott Long, WD8NSD, asks, "I have an unusual interference problem; my television is interfering with *me*! I hear a strong signal on 3.58 MHz every time I hook my TV up to an outside antenna. This is my favorite 80-meter frequency. What can I do to fix this problem?"

A Most cases of "reverse TVI" are from the antenna lead, where either the color-burst signals or the harmonics from the horizontal oscillator are getting into (or onto) the antenna or coaxial-cable wiring.
First, disconnect the antenna lead from the back of the set. If the problem goes away, the signal is definitely being radiated by the antenna or the feed line or coaxial cable. Next, touch only the ground of the coax to the ground of the F connector on the back of the TV, without screwing it on. If the problem comes back, it is a common-mode signal on the shield of the coax; fix it with an FT-240-43 ferrite core (don't substitute unknown material; it may not work). If the problem only comes back when you completely connect the antenna lead, then it is a differential-mode signal *inside* the coax that is being radiated by the antenna itself. In that case, use a high-pass filter; the filter will block the HF signal from getting to the antenna.

Q I was tuning around 8080 kHz last night when I heard a strange signal. It was a rhythmic warbling sound. Sometimes it would stop and there would be a

period of silence. Then, suddenly, I'd hear a tone and the warbling would start again. Any idea what this could be?

A You tuned in a WEFAX (weather facsimile) station. These stations are scattered throughout the world. They broadcast the latest weather maps and weather-satellite photos to ships at sea. The one you heard was probably NAM located in Norfolk, Virginia. Many multimode TNCs on the market today have the ability to decode these signals. All you need is a computer and the proper software. (The software is usually sold by the TNC manufacturer.) Some TNCs can only decode WEFAX maps, while others can decode both maps and photographs. Check with the manufacturer to get the features you want. Keep in mind that the TNCs will decode shortwave WEFAX *only*. You can't use them to decode images directly from weather satellites.

Q Kirk Pengelly, AAØOD, asks, "Most inverted L antennas seem to be designed for 160-meter use. I'd like to try the same design on 80 meters. Is it difficult to scale a 160-meter inverted L for 80 meters?"

A You'll find a description of a 160-meter inverted L on page 4-27 of the 17th edition of *The ARRL Antenna Book*. The antenna depicted is for 160 meters, but you can scale it down for 80 meters. Simply divide the wire length and capacitance by 2. That yields 82.5 to 87.5 feet for the wire

length and 250 to 400 pF for the capacitance.

Q John Harvey, W8HTM, asks, "I see the new hams in my radio club using two different conventions with their keyer paddles—some use the thumb for dots and others use the thumb for dashes. Which is the 'correct' way?"

A The normal convention is that dashes are sent with the forefinger and dots with the thumb (of the right hand). This follows from the days of the semiautomatic key (bug), since the greater dexterity of the forefinger made it easier to manually key dashes than would be possible with the thumb. There is no "correct" way with keyer paddles, but it is advisable for all hams (whether right- or left-handed) to use the same convention (the right-hand thumb, or the left-hand forefinger, sends dots), so they can use one another's paddles when visiting another station, for Field Day, etc.

Q Tracy Miller, KB4ETR, asks, "In January 1992, I took the test for my General class license. Although I failed the written exam, I passed the 13-wpm code test. I'd like to try again. Is my 13-wpm code credit still valid?"

A: Sorry, but your 13-wpm code credit was good for only one year; it expired in January 1993. If you decide to upgrade to General or beyond, you'll need to take the Morse code examination again. **QST**

Build a One-Watt Transmitter in a Kodak Film Box

By Robert S. Capon, WA3ULH
322 Burlage Circle
Chapel Hill, NC 27514

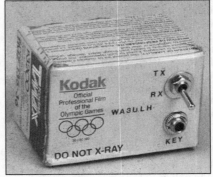

A fun project for beginners that really works!

Have you ever thought about building a miniature one-watt CW transmitter in an unusual enclosure? Well, try a Kodak film box. If you're a novice kit builder, this project can be a lot of fun. It's easy to build, inexpensive, and does not require alignment. Even if you're a veteran kit builder, this project will amaze your friends, amuse your radio club and tantalize your children. When band conditions are good, one watt is plenty of power for you to work DX. And when band conditions are poor, this little gem will look great on your bookshelf.

Selecting a Kit

The basic circuit for the radio is the *Oner* transmitter. It was designed by the legendary British QRP (low power) enthusiast Reverend George Dobbs, G3RJV.

There have been many implementations of the Oner, but the one that I recommend is offered by 624 Kits in Spartanburg, South Carolina. This particular version is an excellent value, because for $13 it includes an output filter *and* a crystal. With the addition of five inexpensive parts available from Radio Shack, you can build the complete transmitter in the film box and be on the air in no time.

The kit is available for bands from 17 through 160 meters. I chose the 20-meter kit, which is my favorite band for QRP DX. The 20-meter version comes with a crystal for 14.060 MHz, the international QRP calling frequency.

The kit is nicely documented. It comes with step-by-step instructions, a schematic (see Figure 1) and a well-prepared parts-layout drawing. The documentation also comes with component information to help you identify the parts. For example, you're told that a 100 kΩ resistor is marked with brown, black and yellow stripes.

The Oner is an interesting little radio. To avoid chirp, for example, the driver oscillator remains on all the time. When you key the transmitter, you are actually keying the final amplifier. As a result, nearby stations will hear two signals: a steady carrier transmitting at milliwatt power levels, and a stronger CW signal with an output power of about 1 W. Stations that are not nearby, however, won't hear the oscillator unless conditions are *very* good.

The Oner is crystal controlled. Because a little trimmer capacitor is used in series with the crystal, however, you're not tied to a single frequency. Rather, the capacitor can "pull" the crystal about 3 kHz above or below its primary frequency.

Unfortunately, because of the capacitance in the circuit, I discovered that the transmitter operates several kHz *above* the crystal frequency. My unit, which uses the 14.060 MHz crystal supplied with the kit, works at 14.066 MHz. As a result, the lowest that I can pull the frequency is 14.063 MHz, which is somewhat above the

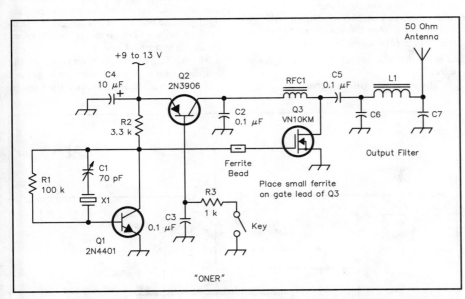

Figure 1—Schematic diagram and parts list for the Oner transmitter, reprinted with permission from 624 Kits.

C1—70pF trimmer capacitor.
C2, C3, C5—0.1 µF, 25-V disc ceramic.
C4—10 µF, 16-V electrolytic capacitor.
C6,C7—
    820 pF disc ceramic (160 meters)
    470 pF disc ceramic (80 meters)
    220 pF disc ceramic (40 meters)
    150 pF disc ceramic (30 meters)
    100 pF disc ceramic (20 meters)
    82 pF disc ceramic (17 meters)
L1—33 turns, #30, T37-2 (160 meters)
    23 turns, #30, T37-2 (80 meters)
    17 turns, #26, T37-2 (40 meters)
    14 turns, #26, T37-2 (30 meters)
    12 turns, #26, T37-2 (20 meters)
    10 turns, #26, T37-2 (17 meters)

Q1—2N4401
Q2—2N3906
Q3—VN10KM MOSFET
R1—100-kΩ, ¼ W.
R2—3.3-kΩ, ¼ W.
R3—1-kΩ, ¼ W.
RFC1—6 turns #26 wire on a ferrite bead
X1—Crystal
*Replacing the ferrite bead with a 10-Ω resistor will avoid possible instability (see Technical Correspondence, *QST*, Nov 1989, p 38, column 3).—*Ed.*

QRP calling frequency. This may not seem like much of a difference, but 3 kHz is really out of the money for most QRP stations who might be monitoring.

If you plan to do a lot of operating with this kit, you might want to purchase a replacement 14.056 MHz crystal from a source like JAN crystals. With a tweak or two of the trimmer, you'll be able to operate on 14.060 MHz.

For your station to work effectively, you'll need a technique to switch your antenna between a receiver and the Oner transmitter. Without such a switching technique, the constant oscillation of the Oner will interfere with your receiver. A DPDT switch will enable you to switch the antenna between the transmitter and receiver, and to turn off the power to the Oner. The wiring diagram shown in Figure 2 shows you how to do this.

Parts List

All of the parts that you will need (other than the film box and kit) are available from Radio Shack (the Radio Shack part numbers are given in the following parts list). The total cost of the radio is about $20:

Oner Transmitter Kit	From 624 Kits
35-mm Film Box	From Kodak
5.5 mm/2.1 mm dc female jack	274-1563
2 phono jacks	274-346
Key jack	274-251
DPDT toggle switch	275-614

Prepare the Box

An easy way to begin the project is to prepare the case. Cut three sides of the top of the case to make a flap, so that the radio can be opened and closed.

To strengthen the box, form two strips of cardboard (I used one of my QSL cards) into a **U** shape, and glue the cardboard into the film box in opposite directions with ordinary white glue. For example, one of the **U**s goes from side to side, and one goes from front to back. This has a lamination effect, and makes the box quite sturdy.

Next, cut two holes in the front of the box, and three holes in the rear as shown in Figure 3. Forget your electric drill for this project. The tool of choice is an X-Acto knife.

Label the case as shown in the photograph. It is much easier to label the case before you've mounted the components on the case. For labeling I used Helvetica 8 rub-on labels that I purchased at a local hobby shop, finished with transparent Scotch tape.

Install all of the jacks. Just finger tighten the nuts for now.

Assemble the Circuit Board

If this is your first kit, take a moment to prepare. Before you open your first parts package, you may want to purchase a plastic compartmentalized parts box, which can be very handy for sorting components. I found some very nice boxes at a local

housewares/kitchen supply store. Alternatively, Radio Shack has a suitable component box that costs a bit more (64-552).

If you're an experienced kit builder, skip this section, dump the parts into a soup bowl, and solder up the board. I've built several of these kits, and the last one took me 25 minutes.

For first-time kit builders, here are answers to some commonly asked questions:

❏ *Can the trimmer capacitors or ceramic disk capacitors go in the wrong way?*

No. Resistors can not be put in the wrong way either.

❏ *Can the electrolytic capacitors go in the wrong way?*

Yes. Electrolytic capacitors have a positive and a negative side. The negative lead is shorter and marked with a stripe and a "minus" mark. The positive lead is longer; it may have a small "+" sign or may be unmarked.

❏ *Can the transistors go in the wrong way?*

Yes. When you install the transistors, be certain to match up the flat side of the transistor with the flat side in the layout diagram.

❏ *How are the toroids wound?*

The documentation comes with an excellent picture of the toroids. You count turns from the *inside* of the toroid. For example, 6 turns on the RF choke will look like 6 turns from the inside of the toroid, but only 5 1/2 turns on the outside.

❏ *How do you solder the coated toroid wires?*

Theoretically, the magnet wire uses a

coating which melts off during soldering. I found, however, that the coating does not melt off completely, and the resulting solder joint does not make a good connection in all circumstances. It's safer to carefully scrape away the coating with an X-Acto blade prior to soldering.

❏ *Can the crystal be put in the wrong way?*
No.

Armed with the answers to these questions, you're ready to populate the little circuit board with electronic components. Identify each of the components and solder them in place. Be sure to keep the leads as short as possible.

Wire the Circuit Board to the Case

The final step is to wire the circuit board to the various components on the box: transmit/receive switch, key jack, antenna jack, receiver antenna jack and 12 V dc jack. Refer to the attached wiring diagram to make the connections. You'll find the job less confusing if you use black wire for the ground connections, red for 12-V connections, and green for all other connections.

If you find it difficult working in the confined space, you may choose to get out your X-Acto knife and slit open the back of

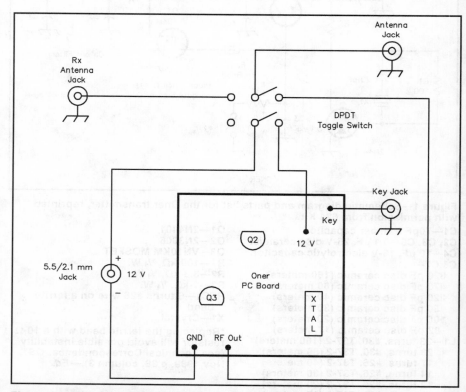

Figure 2—Wiring the Oner to your connectors and the antenna switch.

PHOTOS BY KIRK KLEINSCHMIDT, NT0Z

Figure 3—An inside view of the Kodak-box transmitter. The Oner fits nicely and the jacks are easy to mount.

the case along the vertical sides. This will give you more working room. When you're finished, tape the box shut.

Operating Results

Under normal conditions, I've had good luck with 1-W transmitters into a Cushcraft A-3 tribander beam antenna mounted at

only 30 feet. I've also experimented with QRPp (extremely low power), and worked ZS6KO with 20 mW, which is one-fiftieth the power of the Oner transmitter!

With this QRP experience, I was eager to get my little transmitter on the air. When the radio was finished, I telephoned my friend Ernie, KN4MN, who helps me troubleshoot all of my projects. Ernie lives about two miles away, and he gave me a signal report of S-9 with his 4-element Yagi pointed in my direction. Ernie reported the CW signal was very clean. He also said that he could hear my oscillator running continuously about 1 kHz down from my main signal—even when I wasn't transmitting. The oscillator was much fainter (he gave it an S-4 report).

My first QSO was with LU4VZ, and I received a 529 report. Next, I worked KW1C and received a solid 599 from Fort Kent, Maine.

Later that evening, I went down to the low end of 20 meters with my Yaesu FT-1000 running 200 W. After a bit of searching, I recruited the loudest New Zealand station I could hear, ZL1BDG. Frank said he'd be happy to change frequencies and listen for my Kodak film box at 14.063 MHz. I called him with the Oner …and got a prompt reply! My signal report was 539 and, thanks to Frank's patience and excellent CW skills, we had a pleasant

Contact List

624 Kits
171 Springlake Dr
Spartanburg, SC 29302
tel 803-573-6677

Kanga US
3521 Spring Lake Drive
Findlay, OH 45840
tel 419-423-5643

JAN Crystals
2341 Crystal Drive
PO Box 60017
Fort Myers, FL 33906-6017
tel 800-JAN-XTAL

conversation over an 8000-mile path!

Next Steps

You might want to consider building other Oner projects. Kanga US imports a terrific Oner QSK unit which uses a relay to switch the antenna between the transmitter and receiver. The QSK also includes a sidetone oscillator. It's a logical follow-on project to the Oner transmitter. For more skilled kit builders, Kanga also imports a Oner *receiver* that works in conjunction with a Oner VFO. ■

Q I'm debating whether to buy or build my own equipment. Can you offer any guidance?

A Making two-way radio contacts with a radio you've built yourself is a wonderful experience for radio amateurs. Most people do this with low-power (QRP) Morse code (CW) transceivers. A number of companies make kits just for this purpose. You can probably get on the air with a serviceable home-built station for under $100. Experts can do it for much less by taking advantage of bargains found at flea markets that specialize in Amateur Radio components.

Pushing the state of the art is another great reason to build your own gear. There are bands and modes that aren't popular yet, so that little is available in the way of affordable equipment. The Wright brothers had to build their own airplane. They couldn't have been first in flight if they'd waited for someone to produce a commercial product!

But are there valid reasons not to build? Economics is probably the major factor. Generally speaking, you can't build complicated electronic gear for less than you can buy it. Often, the money spent on home brew gear can't easily be recovered. In other words, you may have a tough time selling your home brew equipment in the future. In contrast, the resale value for commercial Amateur Radio gear is surprisingly high, even for relatively old equipment.

If you decide to roll your own, start with

simple projects. Build simple things, like antennas or electronic keyers. Assembling a modern all-band all-mode radio is more difficult than trying to build your own computer! (And modern radios often have a computer inside that coordinates everything!)

Q I just built a low-power CW transceiver from a kit. It works well, but I keep hearing noises whenever I tap on the cabinet. It's as though the sounds of the bumps and taps are being conducted right into my headphones. Is this common with low-power transceivers?

A With some designs, yes. You didn't mention the manufacturer or model, but I'll wager that your rig uses a *direct-conversion* receiver. In a direct-conversion design, the incoming signal is mixed with a signal from a local oscillator. The frequency of the local-oscillator is nearly the same as the signal you want to receive. They differ by only a few hundred hertz or so. In the mixing process, they combine and the result is a very weak audio-frequency signal. So, the incoming RF is converted directly to audio—*direct* conversion.

The audio signal is passed to a high-gain amplifier that boosts it to a level sufficient to drive your headphones. A direct-conversion receiver relies on this audio amplifier to provide all or most of the gain. This being the case, the audio amplifier must increase the signal level by a huge amount. The gain is so great, the circuitry can function like a micro-

phone, picking up vibrations in wires and components and translating them into electrical impulses. When you tap on your transceiver's enclosure, you hear it in your headphones. The circuit is said to be "microphonic."

Most direct-conversion receivers suffer from this problem to one degree or another. Even so, they provide excellent sensitivity. They're relatively easy to build and adjust, which makes it possible for the manufacturers to offer these kits at affordable prices.

Q Jim Dugan, KA6NVA, asks, "DX stations often ask for my ITU or CQ zone numbers. What's the difference? What are my zones?"

A The question of zones can be a little confusing. First there are the zones created by the ITU, the International Telecommunication Union. Many decades ago, the publishers of *Radio* magazine (now long vanished) also divided the world into a number of zones. The publishers of *CQ* magazine inherited these demarcations (with a few changes along the way) and called them *CQ* zones.

Knowing which zone you're in is useful for contesting and award chasing. That's why the ARRL indicates both zone designations for each country in our *DXCC Country List*. You'll also find ITU and *CQ* zone maps on page 17-57 of the fourth edition of the *ARRL Operating Manual* or on the new *ARRL World Map*. You are located in ITU zone 6 and *CQ* zone 3.

Annie Get Your Gunnplexer!

Are you looking for a band where you can do virtually *anything* The 10-GHz microwave band is ripe with possibilities! Here's an inexpensive way to get started.

By Zack Lau, KH6CP
ARRL Laboratory Engineer

If you've read this far, I assume the use of the word *microwave* or the abbreviation *GHz* hasn't scared you too badly. To be sure, microwave operating departs from the well-worn paths that most amateurs take. The microwave bands are for curious, adventuresome hams.

Am I saying that microwave hamming is difficult? It's certainly more challenging than your usual plug-and-play scenario, but it's a specialty anyone can master. I think the most difficult part is wading through all the microwave jargon you'll find in most books. (There are few microwave books for beginners.) In addition, there are some components and operating techniques that may be unfamiliar to you.

Is microwave hamming expensive? Believe it or not, you can get up and running on the 10-GHz band for less than half the cost of a typical HF transceiver. By using some of the cost-saving ideas we're about to discuss, it can be even cheaper than getting on 2-meter FM.

If this surprises you, your reaction is understandable. Like so many areas of Amateur Radio that are off the beaten path, microwave operation has taken on an exotic air. Hams tend to equate "exotic" with "expensive."

What Can You Really Do on 10 GHz?

Ask most hams about microwave operating and I bet you'll hear, "You'll be lucky just to talk across town—if you can find anyone to talk to!"

Guess what? They're right! If you're looking for long-distance communications, the microwave bands are *not* for you. Except for some propagation enhancements caused by atmospheric conditions, low-power microwave operating is a line-of-sight mode. Some impressive distance records have been set on 10-GHz (several hundred miles or more), but those were under ideal circum-

Kent Britain, WA5VJB, takes his Gunnplexer on the road for the 1992 ARRL 10-GHz Cumulative Contest. Notice that he's using a horn as the antenna.

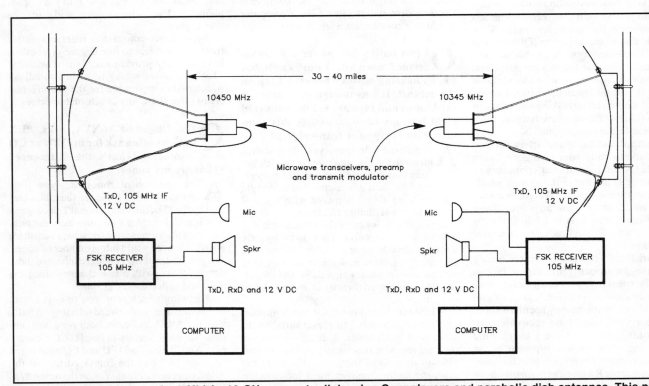

Fig 1—A system diagram of a 2-Mbit/s, 10-GHz computer link using Gunnplexers and parabolic dish antennas. This project is described in detail beginning on page 32-49 of the 1993 *ARRL Handbook*.

stances with good equipment. If you're talking about an antenna on the roof of your house or apartment, a few miles is more likely—depending on how many buildings, hills and trees are in the way.

And it's true that the microwave-active population is small at the moment. Don't expect to haul your equipment to the top of a nearby hill and get an instant response to your first CQ. Unless you're participating in a contest, or unless you've arranged a schedule with another ham, you probably won't be able to contact anyone. Random contacts on the microwave bands are rare events.

Now that I've completely taken the wind out of your sails, I'll list just a few of the many activities that are *ideal* for the 10-GHz band:

❏ **High-speed Data Transmissions:** With the proper equipment, you can swap information at a rate of *millions* of bits per second! (see Fig 1) Why not set up a 10-GHz local network and unleash the power of your computer? For example, I'm sure you've heard of those sophisticated air-combat computer programs that put you in command of a modern fighter jet. Many of these software packages allow you and a friend to "fly" together—as comrades or enemies. Imagine going head-to-head with your buddy using a 10-GHz link to transfer data between your computers at lightning speed. Only the microwave bands give you the room to do this kind of full-throttle networking.

❏ **Repeater Linking:** How about using the 10-GHz band to integrate separate repeaters into one system? You can link several 2-meter repeaters together to cover an area much larger than any single repeater could cover by itself. All it takes are a few interference-free 10-GHz links to transfer signals from one machine to another.

❏ **Remote Control:** You'd like to get on the HF bands, but you don't have room for antennas. Your friend a few miles away has plenty of room for your antennas, but you don't want to run over to his place every time you get the itch to operate. 10 GHz to the rescue! You could establish a 10-GHz link between your homes and operate your HF rigs by remote control. Most modern rigs feature computer control and you already know that you can transfer data on 10 GHz at very high speeds. The 10-GHz band handles voice and CW signals equally well. With a tiny 2-foot dish antenna on your roof, you could control your distant radios and work HF easily.

❏ **Video:** You haven't seen amateur television until you've seen it on 10-GHz! You can send and receive wideband video with crisp, clear images. Talking to a friend on 10-GHz duplex ATV is the next best thing to having him or her in the room with you.

❏ **Contests:** Yes, there are 10-GHz contests. These contests tend to bring all the 10-GHz buffs out of the woodwork. Just take your gear to a high place (a hill, mountain or even a building) and you may be surprised to hear a number of contest contacts taking place. The pace of a 10-GHz contest is very relaxed. It's not uncommon to engage in long conversations with other microwave enthusiasts you happen to find.

With more than 500 MHz of spectrum from 10 to 10.5 GHz, this band is a wide-open frontier. You can let your imagination and inventiveness soar—without someone complaining that you're "hogging the repeater" or "tying up *their* frequency." If I've aroused your curiosity, the next step is to get on the air without breaking your budget.

Those Clever Gunnplexers

The cheapest way to get on 10 GHz is with *Gunnplexer* transceivers. The Gunnplexer shown in Fig 2 will fit easily in the palm of your hand and requires only 12 volts dc to operate. The portion of the transceiver that looks like a funnel is actually the *feed horn* (or just *horn*, for short). It captures *and* radiates microwave energy.

The heart of the Gunnplexer is the Gunn diode oscillator, named after its inventor, John Gunn of IBM. The Gunn diode is installed in a specially designed *resonant cavity*. The diode oscillates and radiates energy at microwave frequencies whenever a dc voltage is applied. (The oscillator frequency is determined by a varactor tuning diode and two mechanical tuning screws.) The energy radiated by the Gunn diode escapes from the cavity and out through the horn.

In addition to creating our transmitted signal, the Gunn diode also acts as the *local oscillator* for the receiver. If you remember your radio theory, you'll recall that the local-oscillator signal is combined with the received signal to create the *Intermediate Frequency*, or *IF*. A Gunnplexer transceiver uses the same technique, but in a very clever way.

When the Gunnplexer is transmitting, a tiny portion of the signal is rerouted to a mixing diode. The incoming signal from the other station is mixed with this signal to create an IF. Think about this for a moment. Can you guess what's actually happening? The Gunnplexer is transmitting and receiving *simultaneously*!

The only catch is that both stations must be on separate frequencies to create a usable IF. For example, to create a 30-MHz IF using the technique we've just discussed, the frequencies of the transmitting and receiving stations must be separated by 30 MHz. Here's how it works:

1. KH6CP is transmitting and receiving on 10.280 GHz. WB8IMY is doing the same on 10.250 GHz.

2. WB8IMY's 10.250-GHz signal arrives at KH6CP and is mixed with the 10.280-GHz signal from his Gunn diode.

3. In the mixing process, the two frequencies are combined and the *difference* becomes our IF. So what's the difference between 10.280 and 10.250 GHz? It's 30 MHz—our intermediate frequency!

Fig 2—Don't let its tiny size fool you. You're looking at a 10-GHz Gunnplexer transceiver. Notice the funnel-shaped horn. It transmits and receives the microwave energy. Connect an inexpensive IF receiver (even an FM radio!) and a microphone and you're on the air!

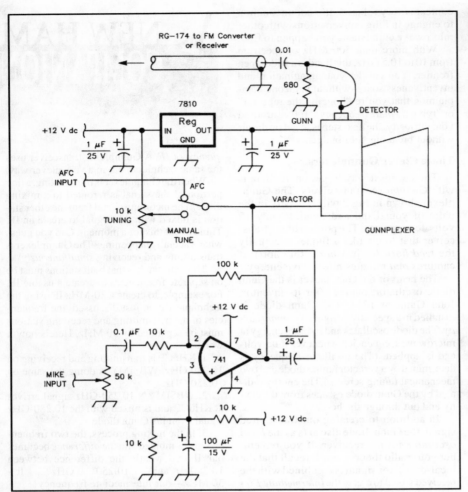

Fig 3—Here is a schematic diagram of a simple Gunnplexer communications system. You can use a standard FM broadcast radio as the IF receiver. The 741 IC is the microphone amplifier. The 7810 is a voltage regulator for the Gunnplexer. This bare-minimum system is described on page 32-44 of the 1993 *ARRL Handbook*.

Recommended Reading

Books

The following books are available from your favorite dealer, or directly from the ARRL. See the publications catalog elsewhere in this issue.

The ARRL UHF/Microwave Experimenter's Manual.

The RSGB *Microwave Handbook.* (Volumes 1, 2 and 3)

Articles

Petersen, "The Care and Feeding of Gunnplexers," *QST*, April 1983, p 14.

Cooper, "$30 Video Microwave System," *QST*, April 1980, p 71.

Steers, "A Simple 10-GHz Dish Antenna," *QST*, June 1986, p 62.

A Gunnplexer transceiver is only one component of your 10-GHz station. Once you convert the 10-GHz energy to an IF, you need an IF receiver to hear the received signal. To send voice, data or other information, you also need a modulator.

If you're strapped for cash, you can use a common FM broadcast radio as your IF receiver. On page 32-44 of the 1993 *ARRL Handbook* you'll find an easy way to do this (see Fig 3). It only requires a handful of parts and includes a simple modulator circuit. To use FM radios as IF receivers, you'll need to separate your 10-GHz transmit and receive frequencies by a frequency between 88-108 MHz. For example...

1. Station #1 transmits on 10.250 GHz.
2. Station #2 transmits on 10.350 GHz.
3. The difference between these two frequencies is 100 MHz, creating an IF that can be received by using an FM radio tuned to 100 MHz.

The disadvantage of this system is that most 10-GHz enthusiasts insist on using a 30- or 33-MHz IF, neither of which is compatible with each other or an FM radio (30 MHz is the most common IF). Many 10-GHz experimenters use modified FM radios or distance-measuring devices known as Telurometers for their IF receivers. The latter was made by Pye Ltd of Cambridge in the UK and apparently has been available inexpensively in Canadian and Australian surplus stores.

Gunnplexer transceivers, modulators and IF receivers can be purchased from a number of sources, including:

SHF Microwave Parts Company
7102 West 500 St
La Porte, IN 46350
(does not do business by telephone)

Advanced Receiver Research
Box 1242
Burlington, CT 06013
tel: 203-582-9409

Antennas

For reliable communications under a mile or so, you can simply use the Gunnplexer's feed horn as your antenna. No kidding! The horn will radiate in a resonably focused pattern and is quite directive for receiving. You can install the transceiver and horn on a roof-mounted mast (with adequate weatherproofing, of course), and keep the IF receiver and modulator in your shack. Use low-loss coaxial cable between the transceiver and the IF receiver.

You'll get much better performance if you use a parabolic dish to focus the energy going to and from your feed horn. A two- or three-foot aluminum dish is perfectly adequate. You can shop for dishes at hamfests and surplus stores. The suppliers noted above often sell dishes, too. Any reflector that's even close to parabolic will do the job. I've seen hams use snow sleds and trash can lids among other things.

Have Gunnplexer, Will Travel

10-GHz buffs like to take their rigs on the road. The challenge is to see just how far you can communicate. In many areas of the country you'll find groups of 10-GHz devotees who periodically gather on buildings, mountains and hilltops to test their mettle. (If such a group doesn't exist in your area, start your own!) They often coordinate contacts using 2-meter FM or SSB. It's easier to make frequency and antenna adjustments when you have direct feedback from the other station.

As I've already mentioned, contests are fun on 10-GHz. Most contesters take their portable Gunnplexers to the highest locations they can find. Contest operating can be a real challenge since you must sweep the band looking for new contacts. In addition to changing frequency, you may have to change your antenna orientation as well.

Conclusion

For more information, I suggest that you check the sidebar, "Recommended Reading." It also doesn't hurt to have some experienced help to get you started. Ask around at your next club meeting and see if you have any microwave-active members. If you're a packeteer, put a message on your local PBBS asking for advice from microwave veterans.

Microwave operating isn't as easy as 2-meter FM, but the best things in this world are rarely easy. When you explore the 10-GHz band, you'll be traveling back in time to the earlier days of ham radio when every mode was a challenge. Gather some friends and try it together!

By George Blahun Jr, KS1U

How to Buy Military Surplus

Have you checked out the goodies at your nearest military base? Why not?
You paid for them!

There probably isn't a ham alive who hasn't noticed the advertisements in the classified sections of some science and electronics magazines. Those that begin with an attention-getter such as: "Fifty-Dollar Jeeps!" or "Airplanes—$300!" The ads then go on to describe how anyone can get bargains like these by attending military surplus sales throughout the country.

As a 12-year-old in 1961, I remember fantasizing about buying an Army helicopter to get to and from high school. My plan was to land in one of the many fields surrounding the school, and I would pity my poor friends who would be stuck driving their old '56 Chevys and Buicks.

Perhaps you've attended a large hamfest and seen table after table of oscilloscopes or signal generators and wondered where they all came from. Maybe you hoped to get just one of those items without depleting your bank account, or envied the merchant with thousands of dollars worth of equipment on his table. Much of that equipment came from the US military and you, my fellow taxpayer, paid for it.

I never bought the aforementioned helicopter, but I've owned and sold enough military equipment to start my own space program. To be candid, it hasn't made me wealthy, but I have acquired electronic equipment that I could never have purchased new without mortgaging everything I own. We've all heard people say "If it sounds too good to be true, it probably is." Armed with sufficient knowledge, however, military sales can prove that adage wrong much of the time!

My initial attempt to purchase surplus can best be described as a learning experience. I was overwhelmed by the procedures and left the sale with no equipment—but plenty of knowledge. My second attempt, though, was extremely successful. For $65, I carried away dozens of pieces of electronic equipment that had originally cost the taxpayers more than $30,000! Among the many items were Hewlett-Packard VTVMs (vacuum-tube voltmeters), Tektronix oscilloscopes, several Variacs, frequency counters, unused components—and some items whose functions are, to this day, still unknown to me.

Get in on the Action

If you've read this far you're probably wondering how you can get in on the surplus bonanza. Don't worry. I'm not going to tell you to send $5 to a post office box in order to receive directions, like the ads in the classified sections do. Because you read *QST*, you'll get the whole scoop for the price of this magazine, whose cover price is *only* $4.95!

This is the best time since the end of World War II to buy military surplus. US bases all over the world are closing and consolidating. As a result, much of the equipment that was used at those bases is being sold. The first thing you'll need to do is compile a list of military bases that are within easy driving range. A look through the blue pages of the phone book is a good way to start your list. Next you'll need to contact the switchboard at the base of your choice and ask for the *DRMO*.

DRMO stands for Defense Reutilization and Marketing Of-

HEY MAC, CAN YOU GIVE ME A TOW? I SUBMITTED THE WINNING BID, AND I GOTTA GET THIS THING OUTTA HERE TODAY

fice. Some small installations may still go by the old name, *DPDO* or Defense Property Disposal Office. Also, there are installations that are too small to have a DRMO and instead send their surplus to larger bases nearby to be processed. Don't be shy about asking questions. Remain polite, but persistent, as you navigate the base bureaucracy. Remember, it's your right as a citizen and taxpayer to have access to this information, and to bid on any surplus.

Once you reach the DRMO, ask when the next surplus sale or auction will be held. Tell the person on the phone that you'd like to receive written notification of the sale and, if possible, a list of items being sold. Several weeks before the sale you'll receive a notice stating the date and time of the sale, the location, the type of sale, and the dates and times for inspection. You'll also receive at least a general description of the items being offered and, possibly, a detailed list.

It's imperative that you thoroughly inspect the items before bidding on them, and understand how long you have to pay for and remove property that has been awarded to you. Failure to remove your purchases by a specified date can result in some hefty storage fees, or even cause a forfeiture of the property and subsequent banishment from any future sales! Generally, there will be a three- to seven-day period during which you will be able to inspect the items prior to bidding.

Going to the Base

Most military bases have armed guards stopping all vehicles. So, it pays to look for signs giving instructions for visitors. Many military installations have small buildings outside the main gate where you can park your car and receive a visitor's pass. To get a pass, you'll need to state your purpose for entering the base and produce the following items: a valid driver's license, car registration and insurance card. You must have all three, or admittance will be denied.

If there are no instructions posted for visitors, simply drive up to the gate. Unless you have a military sticker on your bumper or window, the guard will signal you to stop. Most military guards are polite and respectful, but they take their job *very* seriously.

They are not known for their sense of humor or willingness to ragchew. (This is not the time to joke about having a bomb in your trunk!) Just ask them how to get a visitor's pass, and if none is required, ask for directions to the DRMO.

The typical DRMO consists of a small office building located next to a well-guarded area of several large warehouses and outdoor storage facilities. The entrance to the office is usually well marked and you will be required to sign a log before passing to the inspection areas. Be certain to carry your identification (preferably a driver's license) with you.

If you don't already have one, you'll be given an item list and allowed to pass into the property storage facility. Most of the property offered for sale will be located nearby, but some property will be located elsewhere. For instance, boats may be in a dock—dry or otherwise. Cars and trucks may be located in a guarded parking lot several miles from the DRMO. The item list will give you details about the locations, although it may be necessary to ask for directions from someone at the office.

Sizing up the Territory

When entering a DRMO warehouse for the first time, it's difficult not to be mesmerized by the sheer volume of equipment. There may be acres of high-tech goodies, both indoors and out. Much, if not most, of what you see, however, will not be included in the current sale. Only the items listed on your invitation to bid will be offered.

Property to be sold is usually placed on a wooden pallet and numbered in black ink on a white card. All of the other "stuff" that you see is being processed. If the military can't use it at some other base, chances are it will be available at a future sale or auction. Make note of anything you see that is not currently being sold, but *don't touch any item that is not specifically numbered and listed for sale.* Doing so will bring a great deal of unwanted attention, and may result in your being searched prior to leaving the area! (You're on a military base, remember?)

As I mentioned, inspecting the sale items is essential. The description in the item list will typically read like this:

ITEM 22—COMMUNICATIONS EQUIPMENT. Lot consists of receivers, transmitters, voltmeters, pan adapters, assorted components. 32 items, gross weight 305 lb.

If item 22 interests you, then go to the pallet marked No. 22 and look carefully at the equipment. You'll be permitted to examine any of the equipment, but be careful to return the items as close to their original positions as possible. There are no guarantees that the equipment works. Much of it does, but some is pure junk, so you'll have to know exactly what you're looking at. If you have questions of a general nature, there are workers, usually civilian employees, who can help you. Don't expect them to know much about a specific item. That's your responsibility.

You can get some idea of the condition of the item by looking at its identification tag. The words **EXCESS TO CURRENT NEEDS** are the ones to look for. It means simply that the government doesn't need it anymore and it likely functions as intended. Other items may have numeric codes for indicating condition, or may just say **FAULTY**. Look for inspection stickers, too. Anything the military owns (including people!) must be inspected and calibrated periodically. The most desirable items will have a recent inspection and calibration date. Some tags will give repair dates or indicate what, if anything, is wrong.

When you buy a pallet of goods, *beware*—you might get a mixed bag. There might be three or four 0 to 30-MHz all-mode receivers that you've just *got* to have. But on the same pallet might be 200 pounds of rusted boat-anchor electronics that you'll end up hauling to the dump. That's just part of the game and gamble and, from the DRMO's standpoint, it's a smart move. The bottom line is, *caveat emptor*—let the buyer beware.

While most pallets weigh less than 200 pounds, some can weigh *tons*. Before you decide to bid, make sure you can transport your treasure within the allowable time! You did remember to check about that beforehand, didn't you?

Equipment Manuals

Much of the electronic equipment sold at military auctions comes without manuals. Unless you're intimately familiar with the gear, you'll probably need some documentation to operate or, in some cases, fix it.

The good news is that manual sources are right at hand. The following is a list of suppliers of manuals and other documents for military surplus equipment.

Deane E. Kidd, W7TYR, 27270 SW Ladd Hill Rd, Sherwood, OR 97140; tel: 503-625-7363

Primarily test equipment. Deane has manuals and parts for older Tektronix, Hewlett-Packard, GR and other instruments in addition to some WW II military manuals. Send your "want" list with an SASE.

Keystone Bibliopolist, PO Box 34427, Omaha, NE 68134

Sells used technical manuals.

US Army Military History Institute, Carlisle Barracks, PA 17013-5008; tel: 717-245-3611

Technical manuals for military radio equipment. If possible, include the manual number with your request. If this is unknown, include a complete description of the equipment, including the model name, model numbers and the time period in which the equipment was in use, if known. Once a specific manual is identified, it may be obtained in one of two ways: (1) If the institute possesses three or more copies, one may be borrowed through interlibrary loan procedures. This process must be initiated by your local library. (2) Alternatively, photocopies can be purchased. The minimum cost is $6 for up to 10 pages. Each additional page is 25 cents. Each patron is allowed up to 300 pages per calendar year. Selected bibliographies of Institute holdings are available through interlibrary loan.

Center for Legislative Archives, National Archives, Washington, DC 20408, tel: 202-501-5350

Record group 287 has US Army technical manuals for radio equipment manufactured from 1940 to 1979. Photocopies can be obtained at a cost of 25 cents per page ($6 minimum order). A "Reproduction Service Order" must first be completed by the National Archives to determine the cost of the specific manual you desire. You must identify the desired manual on this form with its proper Army technical manual number. If this number is unknown, contact your nearest US Government Depository Library for assistance. These are usually the main public libraries in large and medium-sized cities. The *National Archives Microfilm Publications Pamphlet*, also available from the Archives, describes this procedure.

Bidding Time

Let's say you've just spent 90 minutes inspecting 127 pallets and you've found 12 worth bidding on. The next step is to determine the *type* of sale. Usually there are just two: *Spot bids* and *auctions*. Occasionally there is a "store" sale, with merchandise offered at a fixed price and on a take-it-or-leave-it basis. This is not very common, and is usually restricted to items such as clothing or furniture. It might be worth checking out, though, especially if you live close to a base.

During a spot bid, anyone interested in bidding on an item will be given a bidding ticket. On this ticket you must write the item number, the amount you're willing to pay and your bidder's number. During some spot bids, bids will be accepted during the inspection days and the bids will be opened on the sale date by DRMO personnel without any bidders being present. The high bidders are then notified by phone or mail. My favorite type of spot bid is when all the bidders are present. Not only can you see how much interest there is in a particular item, you can take advantage of the circumstances, so to speak. I've attended these bids during snowstorms, when the turnout is low, and come away with my best bargains.

During "live" spot bidding, I'll usually prepare two bidding tickets—one with the maximum price I'm willing to pay and the other with my "bargain" price. When the bidding tickets for a particular item are collected by the DRMO employees, I watch closely to see how many bids are going in. If the numbers are few, I'll submit my lower of the bids. It's all a gamble, and can be an exciting game of wits.

After the bids are collected and reviewed, the winning bidder's number and the amount paid is announced. It is wise to record winning bids next to the item list for future reference. It's an easy way to educate yourself as to what the market will bear for certain goods.

On rare occasions, the DRMO rejects a rock-bottom offering, calling it a "token bid." In other words, it was too low for the value of the goods in question. I've only seen a couple of bids rejected in several years, so don't be too concerned about this. A token bid might be five cents for an electron microscope, but I've seen working electron microscopes sold for as little as $12!

The other type of sale is the auction. Nearly everyone is familiar with this format, and it's my personal favorite. One word of caution to those of you who frequent the many ham auctions:

Military surplus auctions are deadly serious! If you bid on something you don't get to change your mind later. Don't wave at a friend who just entered the building unless you want to cart home an old dummy torpedo in the back of your car!

If you're the winner, congratulations! Just pay for your goodies in cash or certified check prior to removing them. No items can be removed before the completion of the spot bid or auction. DRMO employees will load the merchandise into your vehicle if you have a truck. Otherwise, pallets will be brought to your car by forklift and you must load the individual items.

Start Saving

Military surplus auctions are fantastic sources for great equipment at the lowest possible prices. I've seen pallets of 40 oscilloscopes sell for $35, and boats for under $100. Just call the nearest military base, save up a few dollars and maybe I'll see you at the next auction. And by the way, if you happen to see a helicopter with an **EXCESS TO CURRENT NEEDS** sticker on it, give me a call.

George Blahun Jr, KS1U
PO Box 17
Quaker Hill, CT 06375-0017

Q A friend of mine and I were doing some tests on 75 meters recently. I wanted to see if I could hear his signal over the 600 miles that separated us. It was a frustrating exercise because I could hear him pretty well while he was tuning up, but when he switched to SSB, he was very weak. Why?

A When your buddy was operating his rig in the **TUNE** mode, he was concentrating all of his RF power in a very narrow bandwidth. When he jumped to SSB, his RF was suddenly spread over nearly 3 kHz of spectrum. Without getting into heavy-duty analysis, we'll suffice to say that his RF was "watered down," no longer packed into a tight space.

You've stumbled upon the reason why CW is often audible when no other type of signal can be heard. The RF energy in a CW signal is concentrated in just 100 Hz or so of bandwidth. That's why low power (QRP) operators prefer CW. They can run just a watt of power and still be heard hundreds and even thousands of miles away. It's easy to understand why moonbouncers prefer CW, too. They operate at higher power levels—typically more than 500 W—and the narrow bandwidth of CW allows their signals to be audible even after traveling to the Moon and back!

Q I'm just starting to explore the 6-meter band and I'd like more information. Is there such a thing as a Web site devoted to 6 meters *only*?

A There is, indeed. Point your browser to: **http://user.itl.net/~equinox/50dx.html**, the address of *Internet Six News*. This site has a wealth of information about 6-meter activities.

Q Jason Hanson, N9LEA, asks, "Because of my status as an apartment dweller, I have no room for elaborate HF antenna systems. I have no access to the attic and an outside antenna is impossible. What's left? An indoor antenna?"

A Two possible solutions for your apartment-dwelling dilemma come to mind right away. The first is to purchase one of the miniature loop antennas manufactured by Advanced Electronic Applications or MFJ Enterprises (see the advertising pages of *QST*). These multiband loops are only a few feet in diameter and can be tuned remotely. In other words, you can place the loop out of sight in a closet or utility room and install the remote tuning unit beside your radio.

The second solution is to tack a wire dipole onto your ceiling and feed it with 450-Ω ladder line. Don't worry about the overall length of the dipole, and don't concern yourself with keeping the antenna wires in nice, straight lines. Simply put up as much copper as possible, in any direction possible. Bring the ladder line to an antenna tuner with a balanced output. With luck you'll be able to use the tuner to get an acceptable SWR on several bands.

In either case, I strongly recommend that you use low output power, 10 W or less. Beyond the obvious health concerns of generating a strong RF field in your apartment, higher power levels will probably wreak havoc to your neighbors' TV, stereos, VCRs and so on. You won't do much DX pileup busting with a low-power, indoor-antenna station, but you *will* make contacts, probably more than you might imagine.

Q A friend of mine and I keep a regular sked on 20 meters. We both use Yagi antennas and run 100 W output. When I substitute a simple dipole antenna for my Yagi, there seems to be a bigger difference in his ability to hear me than vice versa. I expected a difference, but you'd think it would be roughly equal on both ends of the path. Can an antenna have different gain patterns for transmission and reception?

A Speaking strictly in terms of gain, an antenna's receive and transmit gain are always the same. When it comes to differences in how well a station receives a signal, however, there are several factors that come into play.

Most HF receivers have more sensitivity than they need, particularly on the lower-frequency bands. When hooked to an efficient antenna, they pick up a lot of noise along with the desired signal. If your receiver has an attenuator, try it yourself: You can add quite a bit of attenuation without reducing the readability of incoming signals. This is because the attenuator reduces noise as well as the desired signal, and the ratio between the two remains the same. In effect, your switching from a Yagi to a dipole is like switching in an attenuator in your receiver (except that the dipole will pick up more noise and signals from undesired directions). At your friend's end, though, when you switch it's just as if you cut your transmitter power by the difference in gain between your two antennas. At his end the ratio between your signal, and the noise and undesired signals that he's also hearing, goes down.

As you can see, it's difficult to compare the performances of two antennas at different locations. That's why antenna manufacturers use huge *test ranges* to study and compare their products.

The SWR Obsession

By Steve Ford, WB8IMY
Assistant Technical Editor

Many hams suffer from a cruel obsessive-compulsive disorder. They're driven to achieve the lowest possible SWR—even when it isn't necessary.

There he goes again, scrambling up the ladders to cut another couple of inches from the ends of his antenna. The SWR was at 1.8:1 when he put it up, but that just isn't good enough. He'll run up and down those ladders for hours until he finally achieves the perfect 1:1 reading on his meter. Of course, it's all worthwhile in the end—isn't it?

No.

In this case, our hypothetical ham wasted an afternoon chasing a ghost. Other than burning off a few calories, he achieved nothing. Like many amateurs, this fellow has an unhealthy attachment to his SWR meter. Although they're essential pieces of test equipment, SWR meters have a tendency to dominate our thoughts to an extreme degree. I know hams who swing from elation to depression according to the readings on their meters. ("Oh, happy day! My SWR is 1:1 on 40 meters!")

In the age of instant gratification, I guess it's natural to fall in love with an SWR meter. It tells you all you need to know at a glance—or so many hams believe. It's a bit like an instrument Bones would use in the original *Star Trek* series. He waves it over your chest a few times and declares, "Ah-hah! You have a case of Martian flu!"

In truth, an SWR meter provides valuable information about your antenna system, but it doesn't tell the whole story. The trick is to regard it as just one tool in your diagnostic arsenal. Your SWR meter should inspire your curiosity, maybe even your deep concern in some instances. Never let it dictate your actions, however. When you look at your SWR meter, make sure you're seeing the complete picture.

Before we continue, I have a warning for those who fancy themselves as antenna and transmission line experts: Stop reading now. You won't find complicated presentations on wave mechanics and other arcane topics in this article. Instead, I'm going to make the complex simple. This means cutting some corners and that's sure to make your blood pressure jump a few notches. If you can't live without a dose of math and minutiae, take a look at the sidebar, "Get Out Your Calculators—or Computers" written by Dean Straw, N6BV, another Assistant Technical Editor (and our resident antenna guru) here at Headquarters.

Bouncing Waves

It's a quiet evening at home and you're itching to get on the air. With microphone in hand, you make your first call. As you press the PTT (push to talk) button and speak, the first syllable of your first word is transformed into RF (radio frequency) energy and sent zipping through the feed line. In a slice of time so small it's beyond human comprehension, that wave of energy arrives at the transmitting antenna. Some of the RF has changed into heat because of losses in the feed line, but most of it arrives at the antenna intact.

Everything seems normal so far, but serious strangeness is just around the corner. All it takes is a slight "disagreement" between your antenna and your feed line. This disagreement usually takes the form of an *impedance* mismatch. When the impedance of your antenna and your feed line are not the same, most of the energy is still radiated by the antenna, but the rest is *reflected back to your radio*. When the reflected wave reaches your radio, another odd thing happens: it's reflected right back to your antenna. The wave reaches your antenna and some of it is radiated. The rest—you guessed it!—is reflected back to your radio again.

While this reflected energy is bouncing back and forth like lightspeed Ping-Pong balls, your radio is still generating power. Now we have the energy created at the radio (the *forward power*) combining with the *reflected power*. This is a complex combination of waves, not like

I CUT 2 FEET FROM EACH SIDE LIKE YOU SAID, BUT MY SWR WENT THROUGH THE ROOF!

1 apple + 1 apple = 2 apples. Without going knee deep into math—and I promised you I wouldn't—it's sufficient to say that this combination of forward and reflected power creates what are known as *standing waves*.

When you place a *standing-wave ratio* (SWR) meter in the line at your transceiver, it measures the result of this complex combination of waves and shows it as a function of forward and reflected power. That's why you get readings like 1.5:1, 2:1 and so on. The higher the SWR, the more power is being reflected back to your radio.

SWR and Feed Lines

Common sense tells you that having any amount of reflected power is a bad thing, right? Well…it depends. High SWR is more of a problem—and obsession—for hams today than in the past.

Prior to World War II, most amateur transmitters were designed for *open-wire* feed lines. Open-wire lines consist of two wires in parallel separated by an insulating material, mostly air. The impedance of the line is primarily determined by the spacing of the wires. Since much of the RF loss in feed lines is caused by the resistance of the wires and the nature of the material that separates them, open-wire lines have very low losses indeed! (Air is a good insulator for RF energy.)

With open-wire feed lines, little power is lost between the transmitter and the antenna. Even with a high SWR, the loss is usually minimal. The reflected power bounces back and forth, but most of it is eventually radiated at the antenna. As you can probably guess, few hams concerned themselves with SWR in the days when open-wire line was king.

As America entered World War II, open-wire feed line proved to be a problem for the military. It wasn't shielded from the effects of nearby metal objects, for example. If too much metal was too close to an open-wire feed line, it created an imbalance. This caused an impedance "bump" in the line. Power reflected from this point just like it reflected from a mismatched antenna. Open-wire line didn't take kindly to being wrapped around corners, either. (Open-wire line takes corners well enough, but the curve must be *gradual*.)

The military needed a feed line that was rugged, highly flexible and shielded. So-called *concentric line* already existed, but it wasn't very flexible. (A metal shield entirely surrounded a central wire used to conduct RF energy.) To solve the flexibility problem, manufacturers replaced the solid shield with a braided wire. Flexible insulation ensured that the braid was kept at a uniform distance from the center so that the impedance could be maintained. Before you knew it, *coaxial cable* (coax) was born!

Coax solved the installation problem. You could place coax right up against a large piece of metal and it didn't care. Better yet, you could easily bend and shape it—within reason. After the war, surplus co-axial cable flooded the market and invaded Amateur Radio with a vengeance. Within a few years it became the dominant feed line for all amateur applications.

Coaxial cable has a serious flaw, however. Unlike open-wire line, many types of coax have significant loss. Remember: The air insulation is gone and plastic has taken its place. Plastic isn't nearly as invisible to RF energy as air. You have to spend big money and invest in air-insulated *Hardline* coaxial cable before you have loss figures that rival open-wire lines.

Do you recall what we said about mismatches and reflected power? The greater the mismatch, the more reflected power is bouncing between your antenna and your radio (resulting in a higher SWR reading on your meter). This isn't a serious problem with open-wire line because of its low loss. Coax, on the other hand, may be burning up a significant amount of the power that's traveling up and down the cable. So, if you're feeding an antenna with coaxial cable, a little SWR paranoia may be warranted—depending on the situation.

Is it Okay to be Obsessive about SWR?

Sometimes a little obsession is a good thing. At other times you're just spinning your wheels. The pursuit of the "perfect" 1:1 SWR has the potential for plenty of wasted effort. Let's take a look at a few hypothetical examples and see what we have to gain or lose. The results were calculated using standard transmission line formulas.

Example 1: You've installed a 40-meter wire dipole antenna and you're feeding it with 50 feet of RG-58 coaxial cable. The SWR at the input to the coax is 1.5:1. (This is what you're reading on your SWR meter.)

In this example you're losing about 0.62 dB in total cable attenuation as a portion of your power travels back and forth. This means that only a tiny fraction of your power is being lost. You'd have to lose more than 1 dB before anyone would be able to hear the difference in your signal! If you trim and tweak your antenna to get it down to a 1:1 SWR, you'll gain nothing except the false satisfaction of seeing the result on your meter. (Your power loss will only drop from 0.62 dB to 0.57 dB!)

Example 2: You're still using the 40-meter dipole with 50 feet of RG-58 co-axial cable, but now you're trying to operate the antenna on 20 meters. The SWR on your meter is reading an astonishing 67:1. (Most SWR meters won't really read this high and most transceivers without antenna tuners would shut down.) When the SWR is high, the loss in the coax becomes *very* significant. In this situation, you're losing about 7 dB of your power in the cable. If you were transmitting 100 W, less than *25 W* would actually be radiated by the antenna.

Example 3: You're determined to use your 40-meter antenna on 20 meters, so there's only one thing to do: replace that 50 feet of RG-58 coax with open-wire line. In this case we'll assume that you're using common 450-Ω ladder line. Because the im-pedance of the open-wire line is different from that of your RG-58, the resulting SWR is different, too. Now you're dealing with an SWR of 7.5:1. That's better than 67:1, but it's still high. Even so, the open-wire line loses only *0.17 dB* of your power! With an antenna tuner to match the open-wire line to your transceiver, you can use your 40-meter antenna on 20 meters with little difficulty—or loss.

I should point out that the term "antenna tuner" is a misnomer. An antenna tuner doesn't tune the antenna at all. You can only do that at the antenna itself. Instead, an antenna tuner acts as a resonator and an impedance transformer. It matches the impedance at the shack end of the feed line to a value (usually 50 Ω) that will make your transceiver happy. That's why many amateurs prefer to call them *transmatches*.

Example 4: Let's head up to the 2-meter band. Here we have a beam antenna fed with 100 feet of RG-58 coaxial cable. Unfortunately, something is wrong at the antenna and the SWR is 4:1. If you thought that RG-58 was lossy on the HF bands when the SWR was high, wait until you see what happens on 2 meters. The result is a loss of 8.45 dB. If you were running 25 W, your antenna would be radiating only about *3 W*—and you wouldn't hear very well either! (It's not only the transmitted energy that's lost in the line, received signals are attenuated, too.)

In a situation like this, your SWR meter down in the shack can fool you about what's happening at the antenna. The loss in a feed line can hide a bad mismatch, making it look much better than it really is. In this case, the SWR meter would show a 1.7:1 SWR—even though the SWR at the antenna is really much higher!

Example 5: We fixed the 2-meter antenna and replaced the lossy RG-58 coax with a superior feed line (Belden 9913 or equivalent). The SWR at the antenna is now down to 1.5:1. With our 100 feet of 9913 cable, the total loss is 1.68 dB and we can trust the SWR meter again! We can rest assured that most of our 25 W output is being radiated by the antenna.

I'll bet some of you are saying, "If the SWR is down to 1.5:1, we can go back to using the RG-58 coax, right?" Sorry. Feed-line loss increases as you go higher in frequency. Even with a low SWR, the loss at 2 meters with 100 feet of RG-58 is still an appalling 6.58 dB. That's why you should never use RG-58 cable at VHF or UHF unless the length is *very* short (mobile applications, for instance).

What Have We Learned?

All five examples have one thing in common: They show that power loss in feed lines is a function of the type (and length) of feed line you're using, the frequency of the signal *and* the SWR. All of these factors act together in complex ways. The bottom line on SWR is that it isn't the evil beast it's cracked up to be. A high SWR isn't necessarily a bad thing at all—*if your cable isn't eating up your power.*

Taking this idea to extremes, imagine 10,000 feet of totally *lossless* feed line. (Maybe 10-inch diameter Hardline bathed in liquid helium?) At one end of the line you have the mother of all antenna tuners, able to match virtually any impedance to 50 Ω for your transceiver. At the other end, you have a hideously mismatched antenna with an SWR of 99,999:1 at 3.8 MHz. Will this ridiculous setup work? The answer is "yes." Despite two miles of cable and an SWR the likes of which God has never seen, the vast majority of your transceiver's power will be radiated at the antenna.

Remember what we said about the bouncing waves. The power that isn't lost in the feed line or at other points in the system has to go somewhere. That "somewhere" is out your antenna! So, when you see the SWR reading on your meter, think carefully and take all the other factors into account *before* you get out your ladder!

When to Worry about SWR—and When Not to Worry

❏ Don't worry if you're feeding an HF antenna with 50-Ω coaxial cable and the SWR is 3:1 or less. If the length of your feed line is within reason (100 feet or less), the difference between an SWR of 3:1 and 1:1 isn't worth your trouble. You can even run as high as 5:1 SWR with good-quality coax and suffer relatively little loss. If your radio is cutting back its output because of an elevated SWR, use an antenna tuner to provide the 50-Ω impedance it needs.

If you're running over 500 W output, achieving a lower SWR may be in your best interest. Feed line, filter or antenna tuner damage may result if you try to run too much power with an elevated SWR.

❏ Don't worry if you're feeding an HF antenna with open-wire line and an antenna tuner. SWR has little meaning in this situation until you start talking about SWRs in the range of several *thousand* to one. Simply adjust the tuner for a 1:1 match at your radio and enjoy yourself.

❏ *Worry* if you're operating at VHF or UHF and the SWR is higher than 2:1 at the antenna. Even high-quality coax has substantial loss at these frequencies when the SWR starts creeping up. Adjust the antenna to bring it down to something less than 2:1. *DO NOT* use a so-called VHF/UHF antenna tuner! The tuner will provide a 1:1 SWR for your radio, but you're living in a fool's paradise. The SWR is still unacceptable on the *antenna side* of the tuner and that's where you're losing power.

❏ *Worry* if the SWR on your antenna system changes substantially (up or down) for no apparent reason. Some fluctuation is normal, such as when ice coats open-wire lines, but big changes are a warning. Your antenna system may have a problem and you'd better check it out. **QST**

Q I am confused by the meaning of solar flux, A index and K index. What do these numbers mean in terms of HF band conditions? Where can I get the latest data?

A Solar flux is an index of energy from the sun that correlates with the density of ionization in the ionosphere. In simpler terms, a higher flux value usually translates to a higher Maximum Usable Frequency (MUF) and better HF propagation. Solar flux roughly corresponds to a sunspot number, which is based on the size and number of sunspots on the visible solar disk.

The A and K indices have to do with geomagnetic disturbances. Higher A and K values correspond to greater *absorption* of radio waves, rather than refraction. This is bad news for HF propagation. When conditions are stable, the K index may get as low as one or zero. When conditions are truly awful, it may reach five or even seven. A change of one point in the K index is significant.

The A index is also a measure of geomagnetic stability, but a change of one point is not significant. It is based on the K index for the previous 24 hours. When the K index is three, the A index might be ten. A change of a point or two in the K index may send the A index to 20 or higher. When a severe geomagnetic storm appears and the HF bands shut down, the A index may reach 35 or more.

High A and K indices are typically a result of solar flares or coronal holes on the sun's surface. Both may shoot protons at the Earth, which neutralize the desirable ionization of the ionosphere, cause the geomagnetic field to become unstable and increase absorption of radio waves. To span great distances, you want your radio waves to be refracted (bent) by the ionosphere, not absorbed!

Solar reports are transmitted regularly by W1AW and by "time" stations WWV and WWVH. If you have packet radio capability and a *DX PacketCluster* network nearby, you may find solar reports there as well. Just connect to the system and send the command: SHOW/WWV. (*Our thanks to Tad Cook, KT7H, for supplying this information.*)

Q Fred Hatfield, W9MMZ, asks, "What are the consequences of operating a hand-held transceiver with the battery charger connected?"

A The answer depends on the type of hand-held rig and the design of the charger. For example, some charger cords act like antennas at VHF and UHF frequencies. When you transmit, the RF is picked up by the cord and conducted back into your hand-held transceiver. The result is usually a distorted signal.

If your batteries are low, operating on the charger can cause hum in the transmit and receive audio, too. The batteries may be too weak to supply sufficient current when you're transmitting and the charger isn't much help.

Q Roy Friday, N7JFO, asks...

I've been a ham for nine years,
And enjoy it a lot.
But what has happened lately,
Has tied my mind in a knot.

When my 3-element Yagi is sending Morse code,
The strangest thing takes place.
The lawn sprinklers next to my shack,
Give the code a race.

When I am sending code on 40 meters,
Those sprinklers send out water.
And when I stop, they also stop.
Boy, what a rotter!

Can you tell me what to do,
So this will cease to happen?
I want to send out code,
But not the lawn to dampen!

A Ouch! That loud rumble you hear is William Shakespeare spinning in his coffin at 3000 rpm. One poetic turn probably deserves another, but I can't find a rhyme for "FT-240-43 ferrite core."

Anyway, your 40-meter signal is getting into your sprinkler controller in a big way. It may be wreaking havoc with the microprocessor, or with the electrically operated valves.

Try placing the aforementioned ferrite cores (available from Ocean State Electronics, tel 800-866-6626, among others) on each wire going to and from the controller. Wind about 10 turns of the wire onto each core and install them as close to the controller as possible. You may have to perform the same procedure on the remote valves.

If this fails, contact the Technical Coordinator for your area for more assistance.

Q Edwin Robertson, W5CYF, asks, "I want to use my Swan 350 transceiver as a monitor for my Swan 500 rig. The 500 has developed a hum in the transmit audio and I need to listen to it while I search for the cause. Is there any way I can do this without overloading the Swan 350's receiver?"

A When you're using a nearby radio to monitor the transmissions of another, you need to reduce the output of the transmitting rig *and* the sensitivity of the receiving rig.

The first step is to connect the transmitting rig to a dummy load. This will reduce radiated output substantially. (Several *QST* advertisers sell dummy loads, or you can make one yourself.) In addition, see if your transceiver has a control that adjusts the RF output level. If so, use it to reduce the radiated output even further.

The second step is to use a short piece of wire as the antenna for your receiving radio—or try using no antenna at all. If the receiver has an **RF GAIN** control, adjust it to make the rig less sensitive.

The Lure of the Ladder Line

I was feeding a short, limited-space antenna with coaxial cable. Everything seemed to be okay, but was it?

By Steve Ford, WB8IMY
Assistant Technical Editor

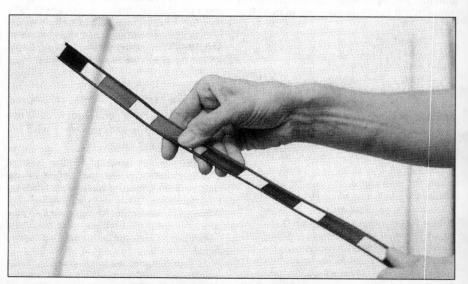

L ike many hams, I live in a home that's inhospitable to antennas. My house sits on a 100-foot square lot with trees along the back. I always hoped to be the proud owner of a tower and an HF beam antenna, but that was out of the question. What about a vertical? Well, I'd have to bury plenty of radial wires in the rocky Connecticut turf. That didn't sound like fun. I could buy a vertical that didn't require radials, but those antennas were a bit out of my price range—and their awkward, spiky appearance didn't blend well with the landscaping. A wire antenna seemed to be the ideal candidate.

Hanging a wire between two trees wasn't a problem, but there was still the *aesthetic* issue to consider. As much as I love ham radio, I didn't want to arouse the anger of my wife and neighbors by installing a copper monstrosity that looked as if it was spun by a mutant spider. All I wanted was a simple, low-profile dipole that I could operate on a number of HF bands.

Perhaps I could string up a single dipole and feed it with coaxial cable, using an antenna tuner to load it on several bands. The length of the antenna wouldn't be critical. I'd put up as much wire as possible and let the tuner worry about transferring power to the system. Even under high SWR conditions, where lots of energy is reflected back and forth between the tuner and the antenna, a substantial amount of RF would still be radiated. That sounded fine to me.

I put up a 66-foot dipole and fed it with low-loss coaxial cable. Sure enough, my antenna tuner was able to load it on all bands from 40 through 10 meters—more or less. The tuner balked a bit on 17 meters and it was very touchy on 10 meters. (Sometimes it arced with a startling snap!) Despite the problems, I used my system to work 75 new countries in just a couple of months, finally clinching my DXCC award. I also enjoyed many stateside contacts.

The SWR was quite high on most bands. At 100 watts output, however, the heavy-duty coax withstood the mismatch without noticeable heating. (I'd certainly notice it at higher power levels, though!) The antenna looked great and seemed to be performing well. Even so, I knew I was losing power in the cable and I wondered how it was affecting the overall performance.

While considering the alternatives, my thoughts drifted to *trap* dipoles. Yes, a trap dipole can be resonant on several HF bands, but the coil-and-capacitor traps tend to be bulky and prone to loss. How about a *fan* dipole? Simply attach several resonant dipoles to the same center point and feed them all with one cable. Too big and ugly! (We're back to the spider-web problem again.)

How Bad Can it Be?

I allowed my thoughts to drift for more than a year—until I met Dean Straw, N6BV, our new Senior Assistant Technical Editor here at League Headquarters. Dean's field of expertise is antennas and propagation, so I peppered him with questions about my antenna situation.

Yes, he said, my original assumption was correct. A nonresonant antenna will work—even with sky-high SWR—*if* the feed-line loss is low enough. My cable provided a low loss. The *ARRL Handbook* chart indicated that its loss was less than 1.5 dB per 100 feet at 100 MHz. I was only using 50 feet and my highest operating frequency was 29.60 MHz. (Cable loss decreases as feed-line length and frequency decrease.) So how bad could my losses be?

Very bad!

I made the mistake of underestimating the loss *under high SWR conditions*. Dean used a computer program to calculate the loss on various HF bands when used with my 66-foot dipole. You can see the results in the middle column of Table 1. I was shocked, to say the least! My 100-watt signal was reduced substantially on some frequencies. (The higher

the dB figure, the more power is lost in the cable. A 3-dB loss represents a 50% reduction.)

Since I insisted on sticking with a single-dipole design, Dean suggested that I replace my coaxial cable with *ladder line*. Unlike coax, where one conductor completely surrounds another, ladder line places both conductors in parallel. Insulating material is used to maintain a consistent separation. As a result, the fields radiated by the conductors cancel each other and the line is *balanced*. In 450-ohm line, sections of insulating plastic give the cable a ladder-like appearance, hence the name (see Fig 1).

"Oh, no," I said. "I know all about ladder line. It radiates RF in your house and you have to keep it away from metal or it won't work."

Dean simply smiled. He ran the loss calculations again, but this time he substituted

Fig 1—This type of 450-ohm ladder line uses plastic insulating material to maintain a consistent separation between the two conductors. The air gaps between the insulation gives it its ladder-like appearance. Other types of open-wire line are available, but 450-ohm ladder line is the most common.

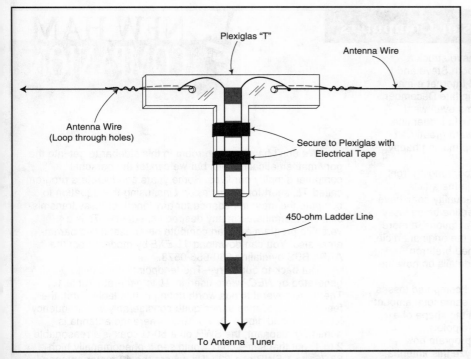

Fig 2—You can use a piece of Plexiglas to reinforce the ladder-line connection at the antenna. The Plexiglas acts to reduce the flexing of the wires where they connect to the antenna.

ladder line (see the right-hand column of Table 1). Wow! On 40 through 10 meters, the loss hardly exceeded 0.3 dB. Now he had my attention. But what about all those ladder-line problems?

"If the ladder line is balanced, it doesn't radiate RF," he replied. "As far as metal objects are concerned, you need to keep the line a few inches away from big sections of steel, aluminum and so on. The fields around the conductors can couple to metal and this creates an imbalance. Unless you intend to tape the ladder line along your gutters, however, I wouldn't worry about it. Your tuner should be able to handle any imbalance that occurs."

Table 1

Loss Comparisons for Belden 8214 Coaxial Cable and 450-ohm Ladder Line.

Cable length: 50 feet.
Antenna: 66-foot dipole at a height of 30 feet.
Calculated by Dean Straw, N6BV,
Senior Assistant Technical Editor

Frequency (MHz)	Loss (in dB)	
	8214	Ladder line
1.9	26.9	8.62
3.8	13.7	1.37
7.15	0.19	0.07
10.14	2.85	0.07
14.27	5.30	0.15
18.14	6.96	0.31
21.40	0.78	0.12
24.90	3.94	0.13
28.50	5.69	0.18

The Test

I was determined to put Dean's statements to the test. I purchased a 100-foot roll of 450-ohm ladder line and attached it to the center of my dipole. Since this was a temporary installation, I routed the line across the roof and into the window of my radio room. Along the way I passed over a couple of gutters, across some chimney flashing and along some aluminum siding to my window—which was equipped with metal sashes!

After attaching the line to the balanced-antenna posts on my tuner, I fired up the radio. "This will never work," I mumbled.

The tuner loaded easily on 40 meters, but that proved nothing. The antenna was resonant on 40 meters anyway. I started moving up, band by band. Each time, the tuner reduced the SWR at the transmitter to a flat 1:1 match without difficulty. No arcing. No RF interference. I was stunned!

On 15 meters, I heard a pileup centered on a station in the Marshall Islands. I grabbed the microphone and announced my call sign when he said, ". . . standing by for calls." He answered me on the first attempt!

"I know what I'll do," I said with a fiendish laugh. "I'll load the antenna on *80 meters*. It's way too short to load on 80!"

Wrong again. The tuner quickly brought the SWR down to 1:1. I then proceeded to make several contacts and received outstanding signal reports. This was the first time that I was ever able to use my dipole on 80 meters. I tried 160 meters, but that was pushing it a bit too far for the tuner. A muffled frying sound indicated its displeasure.

The performance of the antenna fed with 450-ohm ladder line has been excellent on all bands. As you might guess, the improvement is most dramatic on the bands where the SWR is highest. Thanks to ladder line, the vast majority of my output power is now radiated at the antenna—not lost in the feed line.

Not a Cure-All

It's important to point out that my nonresonant dipole is a compromise solution designed for the restrictions at my home. The ladder line isn't magical. It simply allows a mediocre antenna to perform much better than it might otherwise. I must keep my output below 150 watts or risk dangerously high RF voltage levels on the feed line (now you know why the tuner arced on 160 meters!). Some antenna tuners may arc even at relatively low power levels. If you decide to attempt this type of antenna design, I recommend a heavy-duty antenna tuner rated at 1 kW or higher. The tuner must provide a *balanced* output (not all tuners do).

Of course, if I had a resonant antenna instead, I could go back to my low-loss coaxial cable and enjoy equally good performance. I probably wouldn't need an antenna tuner and I could run much more power.

Ladder line can be affected by weather. (Ice, water or debris between the conductors can upset the balance.) Unless you reinforce the connection at the antenna (see Fig 2), the line is likely to break rather quickly. And ladder line can be difficult to locate. (If your local dealer doesn't sell it, check the advertising pages of *QST* for wire and cable suppliers.) These disadvantages notwithstanding, ladder line is an excellent choice for almost any kind of HF antenna. Not only is it inexpensive, the loss figures at HF frequencies are very low.

Apartment and Condo Dwellers

If you're an apartment/condo dweller, or anyone else suffering under antenna restrictions, ladder line may offer a way for you to get on the air. If you have an attic, for example, install the longest dipole you can and feed it with ladder line. Don't worry about the length of your antenna. Just make sure that both sides are equal. Use your antenna tuner and determine on which bands you can achieve a 1:1 SWR. You may be surprised to discover that you can become active on at least some HF bands after all!

NEW HAM COMPANION

"The Lure of the Ladder Line"[1] must have struck a responsive chord (or a nerve) out there—both Steve and I received many letters, telephone calls and Internet e-mail messages as soon as *QST* hit the streets in late December. Despite the snow and ice, some brave hams even went outside to change their feed lines from coax to ladder line. They excitedly reported that their signals were greatly improved—in fact, several just couldn't stop making happy noises to us!

There were some adverse reactions too, ranging from mild surprise to outright disbelief. Table 1 in the article caused the most shock—why should good-quality coax have so much loss? And why should even ladder line be so lossy at 1.8 MHz? Unfortunately, due to space limitations, a more detailed table of values had to be cut from the original article, leaving some of our more technically inclined brethren scratching their heads. So here are some details on how the loss figures were derived.

Just to spice things up a bit, this time I computed losses for a slightly different antenna—I used the same total amount of wire, 66 feet, but assumed that it was in the shape of a typical inverted-V, rather than a horizontal dipole.

I used *NEC2*, a mainframe computer program now available for use on high-end PCs, to analyze this antenna, rather than a *MININEC*-derived program. *MININEC* programs lose accuracy rapidly when the antenna is less than about 0.2 wavelength above ground. I specified "average" ground, having a conductivity of 5 mS/m (millisiemens per meter) and a dielectric constant of 13.

Once I had determined the feedpoint impedances for the multiband inverted **V**, I explored the feed-line loss for two types of transmission line—450-Ω "window" ladder line, which Steve had used for his antenna, and RG-213 type coax, which he had used before he discovered ladder line. In this illustration, each line was to be 100 feet long, a number I thought representative for a typical amateur installation (50 feet up the tree, 50 feet back to the shack).

By the way, this is a good point to digress just a bit. The wave mechanics in a transmission line can be a little mystifying to a novice (or even an old-timer like me). Books on transmission-line theory usually start out by analyzing a "theoretically perfect, lossless line." They look at such a line when it is matched, and then when it is mismatched. At this point they launch into detailed descriptions of forward and reflected waves, and all the complicated interactions they create. Sorry, but my eyes usually begin to glaze over by the second page.

There is a much simpler way to look at a practical (that is, lossy) transmission line that is not terminated in its characteristic impedance—*at any point on that lossy line a unique impedance exists*. If we insert an SWR meter (also called, more accurately, an *SWR bridge*) in the line, what we are measuring is the difference between the characteristic impedance of the line and the unique impedance at that point.

The value of the unique impedance at any one point on the line is determined by lots of factors—for the line itself, we have the characteristic impedance, physical length, velocity factor, and loss characteristics. Then we throw in the frequency and the terminating impedance (usually an antenna) at the end of the line. All these factors are elegantly and succinctly described by the Transmission Line Equation.[2]

[1] S. Ford, "The Lure of the Ladder Line," *QST,* Dec 1993, pp 70-71.
[2] *The ARRL Antenna Book*, 16th Edition, pp 27-29 to 27-30. See Eq 18.

We don't have enough room in this sidebar to get into the gory mathematical details, but we can let the personal computer simplify our lives. Some years ago I wrote a program called *TL*, short for *Tranmission Line*, using this equation to compute the input impedance for any length of lossy transmission line, terminated in any desired impedance. *TL* is a versatile program and can compute other useful line parameters also. You can download *TL.EXE* by modem from the ARRL BBS by dialing 860-666-0578.

But back to our story—The feedpoint impedances generated by *NEC2* were used in *TL* to generate Table 1. There are several things worth noting in this table. First, the feedpoint impedance varies quite considerably with frequency for a multiband dipole. At 7.1 MHz, where the antenna is nominally resonant, the SWR on a 50-Ω coax is a reasonable 2 to 1, but that same coax would see a phenomenally high 63,761 to 1 SWR at 1.83 MHz, where the 40-meter antenna is only an eighth-wave long! Due to the *extremely* high SWR at 1.83 MHz, the loss in 100 feet of RG-213 coax is 32.5 dB. If 100 W were fed into this line, only 0.06 W would appear at the antenna end. That's right—60 *milli*watts—instant QRP!

When trying to feed an extremely short antenna like this at 1.83 MHz, even low-loss 450-Ω ladder line would see a huge SWR of 7,355 to 1. Ladder line loses 11.2 dB, even though the matched-line loss at this frequency is a miniscule 0.01 dB per 100 feet. Another very nasty thing makes its presence known when extremely high SWRs are encountered for 1500 W of power at 1.83 MHz, *TL* computes the maximum RF rms voltage is almost 40,000 V! That will fry most antenna tuners, or at least cause them to arc over internally. Steve was not kidding when he stated that his kW antenna tuner was not a happy camper on 160 meters, even when he had backed the power down to less than 20 W!

So the moral of this tale is simple—as versatile as multiband dipoles may be, especially to a ham who can't put up separate antennas for all the HF bands, they do have limitations. If they are electrically very short, for example on 160 meters, there will be losses in whatever transmission line feeds it. Using coax cable to feed a simple multiband antenna will result in far greater losses than for open-wire feeders, on all frequencies.—*N6BV*

Table 1

Inverted-V Dipole, 50 feet high, 66 feet long, fed with 100 feet of 450-Ω "window" ladder line, or 100 feet of RG-213 coax.

Frequency (MHz)	Antenna feedpoint impedance	SWR for ladder line	Total loss (in dB) for ladder line	SWR for RG-213	Total loss (in dB) for RG-213
1.83	$1.6 - j2256.6$	7355	11.2	63761	32.5
3.80	$10.3 - j878.8$	210	2.2	1505	18.1
7.10	$64.8 - j40.6$	7	0.2	2	0.7
10.10	$21.6 + j648.4$	64	1.8	392	14.9
14.10	$5287.1 - j1309.5$	13	0.5	112	9.7
18.10	$198.2 - j819.9$	10	0.6	72	9.4
21.20	$102.9 - j181.2$	5	0.3	9	3.2
24.90	$269.3 + j569.6$	5	0.4	30	6.9
28.40	$3088.9 + j774.0$	7	0.6	66	10.1

Do You Need an Antenna Tuner?

Maybe yes, maybe no. It all depends on the type of antenna and feed line you're using.

By Steve Ford, WB8IMY
Assistant Technical Editor

There is a great cloud of mythology surrounding antenna tuners, particularly when the conversation turns to what they can and cannot do. Make no mistake, they are useful devices in the right applications. The trick is deciding whether you need one!

When Rigs and Antenna Systems Disagree

Every antenna has an *impedance* expressed in *ohms*. The same is true of the feed line you use to connect your transceiver to the antenna. Impedance sounds like a complicated beast and, to a certain extent, it is. In simplest terms, it is a combination of *inductive reactance*, *capacitive reactance* and garden-variety *resistance*.

It's probably best to avoid a long discussion about the meaning of reactance. This is "New Ham Companion," not the *Proceedings of the IEEE*. If I had several more pages to devote to this article, I'd be more than happy to bore you to tears with reactance theory. For our purposes, think of reactance as opposition to the flow of an ac signal in a circuit. In this case, the ac is the RF generated by your transceiver and the circuit is your antenna system. File this idea away for the moment. We'll come back to it later.

Meanwhile, back at the radio ranch....

The impedance of the antenna depends on a number of factors, including the length, operating frequency, height above ground, proximity of metal objects and even weather conditions (such as ice on the antenna). The impedance of the feed line depends on how the cable is constructed.

Your feed line does more than simply connect your radio to your antenna. It acts as an impedance *transformer*. That is, the impedance of your antenna is transformed by the feed line into the value your radio "sees" when you connect it to the cable. This *system impedance* acts as a *load* for the energy created by your radio—just like a light bulb is a load for the energy supplied by a battery.

Most amateur transceivers are designed to work with a load impedance of 50 ohms. When your radio sees an impedance of 50 ohms, or something close to it, you're on easy street. You press the mike switch, close the CW key or type on your keyboard and all is right with the world.

But what happens when the impedance *isn't* 50 ohms? Now you have a situation known as a *mismatch*.

When a mismatch exists, a certain portion of the power generated by your radio is *reflected*—like light is reflected by a mirror. This reflected power comes shooting back down the cable to your radio. When it reaches the radio, it is reflected back toward the antenna. The reflected power combines with the *forward* power being generated at the radio to create *standing waves* in the feed line.

By using a *standing-wave-ratio* (SWR) meter, you can measure both the forward and reflected power. A 1:1 SWR reading indicates that no power is being reflected back to your radio. This is good. On the other hand, an SWR of 3:1 or more means that a substantial amount of power is being reflected. This is usually bad. (Don't you love these simple concepts?)

A high SWR can cause considerable RF voltages to develop in the feed line and in the output circuits of your radio. This is a dangerous condition for your rig—especially if it is a modern solid-state transceiver. To prevent this, many radios manufactured within the past 10 years include SWR protection circuits. When the SWR gets too high, these circuits automatically reduce the output power or, in some cases, shut down the transceiver altogether (see Fig 1). Older tube radios are much more forgiving, but even they can be damaged when operated under high SWR conditions.

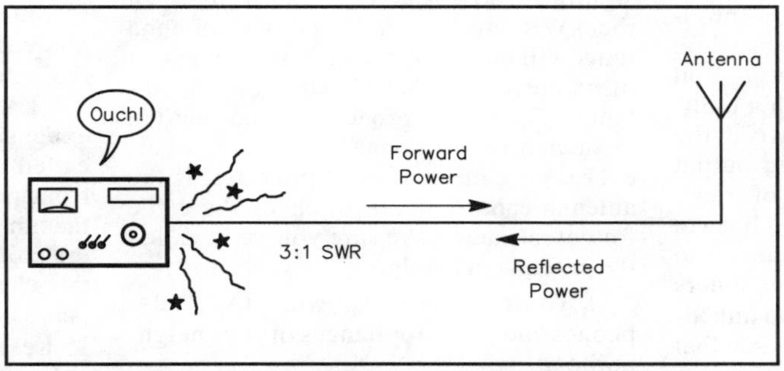

If your antenna system presents a serious mismatch to your radio, what can you do? If you connect your transceiver directly, the protection circuitry will drop your output like a rock. Worse yet, you may find yourself on the receiving end of an expensive repair bill. You need to provide a 50-ohm load for your transceiver—regardless of what is really present. One way to accomplish this is by using an antenna tuner.

How Does an Antenna Tuner Work?

In its most basic form, an antenna tuner is simply a network of variable inductors (coils) and capacitors. By adjusting the coils and capacitors, you counterbalance and cancel the effects of the inductive and capacitive reactance at the *transceiver* end of the feed line. (*Now* you know why I bothered bringing up the subject of reactance in the first place!) As the reactances are canceled, the impedance at the transceiver is transformed to 50 ohms (see Fig 2).

Fig 1—Most transceivers are designed to expect an antenna system impedance of 50 ohms. When the antenna impedance is something other than 50 ohms, a transmission line mismatch occurs and a portion of the RF power is reflected back to the radio. *Standing waves* are created in the feed line and high RF voltages can develop. When the standing-wave ratio becomes higher than 3:1, your transceiver may be damaged.

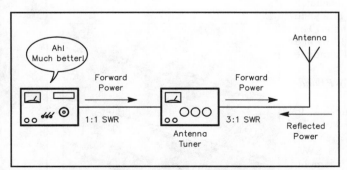

Fig 2—By using an antenna tuner, you can adjust the impedance your transceiver "sees" to a hospitable 50 ohms. The antenna mismatch to the line still exists, but the tuner protects your radio from the RF voltages while allowing it to develop its maximum output.

As far as your transceiver is concerned, the load impedance is matched and it's free to dump all of its power into the antenna system.

I bet a number of you are saying to yourselves, *"Wait a minute! The impedance at the transceiver side of the tuner is 50 ohms, but it's still some other value at the antenna side. All you've done is shift the mismatch problem from the transceiver to the tuner!"*

You're right. The mismatch still exists, but now it's at the output of the antenna tuner instead of the transceiver. By using the tuner, we're protecting the radio while still allowing it to develop maximum output. If the tuner is well designed, it should be able to handle the RF voltages and currents caused by the high SWR.

Of course, the reflected power is still bouncing back and forth between the antenna tuner and the antenna. Some of this power is lost in the feed line. If you're using low-loss feed line, however, most of it is radiated at your antenna. In the meantime, your transceiver is happy and you're happy. Who could ask for more?

Use an Antenna Tuner if...

...you want to feed your antenna with open-wire line.

Open-wire line (or *ladder line*) offers extremely low loss at HF frequencies (much better than coaxial cable). One problem is that open-wire line is *balanced* while your transceiver output is *unbalanced*. You need to use an antenna tuner with a built-in *balun* to form a bridge between the balanced line and the unbalanced output of your radio. A balun is a type of transformer that converts balanced feed lines to unbalanced, or vice versa. (**BAL**anced to **UN**balanced. Get it?) Most antenna tuners use 4:1 baluns that also convert the impedance of open-wire feed lines to a value that the tuner can handle.

...you want to operate your antenna on bands other than those it was designed for.

When you attempt to use, say, a 40-meter dipole on 10 meters, a big mismatch will develop, along with a high SWR. By using an antenna tuner, you may be able to create a 1:1 SWR at your transceiver. (I say "may" because the mismatch can sometimes be so great that it is beyond the capability of your tuner to handle.) The high SWR may cause substantial loss in a coaxial feed line, but at least you'll radiate *some* power at the antenna.

...your antenna has a narrow *SWR bandwidth* on some bands.

Some types of multiband antennas do not offer low SWRs from one end of each band to the other. There is usually a range—expressed in kilohertz—where an SWR below 2:1 can be achieved. For example, a multiband trap dipole may offer an SWR of 2:1 or less from 3600 to 3800 kHz. That's an SWR bandwidth of 200 kHz. If you try to operate above 3800 kHz or below 3600 kHz, you'll encounter an SWR higher than 2:1 and your radio may become displeased. With an antenna tuner, you can operate outside the SWR bandwidth and still load the full output of your radio into the antenna system.

Don't Bother with an Antenna Tuner if...

...your SWR is 1.5:1 or less at the frequencies you operate most often.

An SWR of 1.5:1 or less is not serious and does not require the assistance of an antenna tuner. Most modern rigs will tolerate a 1.5:1 SWR just fine. In fact, many will be happy at an SWR of 2:1. If you are using a good-quality feed line, the loss caused by an SWR of 1.5:1 or even 2:1 isn't enough to worry about at HF frequencies. Many hams are obsessed with providing an absolute 1:1 SWR for their radios at all times. Apparently they also have money to burn!

...you have a high SWR at VHF or UHF frequencies.

VHF/UHF antenna tuners are available, but my advice is to save your money. Remember that an antenna tuner massages the antenna system impedance *at the transceiver*. The mismatch still exists and the SWR is still high at the antenna side of the tuner. Even the best coaxial cables have significant losses at VHF and UHF when the SWR is high. A VHF/UHF antenna tuner will make your radio happy, but most of its power will never make it to the antenna. The best approach is to correct the mismatch at the antenna by adjusting whatever tuning mechanism it provides. If the antenna cannot be tuned, check the cable for defects and make sure you've installed the antenna properly.

...you're interfering with TVs, telephones and other appliances in your neighborhood.

Despite what you may have heard, an antenna tuner will not necessarily cure your interference problems. It's true that most antenna tuners will reduce the level of *harmonic radiation* (signals your radio generates in addition to the ones you want), and if the interference is being caused by harmonics, a tuner may help. Most interference, however, is caused by RF energy that's picked up indirectly by cables or wires, or directly by the device itself. By using an antenna tuner, you'll probably radiate more energy at the antenna than you did before. That may make your interference problem worse!

Looking for Mr Goodtuner

So, you've decided that you need an antenna tuner after all. Antenna tuners come in all shapes and sizes. What features should you consider?

❑ **A built-in SWR meter**—An SWR meter of some type is a must if you want to use an antenna tuner. When adjusting your tuner, you need to keep your eye on the *reflected power* indicator. Your goal is to reduce the reflected power to zero—or at least as close as you can get. When the reflected power is zero, the SWR is 1:1 at your transceiver.

Many tuners feature built-in meters. If not, you can purchase one separately. Your radio may even have its own SWR meter.

❑ **A roller or tapped inductor**—More expensive tuners feature a variable coil called a *roller inductor*. As you turn the front-panel inductor knob, the coil inside the tuner rotates. A metal wheel rolls along the coil like a train on a railroad track. As the wheel moves along the coil, the inductance increases or decreases.

Less expensive tuners do not use roller inductors. Instead, there is a coil with wires attached at various points. On the front panel, a rotary switch selects the wires. According to how the inductor is wired in the circuit, selecting one *tap* or another

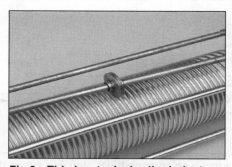

Fig 3—This is a typical roller inductor. Notice the wheel that rolls along the coil windings. As the wheel moves, the inductance changes.

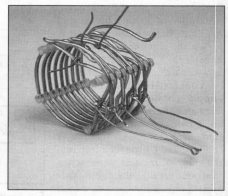

Fig 4—Tapped inductors have wires attached at various points. By selecting a particular wire, you get a fixed amount of inductance.

varies the inductance. This is known as a *tapped inductor*.

There are advantages and disadvantages to both approaches. Roller inductors offer the best tuning performance, but they are subject to the woes of mechanical wear and tear. For example, if corrosion builds up on the wheel or the coil windings, the electrical quality of the connection will deteriorate. Roller inductors are also cumbersome to use. You may have to twist the control many times when moving from one band to another.

Tapped inductors are easy to use and free of mechanical problems (unless the switches get dirty). However, you may find that they restrict the operating range of your tuner. When you turn the switch, you select a *fixed* amount of inductance. You can't easily change it to tune a particularly difficult mismatch situation.

❏ **A built-in balun**—If you intend to use an open-wire feed line, buy a tuner with a built-in 4:1 balun. These baluns often dissipate quite a bit of heat, so always choose a large balun over a small one.

❏ **Multiple antenna capability and dummy loads**—Some tuners offer the ability to connect more than one antenna. This is handy in all sorts of applications. Let's say you have a vertical antenna for 40-10 meters and a wire dipole for 80 meters. You can connect both feed lines to your tuner and easily switch between them.

Built-in dummy loads are convenient, but not necessary. A dummy load is a resistor (or group of resistors) that absorbs the output of your transceiver while allowing very little energy to radiate. It's used for making transmitter adjustments and other tests. If your tuner lacks a dummy load, you can purchase one separately.

❏ **Automatic operation**—Most transceiver manufacturers offer *automatic* antenna tuners. These tuners are usually built in the radio itself, or they're offered separately. Automatic tuners are convenient when you need to change bands or frequencies quickly. You simply push a button and your tuner adjusts its coils and capacitors to achieve the lowest SWR. Some automatic tuners sense when you've changed frequency and will readjust immediately! (You don't have to lift a finger.)

Automatic antenna tuners are expensive and their tuning range is limited. If your operating style requires you to jump from band to band rapidly (contesting is one scenario), consider an automatic tuner. Otherwise, conserve your cash and invest in a manual tuner.

A Word About Power Ratings

If your transceiver produces only 50 or 100 watts of power, a 200- or 300-watt tuner should do the trick, right? Well…yes and no. Remember what we said about mismatches causing high RF voltages in the tuner? If you're trying to use your tuner in a high-SWR situation, the RF voltages at the tuner may cause an unpleasant phenomenon known as *arcing*. That's when the RF energy literally jumps the gaps between the capacitor plates or coil windings. When your tuner arcs, you'll usually hear a snapping or buzzing noise. The reflected power meter will fluctuate wildly. Interference to your TV and other devices will increase dramatically. You may even see brilliant flashes of light inside your tuner!

Arcing is obviously bad news for your tuner. It's your tuner's way of saying, "Stop! I can't handle this mismatch!" There are two cures for arcing: reduce your output until it stops, or get a tuner with a higher power rating.

High-power tuners use large capacitors and coils. The gaps between the plates and windings are greater, making it more difficult for an arc to occur. If you can afford it, you're always better off buying a tuner with a 1.5 kW rating or better. (The exception is QRP operating where you're running low power levels.) A hefty tuner costs more, but it will serve you well in the long run.

Buy or Build?

As you comb through the advertising pages of *QST*, you'll see many new antenna tuners for sale. The prices are often reasonable and the quality is usually good. Keep your eyes open for used tuners, too. If an old tuner is in decent condition, it's every bit as usable as a new one.

If you like to build things, however, consider an antenna tuner as your next project. Antenna tuners are relatively easy to construct. You can find capacitors and coils at hamfest flea markets at low prices. Even roller inductors—the most expensive part of a roller-inductor tuner—can be found for less than $40 if you look carefully.

Your chances of success with an antenna tuner project are excellent. You have to try pretty hard to build one poorly! Best of all, you'll have the satisfaction of using a piece of equipment that you've put together yourself. The *ARRL Handbook* offers several tuner designs you can try. Heat up your soldering iron and go to it! **QST-**

Q Robert Clark, N1SOR, asks, "I'm a relatively new ham and I operate 2-meter FM, mostly on repeaters. My problem is striking up a conversation. It seems like everyone knows each other and I feel like an outsider. Any suggestions?"

A On most repeater systems it does seem as though everyone knows each other. Because the local hams have much in common, their conversations flow easily. When it comes to speaking with strangers, however, they tend to freeze up!

The best way to enjoy a repeater is to shed your "stranger" status as soon as possible. As you become better known among the locals, you'll find the conversations are much more pleasant—and frequent. Here are two effective strategies:

❏ Get involved in discussions that interest you. Let's say that you're into computers and you hear a group of hams talking about video cards. If you can contribute something (answer a question, perhaps), break into the conversation. Most hams will welcome your input. Better yet, if you have a question, join the group and ask. Everyone likes to show off their expertise and they'll welcome the opportunity to do so on the repeater! Do this often enough and you'll no longer be a stranger.

❏ Most repeater systems are maintained by clubs. Join the club and volunteer for anything and everything. Public-service events are particularly fun. You'll be amazed at how fast you'll become a familiar voice. It may take a few months, but when you key your radio and say, "N1SOR listening," it's likely that someone will respond with a question or comment. After all, they *know* you! ("Hey, Bob, are you going to be net control for the race this weekend?")

Q I was listening around 14.230 MHz this weekend when I heard some strange activity. I heard a guy say, "Here it comes, Charlie. Scotty one." This was followed by a warbling tone that lasted a minute or so. What was going on?

A What you heard was a group of slow-scan television (SSTV) operators. When the fellow said, "Here it comes, Charlie. Scotty one," he was telling Charlie that he was about to transmit a picture. In this case, the image was sent in the *SCOTTY 1* format. There are several popular SSTV formats, so it's helpful to alert everyone before you transmit so they can adjust their gear accordingly.

The image information is translated into shifting audio tones for transmission. That's the warbling sound you heard. SSTV images can be sent in black and white or color. If signal conditions are good, the result at the receiving end is often dramatic! Due to the nature of the format, SSTV images are still photographs. The scan rate is too slow to permit movement.

You can join the SSTVers with just a modest investment on your part. Read "An Inexpensive SSTV System" by Ben Vester, K3BC, in the January 1994 *QST*. Ben's system will get you on the air at minimal cost. Also, if you have a *SoundBlaster* card in your computer, you can use it to send and receive SSTV. Check the advertising pages of *QST* and other Amateur Radio magazines for compatible software.

A Townhouse Dipole

If you think it's impossible to use a commercial HF antenna in an apartment or condo, you'd better read this article!

By Mark L. Gress N0OQC
8163 Curtis Ln
Eden Prairie, MN 55347-1118

If you live in a townhouse or other restricted area, global communication *is* still possible! My station is living proof.

When I purchased my townhouse in the summer of 1988, I had no idea I would soon be interested in becoming an Amateur Radio operator. Since then I've earned my Extra Class license and I've been exploring the mysteries of the HF bands *despite* my antenna limitations.

The solution was relatively simple: I installed a Cushcraft model D3 triband 10, 15, and 20-meter rotatable dipole in my attic. It didn't have to be a Cushcraft; this is just my personal preference. There are several commercially available rotatable dipoles. Pick up any Amateur Radio equipment catalog and you'll see what I mean.

Why use a rotatable dipole? Unless you have a truly monstrous attic, you certainly won't be rotating it! Why not just string up a common wire dipole instead?

Commercial rotatable dipoles are made from aluminum tubing and they're designed to work with minimal fuss. They're extremely easy to adjust. No cutting or soldering! Best of all, they are very "broad" when it comes to the SWR bandwidth. In the case of the D3, I can transmit anywhere on 20 or 15 meters—and throughout most of 10 meters—and enjoy a *maximum* SWR less than 2:1.

You can achieve the same performance with an antenna of your own making, but that takes precious hours out of an otherwise busy schedule. For the active ham who doesn't have time to experiment, this type of antenna makes perfect sense.

I call the D3 my "nonrotatable rotatable dipole." Even though the antenna doesn't move, I can work almost every station I hear. I'm limited to only 28.5 feet of attic space, so I had to settle for the shorter D3. There are several options and combinations available, so look around and be inventive. I could have installed the D4 for 10, 15, 20, and 40 meters *and* the D3W for 12, 17 and 30 meters if I had enough space. This combination would give you seven HF bands with no tuner required. You could install the dipoles above each other about a foot apart. Interaction problems are almost unnoticeable.

Installing the D3

I opted to suspend my D3 about 15 inches below the apex of the attic rafters by using flexible nylon webbing (the kind used for sport climbing). This webbing is available at outdoor recreation stores that carry rock-climbing equipment. Any nonconductive material can be used as well. Three-foot lengths of webbing support the D3 in the middle and between the two traps on either side (see Figure 1). I simply made a **U**-shaped loop with the nylon webbing and nailed it to the rafters above. This part of the installation took all of five minutes!

I coiled the air-core balun according to the manufacturers' instructions and fed the antenna with RG-8/U Extraflex No. 9095 coax. This is the half-inch foam-core coax rather than the RG-8/X mini-foam Cushcraft recommended. I routed the coax from the attic through the interior walls, following existing pathways for the house wiring, down to the lower level where my shack is located. I tuned the D3 according to the instructions and I was ready to go within 30 minutes!

Helpful Hints

If you want to try this approach in your house, apartment, townhouse or condo, here are a few hints that will help ensure your success.

❑ Climb into your attic and assess the space before you even think of buying your antenna. Don't rely on your best guess. Measure the length and make certain that a rotatable dipole will fit safely. The antenna

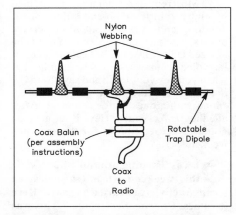

Figure 1—The rotatable dipole hangs from the attic rafters, supported by nylon webbing. Because your antenna is out of the weather, there's no need to worry about waterproofing your coax connectors and so on.

must not touch anything except the antenna supports and the feed line. Keep the antenna a minimum of 12 inches from any other materials in the attic.

❑ Determine how you'll route your coaxial cable to your radio. The simplest choice is to follow the house wiring. Ask a friend to help you. (And if you have a friend who happens to be an electrician, you've got it made!) You might want to run several cables in case you get the urge to set up more attic antennas in the future. At least the cables will be in place and ready to go!

❑ Assemble your antenna before taking it up to the attic. Make sure everything fits properly. Then, separate the antenna into several pieces. After you carry the sections into the attic, it's usually a simple matter to slide them back together.

❑ Tune the antenna for lowest SWR, beginning with the highest band and progressing to the lowest. Then, tighten all the antenna hardware. When in doubt, read the instructions!

❑ Double check everything before you leave the attic. You don't want to make another trip up there if you don't have to.

Depending on the height of your attic, this may be a low dipole indeed. Even so, it has worked very well for me. I consistently receive outstanding signal reports in all directions despite the dearth of sunspots.

You're probably wondering about EMI and I can't blame you. This is a common problem with attic installations. I avoided interference hassles by EMI-proofing my telephones, TV and other electronic devices. At the radio I've installed a Bencher YA-1 low-pass filter as well. I've assisted my neighbors by recommending filters and the result has been terrific. The ARRL book *Radio Frequency Interference: How to Find it and Fix It* was very helpful (see the *Publications Catalog* in this issue). You can also minimize any EMI problems by simply turning down the power. Many hams operate QRP (less than 5 W) from their attics with no interference problems at all.

Expanding on my success, I've installed a homebrew 40-meter "shorty" antenna just below the D3. And if that wasn't enough, my attic antenna farm also includes a Cushcraft AR-270 antenna for 2 meters and 70 cm! Unlike most antenna installations, mine is sheltered from the elements. If I ever need to work on the antennas—or install yet another—I can work in relative comfort despite the weather! ◻

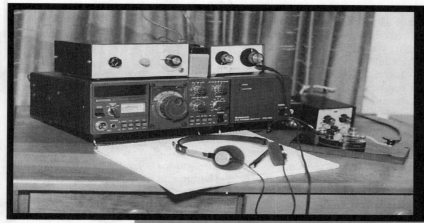

A Practical Stealth Antenna

You can work the world from your apartment or condo—if you're willing to be a little *sneaky*.

By Bruce Muscolino, W6TOY/3
3900 Bel Pre Rd, Apt 5
Silver Spring, MD 20906
Photos by the author

The stealth station of W6TOY/3. Along the top row you'll see an MXM 40-meter QRP transceiver and an NE-4040. On the bottom is the author's TS-130V transceiver. The MFJ antenna tuner is at the lower right.

I know life's too short for *QRP* (low-power hamming) because I saw a T-shirt last year at the Dayton *Hamvention* that said so. But for many years I've been making lots of contacts, with stations all over the world, while operating QRP using a most unlikely antenna. I'm not really sure whether life's too short for QRP or not, but I know for sure it's definitely too short for you to keep missing the fun of operating!

We've all heard, or read stories about, someone loading up their bedspring, window frame, or even a downspout, and earning their WAC, WAS, and DXCC over a long weekend when the sunspot number was less than 1—haven't we? I can remember hearing two or three of those stories almost every year since I was first licensed. So, why tell another one? Because this one is going to show you how to do it, warts and all!

I call this my "stealth antenna" because it's outdoors, yet more or less invisible to the naked eye. Why do we need a "stealth antenna"? Because hams don't seem to live in places where stacked seven-element monobanders are viable options anymore. More often, we live in places where neighbors don't like outdoor antennas, or places where we don't even get a vote with the landlord, or homeowner's associations, or whoever.

Stealth Operation

The "stealth antenna" was born out of desperation. Back when spark ruled the world and electrons were made of stone (flint, probably), I lived in the country on what we lovingly called a farm. It was only five acres with a few outbuildings, but it had enough room for one of the sweetest 137-foot Windom antennas ever created. It seems every place I've lived since then,

mostly apartments and condos, has had some sort of restriction against outdoor antennas.

In the mid-1970s I caught a bad case of "get-back-on-the-low-bands-itis." I simply *had* to make a contact that wasn't "full quieting" into some machine somewhere. If I'd had any sense I'd have bought a house and put up a dipole. But hey, I had to be a ham. Hams, after all, have been responsible for many of the developments in the history of radio. Why not another one? Thus began an almost sacred quest!

The first stop was a series of very successful helically wound dipoles hanging in my living room. The second was a short random wire running alongside my apartment building, under the eaves. "Stealth" was alive!

A year or so later I went home for Christ-

mas. Instead of a farm in Ohio, home was now a third-floor condo in Maryland, where I was introduced to the mind-numbing joys of Covenants, Conditions, and Restrictions (CC&Rs): **No Outside Antennas Allowed. Period. End Of Discussion.**

Fool that I was, I carted my trusty TS-520 transceiver along. First I thought, "Well, I'll just listen around," but the signals I heard got the best of me. Before the day was done I was on the air using an antenna tuner and about 30 feet of wire lying on the floor . I worked stations up and down the East Coast with that setup. You're probably muttering, "So what? That's not great DX." Really? Well, tell me about the last time you worked Florida from a repeater in Maryland, or anywhere else more than a few miles from home, for that matter!

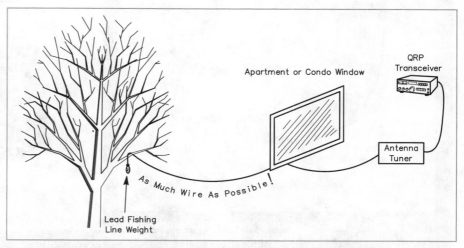

Figure 1—The stealth antenna is simply a random wire. A slingshot launches the antenna through an open window and into a nearby tree. Be sure the window is open before you fire the slingshot!

Home again the next year, I found a slingshot at the local Kmart. That was the start of in my formal stealth antenna development program.

With the help of the slingshot and a nearby tree, I moved the wire outdoors. This expanded my operating horizons considerably! I had created an antenna that could work the world without the problems of visibility and television interference. I wondered what the condo groundskeepers thought as they picked up those pieces of wire while mowing the grass. But they didn't ask and—good citizen that I was—I didn't volunteer!

Traditional wisdom says you shouldn't try QRP operation unless you have a good antenna. Even Doug DeMaw, W1FB, in one of his *QRP Notebooks* says only a masochist would try to operate QRP with a marginal antenna. Even so, I've had pretty good success. Over the 16 or so years that I've been using stealth antennas, I've worked nearly all 50 states and about 80 countries. And except for this past year, I did it all on vacation, operating only one or two weeks each year.

Planning a Stealth Antenna

The antenna is installed behind the condo where my mother and I live. It's a pretty simple design: a length of #26 magnet wire run from my bedroom window, *through the aluminum window frame*, out to a nearby tree (see Figure 1). Not much to it, is there? If I owned the building and the tree, I'd use #14 Copperweld wire and real insulators to make a permanent installation.

Unfortunately, at last count, the building and the tree were jointly owned with about two hundred other souls. If any one of them got upright or uptight about the CC&Rs, the stuff I would find myself in would not be deep clover!

What are the secrets of putting up a stealth antenna? First, and foremost, *planning*. Not only does the antenna need to be invisible, it has to go up quickly, or you may have to do a lot of messy explaining. Finding a location for your station where there's a handy window and a nearby tree or other useable support is the first priority. Once you've found the location, the rest falls into place.

The Dirty Details

Putting up the wire is the hardest part. Using a slingshot and fishing line is the traditional Field Day technique for erecting antennas. It's a great idea, but to keep your neighbors from asking too many questions, skip the fishing line and launch the wire directly. With lightweight wire and the proper spooling system, it's easy.

Figure 2 shows the components of my current design. Note the complete absence of high technology. The slingshot, the large plastic drinking glass, and the fishing weights came from Kmart. The #26 magnet wire was purchased at Radio Shack. You'll also need some double-sided plastic tape, electrical tape, and a "helper" to hold the drinking glass when you actually put up the wire. None of these are hard to find and substitutes are easy to improvise.

The idea of using a tapered core for the

wire coil was inspired by my first job right out of college. You see, my employer built wire-guided torpedoes. Nifty idea, huh? The torpedo is connected to the ship by a wire through which control signals are sent. As the torpedo zips through the water, the wire trails behind it. The wire spools we used were large and carefully wound. The windings were held together by a special lacquer that broke easily when the wire was pulled from the center of the spool.

Since I couldn't duplicate the lacquer, I substituted double-sided tape. Because it's only a single-layer coil, it doesn't matter whether you pull the wire from the center or the outside of the spool! I use a tapered core because it helps the wire feed smoothly. Figure 3 shows the complete stealth antenna, ready to launch.

Start building your own stealth antenna with the launcher. Beg, borrow, or buy a tapered plastic drinking glass. Use plastic so if you drop it you won't cut yourself or have a mess to clean up. Put three strips of double-sided tape on the side of the glass, spaced about 120° apart. Then, wrap one piece of double-sided tape around the top and one piece around the bottom of the

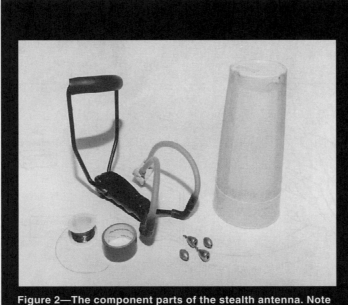

Figure 2—The component parts of the stealth antenna. Note the coil form made from a large plastic drinking glass. (The double-sided tape is already attached to the glass.)

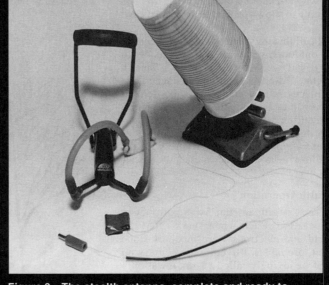

Figure 3—The stealth antenna, complete and ready to launch. Note the small vacuum vise the author uses to hold the wire coil while he operates the slingshot.

glass to anchor the windings. My glass has a step a few inches above the lip. This is where I start my windings. This is also where I clamp the glass in a small vise when I'm ready to launch the wire.

After you've prepared your coil form, get out the spool of #26 magnet wire and start winding. I usually start at the large end of the glass and wind up to the small end. I coil up a leader about 3 feet long and tape it inside the glass. This wire will connect to the antenna tuner.

My coils usually run around 45 to 50 turns, spaced up the glass. There are practical reasons for this. First, that's all the wire I need to reach my tree. Secondly, it's about all the wire my slingshot can pull off one of these coils. (The double-sided tape creates quite a bit of drag.) But, in the true spirit of Amateur Radio, feel free to experiment with either more or less tape; its only purpose is to hold the wire and keep the turns apart. With my system, I found that more than three strips of tape created unacceptable drag on the wire.

When the wire coil is complete, I attach a $1/2$ or $3/4$-ounce lead fishing line weight to the end that's going to be in the tree. I wrap a single layer of plastic electrical tape over the weight and it's off to the launch pad. You'll understand why some strength is necessary in this area the first time you watch your weights sail out in a perfect arc while your wire stays on the coil!

In Figure 3 you see a small vise. This is my "helper," which holds the wire coil while I handle the slingshot. I open the window, point the vise out the window toward the tree, and fire away. I'm not too particular about the time I launch my antenna because the whole process only takes a few seconds, but I prefer daylight so I can see where the wire goes.

Feeding the Stealth Antenna

I've used my stealth antennas regularly on 40, 30, and 20 meters. Like all end-fed wire antennas (called Marconi antennas), the stealth antenna requires an antenna tuner and a decent ground. I've used simple L-network tuners and π-network tuners with about equal success. I simply tune for minimum reflected power, as indicated on an SWR bridge in the coaxial cable between the rig and the antenna tuner..

Ground, though, is a different matter. Without a good RF ground there will be RF everywhere. I use a 33-foot long *counterpoise* wire. Since I'm only running a couple of watts, it's safe to place it under the carpet in my room. The counterpoise is connected directly to the transceiver's ground lug and it serves its purpose well. However, I recently uncovered the MFJ "Artificial Ground" tuner that I'd purchased some years ago and never tried. I connected it in series with the counterpoise and found that I could get the antenna to work on 80 meters. In fact, the power output on all

bands went up a few percent.

The Downside

The stealth antenna is not the strongest antenna in the world. Strength was never a design criteria because I was only going to use the antenna for a couple of weeks, then pack my tent and silently steal away. The antenna shown in this article lasted two months before a strong wind separated it from the window frame. Because this happened during the Christmas holidays, I took it as Mother Nature's way of saying I should be paying more attention to family matters. But I've got another one ready to go now.

I'm sure there are those of you who can and will improve on my basic design to make it longer and stronger. I'd like to hear from any of you who build, use and improve this antenna.

Finally

The stealth antenna has made HF operation a reality for me. Restricting the great majority of my operation to QRP power levels avoids interference problems, too. To any of you who put this kind of antenna to use, I must warn you that the CC&R Gestapo is still out there. Be careful—and don't tell 'em where you heard about it!

QST

Q E.W. Vick, N8NQT, asks, "Why do repeaters operate with offset frequencies instead of just using simplex?"

A To answer your question, we need to talk briefly about how repeaters work. The instant you key your microphone, the repeater relays the content of your signal on its output frequency *while still listening to your transmitted signal*. With its tall antennas and considerable output power, the repeater spreads your signal over a large area—much larger than your transceiver could cover by itself. When you release the mike button, you immediately hear the replies coming back to you through the same repeater (it's listening to the other stations while it is transmitting to you). The act of transmitting and receiving at the same time is known as *duplex* communication.

Engineering necessity requires that efficient duplex radio communication take place on separate frequencies. Otherwise, the transmit energy would overwhelm the receiver, making it deaf to all incoming signals (then there's the problem of horrendous feedback, damage to sensitive components and so on). But if you use separate frequencies for transmission and reception, it's a different story.

Two-meter repeaters usually separate transmit and receive frequencies by 600 kHz. At this offset you can keep most of the transmit RF out of the receiver by using proper filtering. Many repeaters use ultrasharp filters called *duplexers* to allow the repeater to transmit and receive simultaneously *from the same antenna*. The isolating action of the duplexer, in combination with the buffer provided by the frequency separation, makes this feat possible.

This is not to say that you cannot have simplex repeaters. For example, you could use a digital device to record the receive audio, retransmitting the content when the user has finished talking. There is a significant time delay, however, which makes this method unattractive. You might talk for two minutes, then wait for another two minutes while the repeater retransmitted what you said. By the time someone could reply, four minutes would have passed since you first keyed the microphone. Simplex repeaters

are possible through this approach and several others, but they cannot rival the efficiency of duplex systems.

Q Lately I've heard some rare countries on CW. I'd like to try my luck, despite the massive pileups. My problem is that I'm not a CW buff. I own a memory keyer, but I hardly use it. To make matters worse, the DX stations are sending at lightning speeds! Any suggestions?

A Even though the DX stations are sending at high speeds, they're usually sending the same information over and over. If you listen carefully, you'll eventually be able to unravel it all.

The next time you hear a pileup in progress, program your keyer with your call sign in one memory position. In another memory slot, program the exchange that the other stations are sending. (Such as, **QSL 5NN TNX 73 DE** <your call sign>.) Now set the sending speed of your keyer to approximate what you're hearing on the air.

When the DX indicates that he's ready for another call, press the first button and toss your call sign into the melee. Don't worry too much about whether you'll recognize your own call if the DX station responds. You'd be surprised at how well you can decipher your call sign, even at high speeds. If he calls you, he'll likely send the usual exchange. (Listen for the 5NN. It's particularly easy to hear.) That's your cue to hit the second button on your keyer—the one that sends your part of the contact.

This system isn't foolproof, but it works most of the time. Of course, if the DX station suddenly asks you a question and you don't have the answer preprogrammed...oops! After a while, however, you'll discover that you can copy high-speed CW better than before. The simple act of listening will sharpen your ability.

The 5NN? The military has for many years used a system of *cut numbers* to speed the average transmission rate in text that has lots of numbers. Simply, multiple dahs in numbers are replaced with a single dah. Thus, 5NN translates to 599, the world-standard DX signal report these days.

A Four-Band "Tree" Vertical

If the thought of a high-visibility HF antenna *leaves* you cold, it's time to *branch* out and get to the *root* of the problem...

By Mark Weaver, WB3BJF
3260 St Augustine Court
Olney, MD 20832
e-mail: mark.weaver@neteast.com

I live in a townhouse on a small lot in a neighborhood where no outdoor antennas are allowed. That's a fairly typical situation these days. So if I want to operate on the HF bands, am I resigned to an attic dipole or some other indoor compromise? No way! Believe it or not, I'm the proud owner of a four-band full-sized vertical antenna, and it's sitting right in my front yard. And the best part of all is the fact that my antenna is virtually *invisible*. No Klingon/Romulan cloaking devices here, just old-fashioned ingenuity.

The Concept

I tried an attic dipole and had nothing but problems. RF got into everything! It got into the TV and the kids howled. It got into the telephone and my wife howled. The antenna also picked up every kind of noise from my computer, TNC and any other electronic devices in the house.

One day while staring out my front window, dreaming of 100-foot towers and stacked Yagis, my gaze fixed upon a solitary 20-foot tree in my front yard. Wait a minute! I can run a 15-foot hunk of wire up the side of that tree! That's almost a quarter wavelength on 20 meters! But what about 40 meters, one of my favorite bands? I decided to worry about that later. Thus was born my four-band "tree" vertical.

My idea isn't new, although the application may be unique. The antenna is comprised of three quarter-wavelength wires (for 10, 20 and 40 meter), snaking up the side of the tree, more-or-less in parallel, all soldered together at the bottom to the center conductor of the coax (see Figure 1). Several radials are then soldered to the ground braid of the coax. But how do you get a quarter wavelength wire for 40 meters into a 20-foot tree? That's over 30 feet of wire! Easy. Bend the wire at the halfway point and run it to an upstairs window of your house, or some other convenient support. When you're finished you'll have an inverted **L** on 40 meters, a vertical with the top bent over so it looks like an upside down **L**. The 40-meter inverted **L** also works on 15 meters, where it's a ³⁄₄ wavelength.

Construction

Cut three pieces of wire at quarter wave-

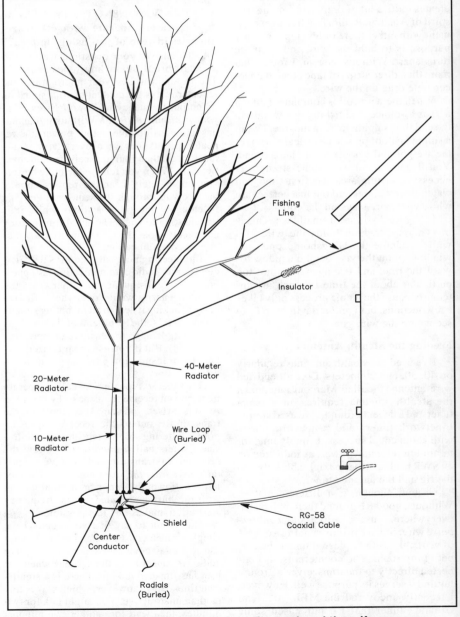

Figure 1—Run the three antenna wires along the trunk and then, if necessary, bend them along the branches. My 40-meter wire is so long that it leaves the tree altogether and attaches to my window frame. Use at least six radials for your ground system, more if you have the space and the patience to place them beneath the soil.

Labels in figure: Fishing Line · Insulator · 40-Meter Radiator · 20-Meter Radiator · 10-Meter Radiator · Wire Loop (Buried) · Shield · RG-58 Coaxial Cable · Center Conductor · Radials (Buried)

lengths on 10, 20 and 40 meters using the formula:

$$\text{Length (feet)} = \frac{234}{\text{Frequency (MHz)}}$$

Choose frequencies that are in the middle of the bands, or your favorite band segments. I recommend #26 enameled wire available at Radio Shack. It's strong and difficult to see.

Examine your chosen tree and the surrounding area. Make absolutely certain that you're not near any power lines. If you see power lines running through the branches, find another tree.

Once you've selected your tree, run the wires up the side of the trunk. If you're an experienced tree climber, work your way up the branches taking the wire along as you go. The alternative is to use a ladder, but make sure you have someone on the ground hold it for you. If inquiring minds want to know what you're doing, explain that you're trimming the tree and/or inspecting the leaves. You can attach the wires to the tree with loops of fishing line, or any other low-visibility means.

The idea is to get the wires as high as possible. You'll probably have to bend the 20 and 40-meter antenna wires, depending on the height of your tree (and your desire to climb it!). The tree in my yard is about 20 feet from the house, so the end of my 40-meter antenna reaches to an upstairs bedroom window. If you use your house as a support, you need to insulate the antenna wire so it won't come in contact with metal siding, storm windows or whatever. I loosened a screw in my metal window frame, tightened it down on a piece of insulated wire and tied the antenna to the wire.

Now build your ground system. Take bare copper wire, preferably something thick like #14, and loop it around the bottom of the tree at ground level. Solder several radial wires to this loop and run them out into the yard. I only used six radials at various lengths, making each one as long as possible. Bury the radials about an inch beneath the soil. (Do this at night if you live in an antenna-restricted area. If anyone asks, just tell them you're checking the lawn for grubs.) The radial wires don't have to travel in straight lines. Zigzag them as much as necessary to fit the available space.

Now install the transmission line. My townhouse, like many, has a water spigot on the front. That means there is a hole through the house for the water pipe to pass through. There was enough extra room in this opening to pass a length of RG-58 coaxial cable. You may need to bury this coax between the tree and the house, so make sure to buy cable that's made specifically for burial in soil.

Back out at the tree, solder all three antennas to the center conductor of the coax and solder the coax braid to the copper radial loop. Weatherproof the coax connections. I used Radio Shack "Outdoor RF Connector Sealant" (part no. 278-1645). Cover the copper radial loop with mulch or soil so it won't be visible. I planted pansies around mine and it looks very nice.

Testing

An SWR meter is all you need for testing. If you measured the antenna lengths correctly, the SWR will probably be no higher than 2:1. If you want it lower, add a few inches of wire to the antenna, or trim it as the case may be. If you have an antenna tuner, you don't have to bother with tuning unless the SWR is grossly out of whack. Simply adjust the tuner for a flat 1:1 SWR. Because your transmission line is likely to be short, an elevated SWR isn't as bad as it seems. On 15 meters you're using the 40-meter antenna on the third harmonic. This means that your SWR might be high, but the tuner should be able to take care of it.

Results

Is this antenna "optimal?" Far from it. No doubt there is some RF absorption by the tree, and the radiation patterns probably look like abstract art. I'm sure that some RF is being used to heat the coax when the SWR is high.

The point, however, is that this antenna solved my problems. It works well and is far enough from the house that I no longer have complaints about TVI and telephone interference. Signals from my computer and TNC are but distant memories.

Many operators are astonished when I describe my antenna. They can't believe that my signal is so strong. When conditions are decent, I even work a fair amount of DX. I've also managed to use the system on 30 and 17 meters with good success.

As far as visibility is concerned, you can't spot the antenna unless you walk right up to the tree. Even then, you need to know what you're looking for. So far it's been completely disregarded by the spies from the homeowner's association.

Take it from me: If you live in an apartment, townhouse or condo, you *can* get on the HF bands with a full-sized antenna. If you can see a tree anywhere on your lot, you've just found a home for your next antenna—and it will probably outperform any indoor design. I must admit, however, that I still stare out the window and dream of 100-foot towers and stacked Yagis! QST

Q **I'm running 100 W to a low dipole on 20-meter SSB. The problem is that few people seem to hear me, although I can hear other stations just fine. Why?**

A Even at this part of the sunspot cycle, 20 meters remains a very popular band, especially for voice communication. Unfortunately, the 200 kHz allocated for SSB isn't big enough to accommodate everyone who wants to use that part of the band. The most successful SSB stations are those with the biggest antennas, coupled with legal-limit amplifiers. (An amplifier by itself isn't going to help all that much—unless you can build a big antenna to go with it.)

Your low antenna "hears" just fine because there are plenty of strong signals on the phone portion of 20 meters, but your antenna is a poor challenger to the larger antenna systems in use on the band. If you were to take the output of a big antenna and chop down the signals by 20 dB, chances are you'd still hear the strong signals. There would be little effect on what really counts, the *signal-to-noise ratio*. Reduce *your* signal by 20 dB on the same antenna and it would probably disappear into the thermal noise floor.

Your present station is analogous to a light-emitting diode—it works fine inside a dark office, but forget trying to use it on a sunny beach. If 20 meters is a sunny beach, you need to find a "darker" (less crowded) band, or make your signal "brighter" with a better antenna, an amplifier, or both. You might also consider CW or one of the digital modes. Not only are these modes more efficient, but the frequencies they use are protected from SSB operations, so the crowding isn't as severe. Many amateurs even find QRP, 5 W or less, enough to make CW or RTTY contacts on 20 meters.

Q **A while back you suggested feeding a dipole with ladder line, and then taking advantage of its low-loss characteristics to use the dipole on other bands. I tried your suggestion. I put up a 40-meter dipole and fed it with ladder line. The ladder line is connected to the balanced output of my antenna tuner. It works well on 40 and, all the bands above, but I can't use it on 80. When I try, the balun in the tuner seems to arc. Any suggestions?**

A Don't give up hope! Transmission lines act as both feed lines and impedance transformers. Try connecting an additional $1/8$- or $1/4$-wavelength piece of transmission line in series with your current line. Loosely coil the new line and tack the coil up on the wall. Often, by changing the length of the line, the antenna tuner will see a different impedance—one it can match more readily without having a high-voltage node right at the connection of the balun in your tuner.

Curtis R. Holsopple, K9CH

Radical Radiators and Weird Wires

Great antennas make for great ham radio, but you can still have plenty of contacts using antennas that are less than the best.

A re you one of those folks who can't get on the air because you can't put up a decent antenna? If so, you're missing a lot of fun. You're also overlooking the emergency preparedness aspect of using make-do antennas.

One of my passions is antennas—I have nearly every edition of the *ARRL Antenna Book* on my shelf. The experts can help you get the most out of your antenna system, no doubt about that. But you're not out of luck if your antenna isn't perfect.

I don't compromise on safety, but aside from that, I've made plenty of contacts on the HF bands with some off-beat antennas. In fact, I've seen and used some skyhooks that have been downright *weird*.

The Cramped Vertical

The long-awaited Novice license arrived in September of my ninth-grade year, and so did my initiation into the world of unorthodox antennas. One of my paper-route customers was also my Elmer—Harold Mahlke, W8QG (ex-W8DOI). Harold had a nice two-element quad on the his roof back then, but his garage sported a vertical for 20 meters that wasn't quite "by the book." Of the four radials in the antenna's ground plane, only two were stretched out straight in the open air while the other two took more devious courses. One ran through Harold's attic while the other crossed his garage roof for a few feet before it doglegged to the right to keep from running into the neighbor's yard. It wasn't quite kosher, yet he made plenty of DX contacts with that antenna.

A Communications Bus

When I got to college I met somebody who was an electronics nerd like myself, Dave Hershberger. He was WA9QCH back then, but now he's W9GR and one of the geniuses behind digital signal processing. Dave and I got acquainted during freshman orientation while swapping ham-radio war stories. He told me about his homebrew 7-W portable 40-meter CW rig that he built into a briefcase.

Dave tried his radio with a trick antenna one night. He'd taken the rig to a high-school play practice. During a slow stretch when he wasn't needed on stage, he looked around for an ad-hoc antenna. His rig included a built-in antenna tuner, so he loaded up a *school bus* using the window frame on a nearby building as his ground! He had no trouble working Michigan from his northern-Illinois location. Come to think of it, the dimensions of the typical school bus are pretty good for a quarter wavelength antenna on 40 meters.

The Dorm Hallway Antenna

During my junior year of college, I decided to take my Heath HW-100 HF transceiver along to the dorm. Putting a wire outside through nearby trees was out of the question—my room faced the administration building! Instead, I used a putty knife to push some speaker wire up between the ceiling tiles in the dorm's hallway. I didn't dare operate during *Star Trek* or the World Series, or I would have earned a Worked All Dorm Rooms certificate (and a punch in the schnoz). But that in-the-ceiling antenna radiated just fine, letting me make plenty of contacts on 40 and 15 meters during carefully chosen operating times. This arrangement worked out pretty well, especially after I made a few phone patches back home for some of the guys in the dorm.

Speaker Wire on Two Meters

During a college summer term in 1972, I was assigned a dorm room facing away from the nearest 2-meter repeater, nearly 30 miles

CURTIS R. HOLSOPPLE, K9CH

Where is the antenna? The ladder is the antenna! With an HF transceiver, SWR meter and antenna tuner, I fed a 20-foot extension ladder as an antenna. My counterpoise was grounded using a 9-foot CB whip lying in a pile of leaves. (Without the counterpoise, the rig was unstable and the SWR meter gave me erratic readings.) I ran 50-W output with this antenna and enjoyed a chat with Bob, N2VDF, on 40-meter CW at a distance of 350 miles.

distant. So I worked out a deal with someone across the hall and mounted a vertically oriented dipole in his window. The sneaky part involved running a feed line across the hall. Coax wouldn't fit around the doors, and it looked unsightly crossing the hallway ceiling. This called for a visually stealthy approach. I used speaker wire zip cord for the feed line, once again stuffing it up between the acoustic tiles glued to the ceiling. Theoretically, speaker wire should be pretty lossy at 146 MHz, but its impedance is 50 to 70 Ω—a close enough match for the rig to work.

A Tuner is a Necessity

Properly adjusted dipoles and beam antennas usually present a good impedance match to today's commercial radios. But if you operate away from their design frequencies, or use radical radiators of any sort, you'll need an SWR meter and some kind of impedance matching network—commonly called an *antenna tuner*.

Figure 1 illustrates a typical home-made tuner. It's a variable inductor and variable capacitor, commonly called an **L** network, connected between the antenna and the SWR meter. If you're not up to designing and building your own tuner, you can buy one new or used. Tuners are critical for sucess with these types of antennas, so I urge you to purchase the best model you can afford.

The electronic theory underlying antenna matching networks gets pretty complicated, but the operation is fairly simple. Try to get a good ground, then adjust the inductor and capacitor in varying combinations until you get a low SWR reading.

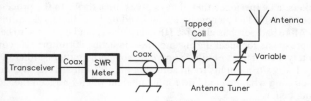

Figure 1—You can consult the *ARRL Handbook* and build your own antenna tuner similar to this one. The alternative is to scan the advertising pages of *QST* and buy one off the shelf. The tuner is an important part of a stealth antenna, so don't cut corners!

CURTIS R. HOLSOPPLE, K9CH

A close-up view of my improvised L network antenna tuner.

By then, I'd begun to see a pattern: If you can't build the antenna you love, try loving the antenna you can get away with. Ideal antennas are nice, but second-best arrays (or worse) still tickle the ether, and this makes contacts even sweeter.

Low Antennas Still Work

After finishing college, Dave went to grad school and a career in electronics design work. I became a nomadic broadcast engineer, teacher and writer, but we stayed in touch by ham radio, often with weekly schedules. Dave had pretty good luck with home-brew antenna tuners (see the sidebar "A Tuner is a Necessity.") and 100 to 150 feet of no. 28 wire strung out the apartment window into nearby trees.

Defying the conventional practice of feeding an antenna from the bottom, Dave's random-wire antennas were often lower than his upper-story dwellings. Yet, he worked some DX and made plenty of stateside contacts with such less-than ideal antennas.

I didn't have an antenna tuner for many years, so I've relied on dipoles cut to my favorite frequency with the help of an SWR meter. Often I've strung these antennas impossibly low, such as the time I had an 80-meter dipole with the feed point about 7 feet off the ground. I didn't crack too many DX pileups with that configuration, but it was great for local and regional net activity because the high radiation angle favored close-in propagation. And running 100 W into a 40-meter dipole at that height was adequate for some DX contacts on 15 meters.

Speaker Wire Has Advantages

I haven't always been able to afford good coaxial feed lines for my dipoles. College loans and graduate school expenses can wreak havoc with a ham's budget, so sometimes I've used speaker wire zip cord for the feed line, soldering it onto the appropriate coax connector and plugging it right into the back of radio. Sure, it's lossy and very far from ideal. But speaker wire is inexpensive compared to coax, and it's easy to sneak this stuff around window sashes and through screens without inflicting any violence on rental housing. Better yet, it's nearly invisible to people more than a dozen feet away. This supports my hypothesis that interference to consumer equipment increases in direct proportion to the visibility of one's antenna farm.

A Flashy Solution

While I was zapping my back yard with HF signals from low-flying antennas, Dave was trying something else at his top-floor apartment in Illinois—he literally hit the roof. Dave had a 2-meter gutter-clip antenna mounted on the edge of the flat roof of his building. The shield of the coax was grounded to the metal roof flashing. One day he discovered that the flashing wasn't grounded ground, so he used the shield of his 2-meter coax as a way to feed the flashing, making a dandy antenna on HF. Outside antenna? What outside antenna?

The Clip Lead Wonder

When my wife Edie and I worked at ARRL Headquarters in the 1980s, we lived in an apartment just a couple of blocks from W1AW. Edie said that working at Headquarters without a ham license was like going to Jerusalem and only eating at a fast food restaurant. So she hit the books and got her ticket. Edie showed a ready aptitude for CW operating, and she upgraded to Extra Class within two years. Naturally, she wanted to get on the air. I stapled a 15-meter dipole to the ceiling of the apartment, once again feeding it with my trusty speaker wire. Edie had the usual new-ham jitters and started out with a couple of incomplete contacts. Then she worked Joe, WA7WLY, in Coos Bay, Oregon. They chatted for more than half an hour until severe fading forced an end to their conversation. Joe did his best to help her have a successful experience, and he even sent a special "First Contact" QSL card.

Edie wanted to try the other bands, so I got out the speaker wire and stapler and went back to work. Before long I had strung up additional antenna wire to lengthen that 15-meter dipole for use on 40 and 80 meters. Carefully labeled clip leads helped me quickly reconfigure the array for each band.

Naturally, we kept the transmitter power output under 100 W with this indoor antenna. (*QST* was just beginning to publish news about the potential biological hazards of RF radiation.) Although the jury is still out on the dangers of RF exposure, I might not try that ceiling antenna now. If you attempt an indoor antenna, I recommend running 10 W or less.

In my case, however, the bigger hazard was in stirring up trouble with the other tenants. I didn't want the Worked All Neighbors award (or another punch in the schnoz), so I made the rounds in the apartment building to explain the situation.

As it turned out, everybody was very nice about it. They agreed not to call the police, and I agreed not to operate during prime time.

That was the year the Boston Red Sox and the New York Mets had a hot baseball pennant race. You can be sure I avoided transmitting while the games were being broadcast.

Worked All Swingsets

Our top-floor apartment was on a small hill, so that ceiling antenna worked great. The feed line was only 10-feet long and the radiating element was high above RF ground. But I wanted more freedom to operate without annoying the neighbors. The apartment management there in Newington was accustomed to ARRL employees and their arcane desire to string wires, so they managed not to notice when I buried 150 feet of coax across the playground to feed a commercial five-band trap dipole in the trees. The coax was routed behind the downspout for the two-story climb up to our apartment. This time I had to drill a half-inch hole in a wooden window frame to bring the feed line into the apartment. Of course I agreed to repair and repaint the frame when we vacated the place.

When I made comparisons between my apartment ceiling antenna and the playground skywire with the long feed line, I noticed that the indoor antenna was better for weak signal work. No problem. I transmitted outside away from the neighbors and received *inside* with the more efficient antenna, using the best of both worlds.

By the way, if you ever rent my old apartment in Newington, that coax should still be there behind the downspout, just outside the kitchen window.

The "Wad" Antenna

You can imagine the receiver overload problems we faced with W1AW's several kilowatts of RF hammering the airwaves just a couple of blocks away. I could see the towers while eating breakfast. Several borrowed rigs struggled to cope with that abuse, but we had excellent luck using the Heath HW-99 CW transceiver at that location (see the sidebar, "The Heath HW-99: A Ramblin' Radio"), even when operating only a few kHz away from W1AW's signals.

The HW-99 was a nice vacation rig, so we packed it along to beach cottages and motel rooms more than once. This led to the creation of more spur-of-the-moment antennas. Once, Edie and I were at a conference in Pennsylvania. We arrived at dusk and just had time to open the motel room window and heave a length of wire into the darkness, hoping for the best. The busy conference schedule prevented us from actually trying to make a contact until about midnight. The sunspot cycle was in the cellar then, just as it is now, but this actually favors nighttime DX propagation on 40 meters. We answered a CQ and knocked off a quick contact with a station in Germany before crawling into bed. Not bad for 30 feet of wire fed with a tuner, I told myself.

The next morning I looked out the window and saw what we were dealing with. When I chucked the wire out the window the night before, I'd hoped that it would spread across a large bush close by. Not so! The wire hung a foot below the window in a basketball-sized wad that nearly touched the ground. I guess I made a 2000-mile contact using 50 W to a *very* short radiator with a large randomly wound end-loaded coil!

The Rain Gutter Configuration

After four happy but hectic years, Edie and I left Newington and moved to her home state of Virginia. We wound up in a brand-new townhouse in Harrisonburg, set in the scenic Shenandoah Valley. The landlord was queasy about allowing us putting up outside antennas at first, but this was 1988 and the sunspot cycle was really heating up. We had to get on the air, so we did our best with a truly invisible antenna.

The townhouse was a bit cramped, so we installed the ham shack in the laundry closet. (We didn't have a washer or dryer. First things first!) I ran a short wire out through the dryer vent to a nearby rain gutter and used an antenna tuner to feed the array. It worked pretty well, and I made plenty of contacts on all bands.

Once the landlord saw that I was causing no interference in the neighborhood, he consented to an outside dipole attached to the gable. That worked better, of course, but the rain gutter array had been more interesting, starting some pretty rich conversations on the air.

The Bunk Bed Antenna

While living in Harrisonburg I held an administrative job at a college. Before long I became faculty advisor and trustee of the college's ham club station, W4RBC. I helped some students get their tickets, an experience that always gives me a thrill. In the process I met Mike, N4TRF, a new ham who lived in the college's dormitory.

Mike had purchased a nice HF transceiver, but he seemed to have no prospects for sneaking an antenna outside the dormitory. He completely lacked trees or other supports. No nearby gutters, either. One day I was sitting in his room admiring his still-unused rig. We were discussing what he could do for an antenna when I noticed the steel bunk bed.

Why not?

Mike's rig came with a built-in antenna tuner, so we used a clip lead to couple it to the bunk-bed frame. Ten meters was open and I finally managed to wrestle a decent match out of the tuner. I worked Joe, W5RYO, a thousand miles away in Texas on SSB. Joe immediately grasped the situation when I told him about the bunk-bed antenna. He said he'd done the same thing when he was in college, and he offered this suggestion: Use the top bunk while transmitting on upper sideband, but move the clip lead to the lower bunk when transmitting on lower sideband. (I'm waiting to see how many readers actually do this!)

Wrapping It Up

I've had a lot of fun using funny antennas. They've allowed me to enjoy my hobby when "correct" antennas were out of the question. And it's a great conversation starter when the ham at the other end of the contact hears those fateful words, "Antenna here is a clothesline full of wet laundry."

So read the books and articles on antennas and put up the best sky wire you can. But if your situation demands compromise or defeat, give radical radiators a try. You might not place first in any contests, but you'll fill your log book with some weird and wonderful contacts.

82 Brennhaven Dr
Newport News, VA 23602
e-mail: curthol@beacon.regent.edu

Q I'm considering the purchase of a low-power (QRP) transceiver. I can only afford a single-band rig, so I face the dilemma of which band to choose. Can you help?

A That's a tough question because the answer depends on your personal preferences. Consider your lifestyle, for example. If you have work and family commitments, and find that your hamming is confined to the nighttime hours, I'd suggest a 40 or 80-meter transceiver. Both of these bands are open and active at night. But if most of your free time takes place while the sun shines, consider 30, 20 or 17 meters. (At this point in the solar cycle, the bands above 17 meters are poor choices for QRP work.)

How much room do you have for an antenna? If space is at a premium, try 20 meters. A 20-meter wire dipole antenna is only about 33 feet long. If you can find about 66 feet to stretch out a 40-meter dipole, 40 is an excellent band for QRP. Unlike the other bands we've discussed, 40 meters is active day *and* night.

If you have access to Internet e-mail, consider joining the QRP-L mailing list. You'll receive as many as 50 messages per day on topics ranging from equipment modifications to propagation—and no shortage of helpful advice. To join the list, send a message to: **listserv@Lehigh.edu**. You can type anything you want in the SUBJECT line; it will be ignored. In the body of your message, enter the following:

SUBSCRIBE QRP-L <first name> <last name> <call sign>

where <first name> is your first name, and so on.

8-Band Backpacker Special

Here's a portable antenna that you can use for backpacking or camping—not to mention Field Day.

By Jim Andera, WBØKRX
506 S Center St
Gardner, KS 66030

Many hams have discovered the value of using Amateur Radio in conjunction with other hobbies ranging from backpacking to bicycling. Those convenient VHF or UHF hand-held radios are great for short-range communications, but what if you need to talk hundreds or thousands of miles? The answer: HF radios, often QRP style to minimize size and weight. A problem you'll run into as you get set up for portable HF operation is finding an easily transportable antenna that's efficient enough to let your QRP signal reach out and touch someone.

A simple dipole antenna, usually strung inverted-**V** style, is hard to beat in terms of efficiency and simplicity. Fan-dipoles work well for two or three bands, but how

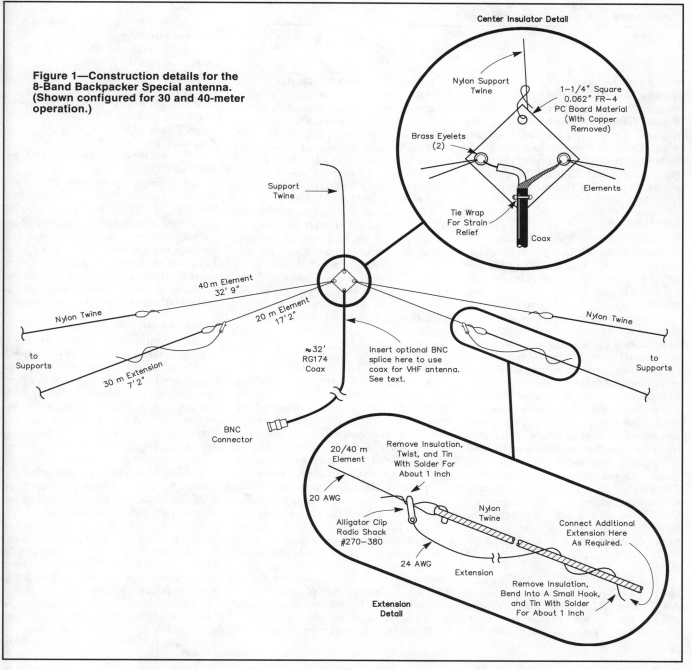

Figure 1—Construction details for the 8-Band Backpacker Special antenna. (Shown configured for 30 and 40-meter operation.)

Center Insulator Detail

Nylon Support Twine

1–1/4" Square 0.062" FR–4 PC Board Material (With Copper Removed)

Brass Eyelets (2)

Elements

Tie Wrap For Strain Relief

Coax

Support Twine

40 m Element 32' 9"

20 m Element 17' 2"

Nylon Twine

30 m Extension 7' 2"

to Supports

≈32' RG174 Coax

Insert optional BNC splice here to use coax for VHF antenna. See text.

Nylon Twine

to Supports

BNC Connector

20/40 m Element

Remove Insulation, Twist, and Tin With Solder For About 1 Inch

20 AWG

Nylon Twine

Alligator Clip Radio Shack #270–380

Connect Additional Extension Here As Required.

24 AWG

Extension

Remove Insulation, Bend Into A Small Hook, and Tin With Solder For About 1 Inch

Extension Detail

Table 1

Eight-band operation can be achieved by extending a 20-meter/40-meter fan dipole. Extensions are clipped to the end of the basic 20- or 40-meter elements.* Carrying an additional pair of 6-inch extensions allows for fine-tuning the antenna.

Band (CW)	Basic Element	Extension Length†	Total Element* Length	Antenna Electrical Length
80 m	40 m	32 ft 11 in	63 ft 8 in	$1/2 \lambda$
40 m	40 m	none	32 ft 9 in	$1/2 \lambda$
30 m	20 m	7 ft 2 in	24 ft 4 in	$1/2 \lambda$
20 m	20 m	none	17 ft 2 in	$1/2 \lambda$
17 m	40 m	7 ft 2 in	39 ft 11 in	$1 1/2 \lambda$
15 m	40 m	1 ft 6 in	34 ft 3 in	$1 1/2 \lambda$
12 m	20 m	7 ft 2 in and 4 ft 9 in	29 ft 1 in	$1 1/2 \lambda$
10 m	20 m	7 ft 2 in and 1 ft 6 in	25 ft 10 in	$1 1/2 \lambda$

*An element is one-half of a dipole.
†Two extensions are required, one for each element.

would you make an easily transportable antenna to cover 80 through 10 meters without creating a tangled mess of wires? Try this 8-Band Backpacker Special! This is what I use on my backpacking adventures; it lets me hop between two bands without even having to get out of my sleeping bag to make adjustments. (See my article, "Operating Backpack Portable," *QST*, April 1994.)

Construction

The Backpacker Special consists of a 20-meter/40-meter fan dipole that has extensions clipped to the ends of the elements to make the overall antenna $1/2$ or $1 1/2$ wavelengths long on each band. (As used in this article, an *element* is one-half of a dipole.) Table 1 shows the lengths of the various extensions that need to be added to the basic antenna to make it cover the eight HF bands; each extension has an alligator clip soldered to one end. Several extensions are reused in the various configurations to minimize the amount of wire carried, reducing the weight and bulk of the antenna. (My pack dog, who carries the antenna on backpacking trips, appreciates the fact that the antenna weighs only 1.4 pounds and doesn't take up much space—it leaves more room for dog chow.) The lengths given in Table 1 typically resonate the antenna on the low edge of the CW bands; for the Novice subband the length of the 40-meter element may need to be shortened about 4 inches, and the 80-meter extension shortened about 18 inches.

Figure 1 illustrates the details of the antenna's construction. I like to use #20 AWG magnet wire for the main elements and #24 AWG for the shorter extensions. The #20 AWG is strong enough to allow it

to be pulled down when tangled in tree branches, without breaking the wire. About 32 feet of RG-174 coax is convenient for the feed line. Make sure to strain-relieve the coax at the center insulator. A BNC splice can be inserted close to the center insulator if you want to be able to steal the coax to use with your VHF antenna (a 30-foot length of RG-174 will have about 3 dB loss at 144 MHz).

Check the antenna with an SWR meter before you take off on your adventure by setting it up in the backyard or in a park. Install it at whatever apex and element height you think you'll usually use. When I use it, the apex is often supported by a tree branch 15 to 25 feet above the ground and the ends of the elements are 6 to 8 feet high. If you let the ends of the elements get too high, it's hard to reach them to attach the extensions!

Materials

You may be able to use your creativity and junk box to reduce the need to go out and buy everything for this antenna. Few, if any, ham dealers will carry the miniature RG-174 coax or connectors. RG-58 is fine if you don't mind the extra bulk and weight. The nice thing about the magnet wire I've specified is that it has a thin film of insulation that will burn off easily during soldering (no need to strip the insulation in advance); but most any type of wire will do. FR-4 PC board material can be identified by viewing the edge of the board and looking for thread-like filaments imbedded inside the material. If you don't have any old FR-4 in your junk box, substitute a high-temperature plastic or some varnished wood (avoid phenolic PC board material because it's too brittle).

If you need a source for the wire and

connectors try your local electronics distributors, or you can order them by telephone from:

Arrow/Capstone: 800-833-3557 ($50 minimum order)

Newark Electronics, either your local outlet or their national order line: 800-281-4320 ($25 minimum order)

Parts list:

#20 AWG magnet wire—Belden 8050 (approx. 160 ft/0.5 lb spool)

#24 AWG magnet wire—Belden 8052 (approx. 404 ft/0.5 lb spool)

RG-174 miniature coax—Belden 8216 (it comes in a 100-foot spool)

BNC Plug for RG-174 (clamp style)—Amphenol type 69475

BNC Plug for RG-174 (crimp style*)—Amphenol type 31-315

BNC Jack for RG-174 (crimp style*)—Amphenol type 31-317

Hardware stores and Radio Shack have various sizes and styles of alligator clips, tie wraps, and brass eyelets that are useful.

*Crimp connectors can be used without a crimp tool by soldering the collar over the coax braid rather than crimping it on. Take care not to melt the coax center conductor. After it's soldered, place a couple of inches of heat-shrink tubing over the collar and coax jacket for strain relief.

Antenna Tips

❑ If you mount the antenna unusually low, the antenna will behave as though it's longer and tune up low in frequency. Clipping the extensions on a few inches from the end of the basic element will help compensate for this effect. If mounted high, the antenna will act as if it's shorter, so you may need to add a short extension (try six inches for starters) to make it tune properly.

❑ Ground conductivity can affect the tuning. Raising or lowering the ends can help compensate for this variation, as can the two remedies mentioned above.

❑ Nylon twine works well as an end insulator and support. Have these ropes pre-cut (the apex rope 50 feet long and the element ropes 20 feet long) and wind them up on some type of form. A few 3 and 6-foot sections are handy, too.

❑ Keep the entire kit in a gallon-size Ziplok plastic bag to keep things together, with smaller items in a quart-size bag.

Bill Wright, GØFAH

Four Bands, Off Center

Every dipole must be center fed, right? Not necessarily. Here's a dipole that's fed *off center*, works on four bands, and doesn't require an antenna tuner.

H ave you ever wondered why you're required to attach your feed line to the center of a dipole antenna? The middle is a good place for a half-wavelength antenna because the feed impedance is low, typically close to 50 Ω, when the antenna is cut to resonance at the operating frequency. This makes for a good match for 50-Ω coaxial cable, and a good match for your radio. But could you get a more versatile antenna by moving the feedpoint *away* from the middle?

Like many amateurs, I often ask other hams to describe the antennas they're using. Most of the time the answer is a wire antenna like the classic half-wavelength dipole. On occasion, however, some European amateurs tell me that they're operating with "FD3" antennas. Being more than a little unfamiliar with this design, I was eager to find out more.

After some research I learned that the FD3 is a single-wire antenna, with the feedpoint not in the middle, but *one third the way from one end*. It's coax fed with a 6:1 balun at the feedpoint. It actually resembles the Windom antenna with the single-wire feed that was popular in the early 1930s.

Studying the FD3 gave me an idea for the antenna shown in Figure 1. This off-center-fed dipole works on four bands: 40, 20, 15 and 10 meters. And, as a bonus, you don't need an antenna tuner! This antenna is similar to the 1950s Windom antenna that was fed with 300-Ω twinlead.

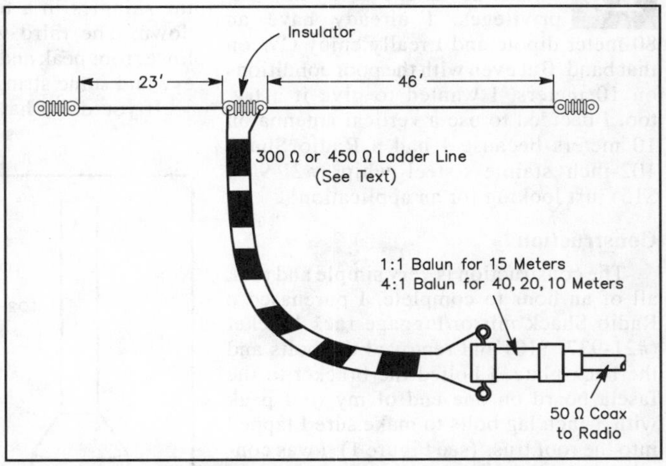

Construction

Imagine that you have 69 feet of #12 copper wire. If you were to cut this wire in two equal halves and feed it with 50-Ω coax, you'd probably find that it is resonant at the bottom end of the 40-meter band. (This depends, of course, on how high the antenna is above ground and so on.)

For your nonimaginary antenna, use 69 feet of bare copper wire, but *don't* cut it into equal halves. Instead, cut one length at 23 feet and the other at 46 feet. Rejoin the two sections with an insulator in between. This off-center feedpoint will have an impedance close to 300 Ω when you apply a 40-meter signal. This same feedpoint will also present a 300-Ω impedance on the 20 and 10-meter bands, at a typical height of 40 feet or more.

Connect ladder line, either the 300 or 450-Ω variety,[1] at the feedpoint. At our one-third feedpoint, the impedance will be very high on the 15-meter band. But if you make the ladder line a quarter wavelength long at 15 meters, it will transform the high impedance at the feedpoint down to a low impedance near your radio.

A quarter wavelength of 300-Ω ladder is about 10 feet for 21 MHz. This is probably going to be a little short to reach your

Figure 1—This off-center fed dipole offers four-band performance without an antenna tuner. Just cut the wires and the ladder line to the proper lengths. You'll need to swap baluns when you want to operate on 15 meters.

radio. You can make it longer on one condition: The overall length must be an *odd* multiple of the 21-MHz ¼ wavelength. For best SWR on all four bands, I recommend either 55 or 111 feet of 450-Ω line (or 50 or 110 feet of 300-Ω line). One of these lengths should get the ladder line to your radio with room to spare.

Now that we have a low impedance at the end of the feeder, we use a 4:1 or 1:1 balun to make the transition to 50-Ω coax. Use a 4:1 balun for 40, 20 and 10 meters, and a 1:1 balun for 15 meters. At my station I have 4:1 and 1:1 baluns that I can plug in as required when I change to and from the 15-meter band. You can purchase 1:1 and 4:1 baluns from a number of *QST* advertisers.

Conclusion

How well does the off-center dipole work? I enjoy the convenience of hopping from one band to another without having to fiddle with a tuner. I found that changing the balun when moving to the 15-meter band wasn't all that cumbersome. By choosing the correct line length, the balun was right next to my radio. Best of all, the SWR never exceeded 2:1 on any of the four bands.

Not only is the antenna easy to use, it rewards me with plenty of contacts. Off center, yes, but *spot-on* performance!

---

[1] 300-Ω ladder line is preferred for this design, but it isn't commonplace on your side of the Atlantic. Call around to several *QST* advertisers who specialize in wire and feed lines and you'll probably find it. If not, don't hesitate to use 450-Ω line.

46 Homestall Rd
East Dulwich, London SE22 0SB
England

A Low-Profile 10-Meter Antenna

Put this simple whip antenna on your roof and have fun!

By Brian Smithson, N8WRL
1670 Edgewood Lane
Milford, MI 48381
E-mail: smithson@acm.org

Because I recently ungraded to a Technician Plus license, I wanted to take advantage of my new HF privileges. I already have an 80-meter dipole and I really enjoy CW on that band. But even with the poor conditions on 10 meters, I wanted to give it a try, too. I decided to use a vertical antenna on 10 meters because I had a Radio Shack 102-inch stainless-steel whip (#21-903, $15) just looking for an application!

Construction

The construction is very simple and took all of an hour to complete. I purchased a Radio Shack mirror/luggage rack bracket (#21-937, $10) and removed the bolts and the back plate. I bolted the bracket to the fascia board on one end of my roof peak with 3-inch lag bolts to make sure I tapped into the roof truss (see Figure 1). I was concerned about strength, but the antenna survived some recent 40-mph winds (gusting to 50 mph)!

This vertical requires a ground plane, and it's best if it angles down to bring the feed-

point impedance close to 50 Ω. I used three radials made of 8-foot pieces of scrap wire I had in my junk box. I crimped a spade connector to one end of each wire and connected these under the lag bolts (Figure 2). My roof line has a couple of levels and this makes radial installation easy. Two of the wires follow the roof line away from the peak at a 45° angle. I shoved the wires under the shingles in a few places to hold them down. The third wire angles toward the lower roof peak and is fastened with a screw eye and some string.

If you don't have a roof line like mine,

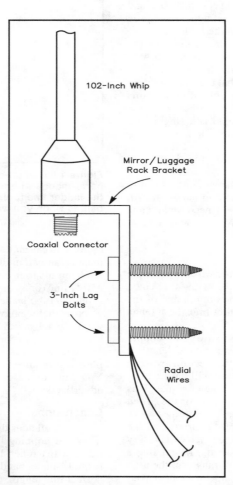

Figure 2—There isn't much to this design. Just remove the back plate from a Radio Shack mirror/luggage mount and thread your lag bolts through the holes. The radial wires make contact with the bracket at one of the lag bolts. The whip screws onto the top of the mount.

it's very simple to mount the bracket along the peak of your roof and run four radials down along the shingles. This might even perform better than my setup!

Connect your coax to the bracket with a PL-259 connector. I sealed my PL-259 against the weather with some Coax-Seal putty wrapped tightly around the mating connectors and the cable. The bracket has a ³/₈-inch threaded stud to accept a whip antenna, so that it accepts the 38-inch threaded stud of the 102-inch whip. So, the last step is to screw the stainless whip into the stud. Don't tighten it down yet, because you'll be removing it for tuning later.

Tuning

The Radio Shack 102-inch whip is cut for 11-meter CB, so we'll have to shorten it a bit for use on the 10-meter amateur band. Since I planned to use this antenna for the 10-meter Novice/Technician phone subband, I decided to aim for a resonant frequency of 28.4 MHz, right in the middle of the subband.

Check the SWR at 28.4 MHz. You'll find it is a bit high, so unscrew the whip and cut off about half an inch. Screw the whip back on the mount and check the SWR again. Repeat this until the SWR gets down to where you want it. Don't cut off too much at a time. You'll have a hard time adding to the whip if you cut too much! If you're fortunate enough to own an SWR analyzer, this process will be much quicker; I had to climb up and down the ladder and basement stairs a few times to take these measurements!

I cut off a total of 2 inches to get the SWR down to 1:1. (Anything below 2:1 is acceptable for most rigs.) At this length, I found that my SWR ranged from 1:1 at 28.1 MHz to about 1.1:1 at 28.5 MHz. Not bad! This tells me the whip probably will have sufficient bandwidth to operate well on the rest of the 10-meter band when I upgrade.

Performance

Luckily for me, there was a good 10-meter opening the day I put up the antenna. I received 59 signal reports all along the East Coast, and 57 to 59 reports in California and the rest of the West Coast. In about two weeks' time I worked 20 states and 15 countries (mostly South Americans)! A DX contest in progress certainly helped!

In all, I'm very pleased with the performance of my whip antenna. It has a low enough profile to pass the marital bliss test, and it is also fairly inexpensive. You might give it a try!

Figure 1—The sleek, low-profile whip antenna is hardly visible against the daylight sky. One radial wire can be seen sloping away from the bracket at roughly a 45° angle.

A Gain Antenna for

28 MHz

Give your 10-meter signal a boost with this simple antenna.

By Brian Beezley, K6STI
507½ Taylor
Vista, CA 92084

Although in coming years the 10-meter band won't provide the excitement it did at the peak of sunspot cycle 22, DX openings will still occur, especially during spring and fall. And who knows? With the large number of 10-meter operators and wide availability of inexpensive, single-band radios, the band may be the hangout for local ragchews that it was before the advent of 2-meter FM.

I'd like to present a simple antenna for 10 meters that provides gain over a dipole or inverted **V**. Similar designs have been published before, but because I never hear them on the air, I think they must not be fully appreciated. The antenna is a resonant, rectangular loop with a particular shape. It provides 2.1 dB gain over a dipole at low radiation angles when mounted well above ground. This represents a power increase of 62%. The antenna is simple to feed—no matching network is necessary. When fed with 50-Ω coax, SWR is close to 1:1 at the design frequency. SWR is less than 2:1 from 28.0 to 28.8 MHz for an antenna resonant at 28.4 MHz.

The antenna is made from #12 wire (see Figure 1). For horizontal polarization at 28.4 MHz, the loop is 73 inches wide and 146 inches high (just larger than 6×12 feet). Feed the antenna at the center of the lower wire. Coil the coax into a few turns near the feedpoint to provide a simple balun. A coil diameter of about a foot will work fine. You can support the antenna on a mast with spreaders made of bamboo, fiberglass, wood, PVC, or other nonconducting material. You can use aluminum tubing both for support and conductors, but you'll have to readjust antenna dimensions for resonance.

This rectangular loop has two advantages over a resonant square loop. First, a square loop has just 1.1 dB gain over a dipole. This is a power increase of only 29%. Second, the input impedance of a square loop is about 125 Ω. You must use a matching network to feed a square loop with 50-Ω coax. The rectangular loop achieves gain by compressing its radiation pattern in the elevation plane. The azimuth pattern is slightly wider than that of a dipole (it's about the same as that of an inverted **V**). A broad pattern is an advantage for a general-purpose, fixed antenna. The rectangular loop provides bidirectional gain over a broad azimuth region.

You should mount the loop as high as possible. To provide 1.7 dB gain at low angles over an inverted **V**, the top wire must be at least 30 feet high. The loop will work at lower heights, but its gain advantage disappears. For example, at 20 feet the loop provides the same gain at low angles as an inverted **V**.

A small, 3-element Yagi can provide 6 dB gain over a dipole and great rejection of signals to the rear. If you can install a beam and rotor, you'll find it much more effective than a loop. But for a simple, cheap, gain antenna that can be thrown together quickly, the rectangular loop is hard to beat.

Note: I used the AO 6.0 Antenna Optimizer program to automatically optimize the dimensions of a rectangular loop for maximum forward gain and unity SWR. I used NEC/Wires 1.5 to verify the design with the Numerical Electromagnetics Code. QST.

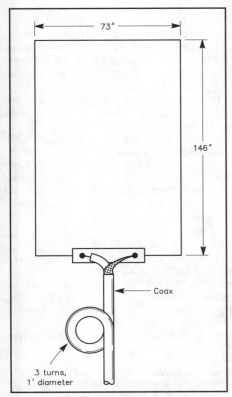

Figure 1—Construction details of the 10-meter rectangular loop antenna.

Radio Tips:

The Trusty Slingshot

Trees make excellent supports for wire antennas, but how do you get a rope over tall branches? Some hams use bows and arrows with good success, but I prefer my trusty slingshot. All you need is some high-strength fishing line and a couple of fishing weights (sinkers). Attach the weights to the line and launch them with your slingshot. If your aim is true, the weights will carry the line over the branches. Tie your rope to the line, find the other end, and then slowly, carefully, pull the rope through the tree!—*WB8IMY*

An *Indestructible* Dipole for 10 Meters

By Chester S. Bowles, AA1EX

RFD 2, Box 335L
Sharon, NH 03458
Photos by the author

NEW HAM COMPANION

*Here's a rugged
10-meter antenna
that'll get you on the
air within an hour.*

I know what you're thinking. "10 meters? That's the *dead band,* right?"

Sure, this is the low point in the sunspot cycle and propagation on 10 is sporadic at best. Don't dismiss the band so quickly, though.

My wife's uncle, WØQHY, (now a Silent Key) operated almost exclusively on 10 meters. Deed, as he was known, was a ham for many years. After his death, I spent a bit of time looking through his logbooks and was amazed to see how well he did on 10, even in the very lean years. Of course, he tended to make lots of local ground-wave contacts when the band was less active, but he was also quite successful in working DX. I'm sure he had to work harder (and listen more) to find band openings, but patience worked well for him. It can for you too.

But why 10 meters?

First, it's the only HF band where Novices and Technician-Plus licensees have voice privileges. That means that 10 meters offers your best chance to make HF DX contacts, unless you want to practice your CW skills on 15 meters.

Second, propagation characteristics being what they are, 10 meters is an excellent band if you find yourself running low power with marginal antennas. You don't need a kilowatt and a beam to compete with "the big boys." Twenty-five watts and a dipole can be nearly as effective.

Third, there are lots of 10-meter radios available on the used market. You can get a very respectable rig for a small investment—often for less than the cost of an H-T.

Finally, antennas for 10 meters are physically small as HF antennas go. That means you can easily mount them in confined spaces in attics and apartments—or on balconies.

So, with all these thoughts in mind, here is a simple, effective and durable antenna for 10 meters (see Figure 1). Spend an hour or two building the antenna, mount it in your attic or on your balcony and have a ball!

The Indestructible Dipole

Everything you will need to build your Indestructible Dipole is available at your local hardware store. Here's the parts list:

2—10-foot lengths of ¹/₂-inch galvanized electrical conduit
2—Stainless-steel adjustable hose clamps
1—⁵/₈-inch wooden dowel

First, cut the electrical conduit to the proper length. I'm sure you remember the formula for determining the length of a half-wave dipole (Length = 468/F in MHz). Here's your chance to use that knowledge. I chose to build my antenna for 28.400 MHz, so the formula told me that my antenna should be about 16.5 feet long.

You'll find that the formula will typically give you an antenna that's too long. That's okay because it's easier to cut a pipe than it is to add it back on. Also, it's usually true that using a larger conductor (and ¹/₂-inch electrical conduit is a large conductor!) means that the physical length of the antenna will be shorter. Knowing this, I made some educated guesses and decided to cut each piece of electrical conduit to a length of 8 feet 2 inches rather than the 8 feet 6 inches called for by the formula. You can use a hacksaw to cut the conduit. If you own a pipe cutter, that's even better. Pipe cutters give you a smooth edge.

Next, you need to do some work on the wooden dowel. The dowel is used to fit the two halves of the antenna together while insulating them from each other. It will slide into the conduit as is, but it is a very tight fit. Use coarse sandpaper to reduce the size of the dowel so it is a snug (but not loose) fit. Leave a gap of about 1 inch between the pieces of conduit. It helps to plug the other end of the conduit with caulking or tape to prevent water from getting inside.

Finally, use the stainless-steel hose clamps to secure the coax

Figure 1—The Indestructible Dipole mounted vertically on the author's deck. A small pine board with a U Bolt supports the antenna. The end of the antenna slips over a small screw in the deck to prevent the antenna from slipping.

Figure 2—Detail of the coax connector. The center conductor goes to one side of the dipole and the outer braid attaches to the other side. A wood dowel joins the two sections. Stainless-steel clamps allow the antenna to be taken apart quickly and easily.

10 Meters is *Not* Dead!

"Dead" is a relative term. If you don't believe me, ask anyone who's spotted Elvis at their local Kmart, waiting on customers in the automotive department along with Jimi Hendrix, Janis Joplin and Jim Morrison. When it comes to Amateur Radio bands, the death of 10 meters has been greatly exaggerated.

I'd be a fool to insist that the band is anything like it was in 1989 and '90 when I worked most of Europe with 25 W and a dipole antenna. Those days are gone—at least until about the turn of the century. From the standpoint of a rabid DXer, 10 meters is indeed "dead" most of the time. But if your goal is to simply enjoy the fine art of conversation and possibly pick up your Worked All States award in the process, 10 meters is very much alive!

For the next five years or so, 10 meters is going to be pretty much as it is now. Is that so bad? During the most recent ARRL 10-meter contest, I worked stations throughout the United States, Canada, the Caribbean and South America without breaking a sweat. Was I using a beam antenna and a kilowatt? Nope. Just 100 W and an antenna similar to the one described in this article.

As the author points out, all you need is patience and a little persistence. The greatest enemy of 10-meter operating is *apathy*. No kidding. So many hams turn on their radios, tune through the band and, hearing nothing, hit the **POWER OFF** switch. Why not try calling "CQ" a few times? The band may be open to who-knows-where, but you'll never find out if no one bothers to call! Also check the 10-meter beacon frequencies. The *ARRL Repeater Directory* lists many of the beacons.

The band tends to be at its best from September through May. During those months, 10 begins to open in the late morning, reaching its peak by early to mid afternoon. Depending on conditions, anything is possible. Be on the lookout for signals from just about anywhere in the US. You'll also hear a fair amount of activity from Central and South America. As darkness falls, so does 10 meters. Even so, you'll often stumble across some long-haul interstate signals—and DX—an hour or two after sunset.

During the summer, 10 seems to enter the doldrums. Again, however, this is relative! You can still enjoy conversations with locals as well as stations hundreds of miles away. The occasional continent-spanning contact is possible and you'll still encounter some South and Central American stations, too.

You can determine the "condition" of 10 meters by listening to the *propagation beacons*. These are automated stations that exist for the purpose of exploring skip conditions on 10 meters. Most use CW to transmit their call signs and other data such as their location, output power and so on.

Tune from 28.189 through 28.300 MHz and listen for the beacons. If you hear a reasonably strong beacon from Texas, for example, chances are good that you can talk to stations there. Tune through the phone band and see if you can find those Texans. If you don't hear any, you'll have to flush them out of the woodwork. Try calling CQ at several frequencies throughout the band (28.400 MHz is a popular spot). If your calls go unanswered, wait about 30 minutes and try again. Don't give up!

You can also use your transceiver scanning functions (or just a scanning receiver) to alert you when the band opens. Set your radio to scan 29.600 through 29.680 MHz. This is part of the 10-meter FM subband. Turn up the volume, set the squelch and go watch television. When you hear voices echoing from your radio room, you may be receiving signals from 10-meter repeaters in various areas of the country. That usually means the band is open! Switch off the TV and head for your radio. (You probably watch too much TV anyway.)—*WB8IMY*

---

to the antenna (see Figure 2). The center conductor goes to one side of the antenna and the coax shield braid attaches to the other side. It helps to put some solder on the coax wires before you clamp them to the antenna. This is called *tinning* and helps make a good electrical connection. It also makes the coax wires more durable. You could use a small screw to attach the coax to the antenna, but I chose to use the clamps so that I could disassemble the antenna quickly.

I checked the SWR and found that the antenna seemed to resonate best at about 28.200 MHz. This meant that it was just a bit too long. So, I cut about 1.5 inches from each end. That gave me an SWR reading of 1.4:1 at my chosen frequency. That will probably be about the best you can do with an antenna like this.

Mount it Anywhere

Dipoles work well horizontally or vertically. If you mount it horizontally, it is best to get it fairly high into the air. On the other hand, vertical polarization is nice because height is less of a factor and, unlike most other vertical antennas, a dipole requires no radials. Also, a vertical antenna focuses most of the transmitter's energy low on the horizon, which means better skip and more DX!

I mounted my antenna vertically on my deck using a small pine board and a **U** bolt. I put a small screw in the deck with the head sticking up about an inch. The end of the antenna slips over the screw and prevents the antenna from slipping. I also left the **U** bolt loose so I could mount or dismount the antenna in just seconds. This could be a very useful feature for someone who lives in an apartment or condo!

Of course there are other creative options for mounting the antenna:

❑ Suspend it in your attic.
❑ Mount it vertically at ground level by installing a board with two **U** bolts.
❑ Drill a hole in one end, put a rope through the hole, and pull the antenna into a tall tree.

Regardless of how and where you install it, the Indestructible Dipole is simple, cheap, effective and very durable! ▮QST▮

Radio Tips: The 10-Meter Band Plan

(All frequencies are in MHz)

28.000-28.070	CW
28.070-28.150	Digital (RTTY, AMTOR, packet, PacTOR, CLOVER)
28.150-28.190	CW
28.190-28.200	New beacon subband
28.200-28.300	Old beacon subband
28.300-29.300	Phone
29.300-29.510	Satellites
29.510-29.590	FM repeater inputs
29.600	FM simplex
29.610-29.690	FM repeater outputs

FM Repeater pairs (input/output)

29.520/29.620	29.560/29.660
29.540/29.640	29.580/29.680

—from the 1993/1994 *ARRL Repeater Directory*

El Dipolo Criollo

A dual-band HF antenna with a Caribbean accent!

By Bill Meara, N2CQR/HI8
Unit 5510
APO AA 34041

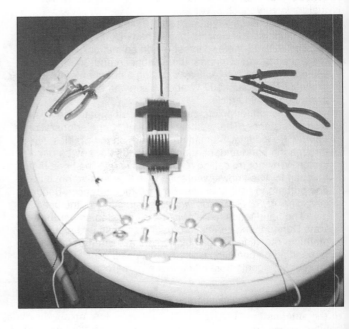

A view of the center insulator/ connector assembly and the coaxial balun.

This is yet another version of that venerable standby of the ham bands: the inverted-**V** dipole. While it might seem as if there are few lessons and little enjoyment in the construction of such a simple antenna, I found that this project was a big help in relearning antenna theory after a long absence from Amateur Radio. I also had a lot of fun coming up with small innovations while putting the antenna together. I call it El Dipolo Criollo. Here in the Dominican Republic the word criollo (pronounced *cree-oh-yo*) is used to connote things grown or produced on the island.

Inspiration

After dusting off my old Hallicrafters HT-37/Drake 2B combination and getting a reciprocal license from the Dominican Republic's telecommunication authority, I found myself repeating some of the rites of my ham radio youth: jerry rigging hastily built dipoles and stringing them through the branches of trees. Assisted by the nearby Caribbean, lots of solar radiation, wet ground and a DX call sign, I had good results. Even so, I wanted to do a bit more in the antenna area.

With simplicity one of the watchwords of my station, I decided to build a dual-band inverted **V** for 15 and 20 meters. This antenna is really just two inverted **V** dipoles (one suspended a few inches beneath the other) fed simultaneously with the same piece of coax. While it might seem like this arrangement couldn't possibly provide good antenna matches on both bands, it works because the RF "sees" only one of the antennas at the proper impedance. the energy is

transferred to that antenna element; the other antenna is "seen" as a high impedance and is "ignored" by the RF.

You can build an antenna like this for almost any combination of ham bands. In fact, you can easily apply the principles described here to build an antenna for three or more of your favorite bands. With sunspots rapidly disappearing, you may want to consider going lower in frequency, say to a 40 meter/20 meter combination. I've noticed recently that my 15-meter element was getting less and less use. (Then I discovered the RS-12 satellite and it swung back into action, but that's another story.)

Hitting the Books

A look at the technical literature provided some interesting review lessons. I was very pleased to see the inverted **V** get good treatment in the 1993 *ARRL Handbook*: "Contrary to statements made in previous editions of this *Handbook* and by various radio amateurs, the inverted **V** is an efficient radiator. Its gain and pattern are very similar to a horizontal dipole at the same height as the apex when the apex angle is 100° or more."

Great! A 35-foot apex would put me at a half wavelength for the 20-meter band. With a 15-foot length of 1-inch PVC pipe on top of a 20-foot roof, I figured I could get the apex up to the required height.

The *Handbook* showed fairly good radiation angles (20°) at this height. You want your radiation going out at a low angle so that it will strike the ionosphere and be refracted back to Earth as far away as possible. With a conveniently placed backyard tree and a second PVC pipe in the front yard for end supports, the 100° apex wouldn't be a problem.

The literature indicated that the **V** shape tends to reduce the input impedance from the 70 Ω normally associated with a straight dipole. Because my transmitter has a 50-Ω output circuit and I'm using 52-Ω RG-58 coax, it seemed that the **V** could actually provide a better impedance match than a horizontal dipole. The *Handbook* says that for an antenna at 0.2 wavelength above ground, an apex angle of 127° would yield an input impedance of 50 Ω; 90° would give 36 Ω. I was shooting for around 100° to 110° so I could have a low SWR. This was important because at this point I did not yet own an antenna tuner. Without a tuner to handle the mismatch, a low SWR was necessary to load the transmitter properly.

Designing a Simple Balun

When I was a teenage ham, I routed all my coaxial feed lines directly to my antennas. This usually works fine, but it raises the possibility of problems. The most troublesome is the fact that current can flow back from the antenna along the outer surface of the coax shield. Because the shield and the inner conductor are so close together, the electric and magnetic fields caused by the RF flowing to the antenna are normally "balanced out" and little radiation results. But the current introduced on the outside of the shield "unbalances" the transmission line and the coax starts radiating. This affects the radiation pattern of the antenna.

The *Handbook* provided a neat and easy solution in the form of a *balun* (meaning *bal*anced to *un*balanced). It suggests a current balun consisting of 6 to 8 turns of coax with a diameter of 6 inches or so, mounted at the center of the antenna. Following the old ham tradition of stealing items from the kitchen for use in radio projects (that's where the term "breadboard" comes from!), I found a Tupperware bowl that was just begging to be used as a coil form. It's now suspended approximately 35 feet above the Dominican Republic.

My balun is secured to the mast. It's light enough that you could simply allow it to dangle as well. In either case, be sure to use a strain-relief clamp on the plywood center section where the coaxial cable attaches to the bolts. Otherwise, the coaxial connections will snap after exposure to a couple of windy days.

Clothespins, Wire and PVC

The centerpiece of my Dominican Dipole was a small rectangular piece of var-nished plywood and some stainless-steel bolts. The bolts serve as the connection points for the two antennas (see Figure 1). I made sure to wrap the wires so that they would be in firm contact with the bolts as I tightened them. (I didn't want to add inductance by inadvertently forming a small coil.) If you have access to thick pieces of Plexiglas or Lexan, you can use this material in place of the plywood.

A visit to a local hardware store yielded a 15-foot length of 1-inch PVC pipe for my mast. I put a smaller diameter PVC pipe inside the main support thinking that it would increase rigidity, but all it did was increase the weight. One of the things that I'd do differently on this project would be to be more careful about weight at the apex point; the PVC is very flexible and weight at the top can make antenna erection look (to the neighbors) like you're wrestling with a bizarre fishing rod! (When you put up this or any other antenna, make sure that you are far from any power lines and that there is no possibility that the antenna will come into contact with electrified wires.) I marked off 1-foot intervals on the support pipe. This helped when it came time to measure the wires for the antenna elements. For your version of the Dipolo Criollo, just about any mast can be used. PVC pipe happened to be best in my situation.

I culled the literature for words of wisdom on element length. My old 1973 *Handbook* advised that, "Because the ends of an inverted **V** are closer to the ground, the antenna will be slightly shorter than a dipole." Regarding parallel dipoles, the 1993 *Handbook* observed that the resonant length of the shorter dipole lengthens by a few percent and advised the builder to adjust the *longer* antenna for resonance *first*.

With this in mind I cut my elements. The 20-meter antenna would be on top and would serve as the physical support for the PVC

mast, so I used a relatively heavy gauge wire (AWG 10). In the tropics, insulated wire is mandatory! Shooting for resonance at 14.175 MHz, I applied the formula 468 ÷ frequency (in MHz) and came up with an antenna length of 33.015 feet—about 16 feet, 6 inches per side. I cut two 17-foot lengths of wire. After attaching the coax and the antenna wires to the apex plate, I ended up with elements that were 16 feet, 8 inches long. Knowing that I would have to do some trimming, I stripped the insulation from the last 8 inches of the wires.

For the 15-meter antenna I used some ordinary insulated hookup wire. Using 21.225 MHz as my center frequency, the formula yielded an antenna length of 22.049 feet or about 11 feet, 1/4 inch per side. I cut the elements to 11 feet, 6 inches. After attaching them to the apex, they were approximately 11 feet, 4 inches long.

I used some modified clothespins to suspend the 15-meter elements below the 20-meter antenna. I just took the clothespins apart, discarded the metal spring and put the wooden pieces flat surface to flat surface (see Figure 2). I used small cable ties to hold the wood together. Looking back, I realize that I should have varnished or painted these separators because, when it rains heavily, the SWR on 15 meters rises. I think this is due to the clothespins getting wet and increasing the coupling between the two antennas (the SWR on 20 meters stays the same). When you build this antenna, take the extra time to varnish the clothespins or whatever wood separators you use, or use plastic separators.

Installation and Operation

Getting the antenna to stand up straight was a bit of a chore. As the PVC mast, coax, antenna elements swung about in the breeze, I had nightmarish visions of the whole thing falling into a hopeless tangle. Finally, after some cajoling and manipulation of two nylon guy ropes (attached at the apex), the antenna was firmly in place. I used an old TV antenna mount that was already on the roof as the base support and simply lashed the bottom of the PVC pipe to what was left of it.

The literature indicates that an inverted **V** with this kind of apex angle will probably not be completely unidirectional; there probably will be some dipole-like signal lobes off the sides of the antenna. I oriented the antenna northwest to southeast in order to place my signal lobes in Europe and the South Pacific. I knew that from the Dominican Republic I'd have no trouble working the US "off the ends."

When the moment of truth arrived, I

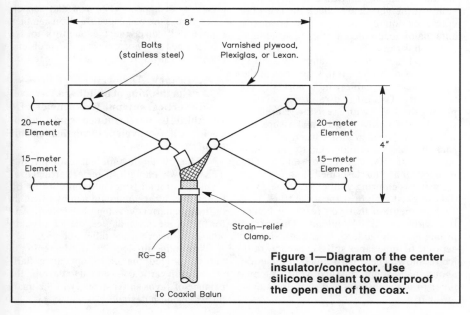

8"

Bolts (stainless steel)

Varnished plywood, Plexiglas, or Lexan.

20-meter Element

20-meter Element

4"

15-meter Element

15-meter Element

Strain-relief Clamp.

RG-58

Figure 1—Diagram of the center insulator/connector. Use silicone sealant to waterproof the open end of the coax.

To Coaxial Balun

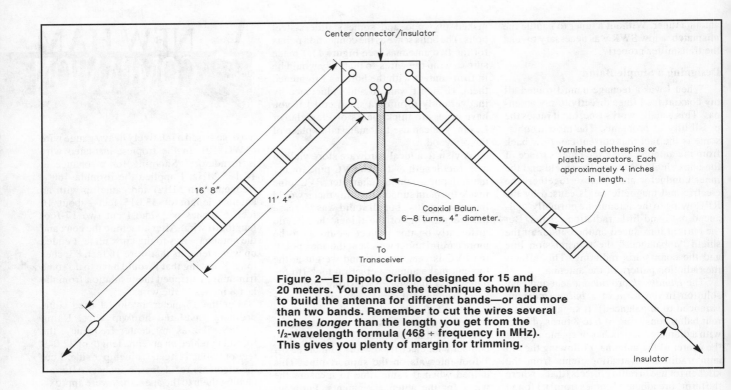

Figure 2—El Dipolo Criollo designed for 15 and 20 meters. You can use the technique shown here to build the antenna for different bands—or add more than two bands. Remember to cut the wires several inches *longer* than the length you get from the ½-wavelength formula (468 ÷ frequency in MHz). This gives you plenty of margin for trimming.

Labels in figure:
Center connector/insulator
16' 8"
11' 4"
Coaxial Balun. 6—8 turns, 4" diameter.
To Transceiver
Varnished clothespins or plastic separators. Each approximately 4 inches in length.
Insulator

---

hooked up my equipment and measured the SWR on several frequencies. Here are the results:

Frequency (MHz)	SWR
14.000	1.1:1
14.175	1.3:1
14.350	1.5:1
21.000	1.5:1
21.225	2.0:1
21.450	2.7:1

Looking at this pattern I saw that my 20-meter antenna was resonant at a frequency lower than I had intended (at resonance, SWR will be lowest, because all of the reactance in the antenna has been eliminated and only resistance remains). I shortened the antenna by a few inches. When I got the 20-meter SWR in good shape, I made similar adjustments to the 15-meter antenna. Just a little trimming and I was done!

Summary

My Dipolo Criollo has provided excellent service through eight months of tropical sunshine and downpours. I've been able to work lots of DX with this antenna, never using more than 50 W. It was a rewarding and educational project. And I think it looks good up on the roof! An inverted **V** has a majestic appearance—it looks like a pair of wings spread for a journey through the ionosphere! If you're new to ham radio and looking for a fun project, put together your own version of my multiband Dipolo Criollo. It's almost certain to work well and when it's done you'll have a taste of the satisfaction that comes from working the world with something you built yourself. **QST-**

Q Stan White, WB2PPN, asks, "My HF antenna system consists of a Mosley TA33 Jr beam fed with coaxial cable and a G5RV wire dipole fed with ladder line. As long as the weather remains dry, the antennas function perfectly. But as soon as it rains, the SWR on both antennas jumps substantially. What's causing this?"

A Concerning the TA33 beam, my guess is that rainwater is finding its way into the coaxial cable or the traps, or both. If coax is not properly shielded against moisture, water penetration can cause serious problems. If water is entering the traps, they should be disassembled and cleaned if possible. At the very least, check the traps for cracks or holes. It also pays to clean the antenna of accumulated grit and structures left by busy insects.

If you can get your hands on a 50-Ω dummy load, connect it to your coax at the point where the cable would normally attach to the TA33. (You're effectively replacing the TA33 with a resistor.) Carefully shield the dummy load to make sure it's watertight. Now, grab a garden hose and soak the coax thoroughly. Go to your radio and check the SWR on the coaxial line. Did it shoot up as you describe? If so, chances are water is entering your coax. If the SWR did not go sky high, suspect the traps.

You mention that you're using ladder line with your G5RV antenna. One of the problems with ladder line is that it is susceptible to impedance shifts caused by rain, ice or snow. There isn't much you can do about this except readjust your antenna tuner to compensate—and pray for sunny weather.

Q Bob Gustafson, KD9GI, asks, "I have a solid-state Hammarlund receiver with an ac hum in the audio. I've checked the ground connections, added a new filter capacitor, and bypassed each power-supply diode with 0.01-µF capacitors. Nothing seems to work. Any suggestions?"

A Your symptom seems to fit the classic problem of an open filter capacitor. There may be another filter capacitor in another part of the circuit that you missed, or the capacitor you installed has insufficient capacitance. You can usually troubleshoot the culprit by adding capacitance across the filter caps with clip leads. The hum will decrease or disappear when you add capacitance across the bad capacitor. You can then sequentially disconnect capacitors to see which ones are *not* causing the problem. (There may be more than one bad capacitor.)

Q Matthew Taylor, KB2QKB, asks, "I'm thinking of building a ½-wavelength vertical antenna for 40 meters. Do you think its performance would be superior to a ¼-wavelength vertical on this band?"

A The low-angle gain that results from a half-wavelength 40-meter vertical over "typical" ground is actually only a tiny bit better than what you could achieve with an ordinary quarter-wavelength vertical. And for higher elevation angles, the gain is substantially lower for the taller antenna.

When the difficulties of designing a means to feed the high-impedance half-wavelength vertical are added to the mix, the balance of favor shifts strongly to the quarter-wavelength design.

Build an HF

Walking Stick

Antenna

By Robert Capon, WA3ULH
322 Burlage Circle
Chapel Hill, NC 27514
Photos by the author

T his antenna project was inspired by the planning that went into an expedition by a group of amateurs to activate Harker's Island off the coast of North Carolina. We had just finished operating the 20-meter CW station with the Orange County Radio Amateurs during Field Day. We had so much fun, we didn't want to wait another year to combine ham radio with a camping adventure.

As with any expedition, one of the central planning questions is, "What do we use for an antenna?" During Field Day, we worked QRP, so we opted for the gain of a 3-element Yagi mounted on a 21-foot mast, held with guy ropes and massive anchors. The mast weighs about 50 pounds, so setting up the Yagi was hard work. Fortunately we had six sturdy hams on hand to do the job safely. But we had only four amateurs for the IOTA expedition, and none of us were excited about setting up the Yagi.

None of us are big fans of dipoles. Dipoles have a rather high angle of radiation, and have nulls that are very inconvenient.

And dipoles can be difficult to put up on a flat, open beach.

This left us with our commercial multiband verticals. I like my Cushcraft R-7 and my friend Paul, AA4XX, loves his GAP. With 100 W, we felt that we could work the whole world with our verticals. In fact, I started my DX career with only 100 W and a ground-mounted Butternut HF6V vertical. I worked over 200 countries before I graduated to a Cushcraft A-3S Yagi.

But our plans for the mini-expedition called for spending most of our time on only two bands: 20 and 40 meters. So why not put together single-band vertical antennas held up with lightweight guy ropes? This would enable us to leave our commercial verticals at home, thus eliminating the need to dismantle our home stations.

With a little effort, I designed a monoband vertical antenna that can be fit into a walking stick that weighs about 3 pounds. The antenna can be fabricated in less than two hours, assembled in the field in less than 15 minutes (either free-standing or suspended from a tree), and built for about $30. Not bad, considering that regular walking sticks found in trail shops run about $70!

In addition to use as an expedition antenna, the walking stick vertical is an excellent monoband antenna for the new ham. It provides performance on par with commercial vertical antennas, except that it only works on a single band and it's very inexpensive. The antenna is ideal for both QRP and full-power operation.

Before we proceed, please keep in mind the cardinal safety rule when working with vertical antennas. Do not allow the antenna to come into contact with a power line or power source of any kind—you could be killed. That's why commercial verticals carry a precautionary warning label. Please use caution whenever you are in the vicinity of electrical outlets, fixtures and overhead power lines.

Quarter-Wavelength Verticals

The walking stick is a design variation of the classic quarter-wave vertical antenna. The design is optimized when a vertical quarter-wavelength radiator is combined with a tuned quarter-wavelength radial system.

The vertical element can be as simple as a quarter wavelength of wire or ladder line, suspended from a tree using nylon rope and an insulator. Three to four wires, also trimmed to a quarter wavelength, work very well for the radial system.

To determine the length in feet of a quarter wavelength, use the following formula:

Length (in feet) = 234 / f(MHz)

This works out to the dimensions shown in Table 1. You'll notice that the lengths for the CW and phone portions of each band are only a few inches apart, so the same antenna can be used for different parts of the band without adjustment. Further, the same antenna can be used for any of the higher bands

Table 1

Band	CW (ft)	Phone (ft)
10 meters	8.3	8.2
12 meters	9.4	9.4
15 meters	11.1	11.0
17 meters	12.9	12.9
20 meters	16.7	16.5
30 meters	23.1	—
40 meters	33.3	32.4

by compressing its size during assembly in the field.

A quarter-wavelength vertical exhibits excellent characteristics for working DX because it has a very low angle of radiation. The antenna has a low impedance at the feedpoint, it is omnidirectional, and it exhibits very broadband coverage for the band of interest.

Unfortunately, even multiples of a quarter-wavelength vertical do not work well because they have a high impedance at the feedpoint. Therefore, a quarter-wave vertical on the CW portion of 20 meters that's a half wave on 10 meters will exhibit unacceptably high impedance on 10 meters (the SWR will be high).

Odd multiples do resonate, but their angles of radiation increase to the point where they become much less effective. For example, a quarter-wave vertical on 40 meters is approximately ³/₄ wave on 15 meters and will resonate on 15. But at ³/₄ wave, the antenna has a high angle of radiation and is much less effective for working DX on 15 meters. So the magic number for the monoband walking stick vertical is a quarter wavelength.

Parts List

All of the parts that you will need are readily available, and the total cost of the antenna is about $30 (see Table 2).

I was surprised at how difficult it was to locate telescoping (nested) aluminum tubing at my local hardware stores. The ⁵/₈-inch tube was impossible to find. Fortunately, my DX buddy Ernie, AD4VA, came to the rescue by suggesting that I contact a mail-order supplier. Sure enough, I was able to order the four lengths from a mail-order supplier for $16.50, plus shipping.

When the aluminum arrived, I found that two of the sections did not fit together at all, and I had to swap the ³/₄-inch tube with a section from the hardware store to build the antenna. My friend Paul, AA4XX, who built a 40-meter walking stick vertical, encountered the same problem. In fact, two of his sections became stuck together and could not be separated.

Be careful. The reason that the pieces can fit improperly or become jammed is that aluminum suppliers ordinarily cut aluminum to length without further preparation of the ends. Before you attempt to nest the tubing, you must bevel and deburr the ends with a rounded metal file, and carefully clean away the aluminum filings. To clean away the filings, place a wad of soft cotton cloth sprayed with WD-40 in each tube, and push the oiled cloth through the length of the tube (like a ramrod) with the smallest diameter tube that you have.

Remember, the aluminum sections have extremely tight tolerances. If a single particle of aluminum remains inside an aluminum tube, the tubes will likely jam.

Building the Aluminum Sections

I spend most of my time on 20 meters, so I built my walking stick vertical for that band. This choice also enables me to compress the antenna during assembly in the field to work on 10 through 20 meters as the need arises.

Begin constructing the antenna by cutting the aluminum tubes to the proper lengths with a hacksaw. The aluminum tubing cuts easily, but please be sure to wear safety glasses. Cut the three smaller diameter tubes to a length of 4 feet, 5 inches. Cut the 1-inch tube to a length of 4 feet, 8 inches.

Next, prepare the antenna for assembly by cutting 2-inch slots in one end of the 1-inch, $^7/_8$-inch, and $^3/_4$-inch tubes. (The $^5/_8$-inch tube does not need a slot.) To slot the tubes, gently place them in a wooden vise, and cut the slot with a hacksaw. Be sure not to make the vise too tight, because this will compress the tubing, and make it harder to nest the tubes later. After cutting the aluminum, gently file off the burrs with a fine-grade, curved metal file and clean away the filings.

When you assemble the antenna in the field, place the hose-clamps over the slotted ends of each of the aluminum tubes

and attach the unslotted tube of the next smaller size. (Slide the $^7/_8$-inch tube into the 1-inch tube, and so on.) Gently tighten the hose clamps for a snug fit.

Measure the length of the vertical for the band of interest, and label the three smaller tubes with a permanent laundry pen or a scribe mark to facilitate setting up the an-

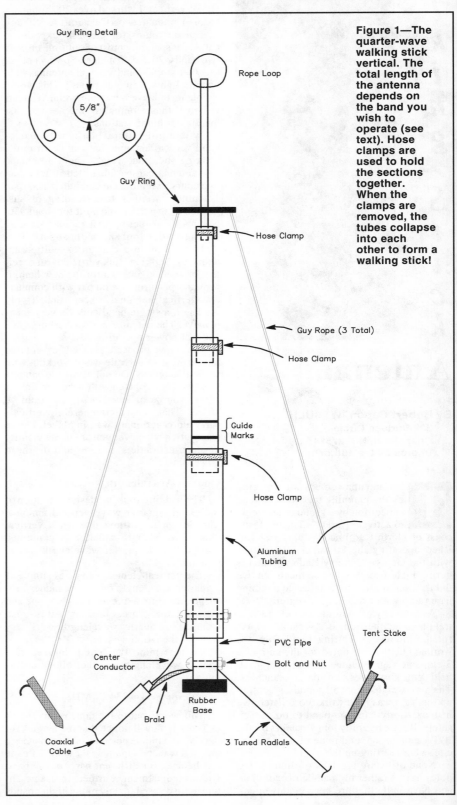

Figure 1—The quarter-wave walking stick vertical. The total length of the antenna depends on the band you wish to operate (see text). Hose clamps are used to hold the sections together. When the clamps are removed, the tubes collapse into each other to form a walking stick!

Table 2

Note: The lengths shown are for 10 through 20 meters

Aluminum Tubing: (use 0.058" wall thickness for proper telescoping)	1-inch×72 inches $^7/_8$-inch×72 inches $^3/_4$-inch×72 inches $^5/_8$-inch×72 inches
Guy ring	Scrap of wood or closet bar hanger
Guy rope	Nylon, $^1/_8$ inch or braided mason line, 60 feet
Tent stakes (3)	Lightweight stakes
Radial wire	50 feet insulated #22 or heavier
Hose clamps (3)	1$^1/_4$-inch hose clamps
Rubber walking tip	Cane tip (purchased used from medical supply store)
Rubber antenna tip	Rubber chair tip, from hardware store
Hand grip	Black cloth tape or tennis racket grip
Decorative knob	2-inch diameter wooden sphere
Ground radial post	$^1/_2$-inch-diameter PVC or fiberglass tube
Fishing Weights (4)	$^1/_2$-oz brass fishing weights

tenna in the field. I marked the tubing for the middle of the 20-meter band. I also marked the 7/8-inch tube for several of my other favorite bands. (The 7/8-inch section is ideal for length adjustments because you can reach it from the ground.)

Finally, drill a 1/8-inch hole approximately 1/2 inch from the top of the 3/4-inch aluminum tubing. Thread a small piece of nylon rope through the hole and tie the rope into a small loop. This loop will come in handy in situations where it is more convenient to suspend the vertical from a tree limb, rather than erecting it as a free-standing antenna with guy ropes.

Install the rubber cane tip on the end of the 1-inch aluminum tube. I went to a medical supply store where the clerk advised me that new cane tips cost $9.30 a pair. I noticed that there was a box of assorted used cane tips for 30 cents each, and I opted for one of these. This tip is used when the antenna is in the "walking stick mode." You can also buy chair tips, which are not as sturdy but are much easier to find and cheaper to buy, in most hardware stores.

Building the Guy Ring

To build the guy rope ring find a scrap disk of wood or heavy plastic, approximately 2 to 3 inches in diameter. Almost anything will work for this application. I used an item commonly found in hardware stores: a heavy plastic disk designed to hold a closet pole. Drill a 5/8-inch hole in the center of the disk. Then drill three 1/8-inch holes, equally spaced 120° apart on the perimeter of the disk (see Figure 1).

Tie three 17-foot lengths of nylon rope onto the guy rope ring, using a non-slip knot. I used braided mason "snap line" for my guy ropes to support this very lightweight antenna.

When you assemble the antenna in the field, slide the guy ring down the 5/8-inch aluminum rod. The ring is held in place by the 3/4-inch tube, so the guy ropes will go approximately 3/4 of the way up the antenna.

Building the Ground Radial System

Cut three ground radials for the band of preference to the same length as the antenna. Figure 2 shows the detail for connecting the ground radials to the antenna. The center conductor of your coax feed line goes to the vertical aluminum tubing, while the coax braid goes to the radials. Attach a small fishing weight to the end of each radial. This helps weigh down the radials in the field. These fishing weights are also commonly available in brass, which is much safer to handle than lead weights.

To insulate the ground radials from the center conductor, I used a 6-inch length of 1/2-inch inner diameter PVC plastic mounted with a 1/8-inch bolt to the bottom of the 1-inch aluminum tube section (Figure 2). I finished off the PVC section by installing a rubber chair tip on the end of the PVC insulator tube.

This PVC ground section is installed

Figure 2—Base detail of the walking stick vertical. The center conductor of the coax is bolted directly to the aluminum tube. The shield is bolted to the PVC pipe along with three tuned radial wires. The rubber tip at the bottom of the PVC pipe doubles as the walking stick base.

when the antenna is operational. To avoid damaging the PVC tube, remove the tube when you are back in "walking stick mode," and replace it with the rubber cane tip (directly mounted on the aluminum tube).

Finishing Touches

I used a wooden knob for the top of the antenna to give it the "Professional Walking Stick Look." I used a 2-inch-diameter wooden ball (an inexpensive cabinet pull from the local hardware store), and drilled a 1-inch hole in the bottom to form the knob. Finally, I stained and sealed the knob with tung-oil finish.

To put the final touches on the antenna, I fashioned a walking stick grip at the top. Black cloth electrical tape would be sufficient for the purpose, but I used a tennis racket replacement grip, which winds onto the tube like tape. (These replacement tennis racket grips can be found at almost any sporting goods shop that sells tennis accessories.) I also purchased a small nylon pouch to provide a convenient place to store the miscellaneous parts, guy rope, and ground radial wires of the antenna.

If you want a classy extra touch, consider putting a compass into the wooden knob. (My wife and kids love this feature.) I found

An antenna that gets you on the air and keeps you on the path.

a very nice compass built into a $2.99 survival kit at a department store. I pried the compass out of the plastic kit, drilled a shallow hole into the top of the wooden knob, and cemented the compass in place.

Operational Test

In preparation for our expedition to Harker's Island, I assembled a team to go out to a local baseball field to set up the antenna and test it out: Ernie, AD4VA; my son Howard, KE4RUZ (age 7); and myself. We opted for the guy rope method of installation because we were anxious to try out the portable guy system.

My heart skipped a beat when we hooked the antenna up to the SWR analyzer and saw high readings on all frequencies! I got out my digital multimeter and began testing the coaxial feed line when Ernie and I simultaneously noticed that the center conductor of the coax had broken off. We fixed the connector and were in business.

Note that three on-ground radials don't make for a terribly efficient 1/4-wave vertical antenna, but our saltwater location helped even the score. The vertical will work even better if you can get the antenna base and radials 8 or 10 feet in the air.

I brought along my Index Labs QRP Plus 5-W rig and we put the antenna through its paces. Signals were loud and seemed to be coming in from every direction. In about 15 minutes of operation we logged two contacts: VE3DMC, in Ottawa, and W5RRR, the station at the Johnson Space Center in Houston. We made contact with both stations on the first call and received reports of 579 from each. I was running just 3 W at the time.

Paul's walking stick vertical for 40 meters delivered similar performance. His antenna had seven 5-foot sections, with the largest section made of 1 1/4-inch aluminum. Paul's 40-meter antenna was so tall, he used two sets of 1/8-inch guy rope to erect it. Paul tested his antenna on 40 meters and obtained an SWR of 1.3:1 or less over a bandwidth of 300 kHz. Paul tested the antenna for approximately 30 minutes running 100 W and worked five European stations including: EC5ABU, OK1DOZ, UA2FCC, and F9OQ.

Next Steps

You may want to experiment with an assortment of mounting possibilities to set up the walking stick vertical for semi-permanent use at your home. After you have mastered the monoband walking stick vertical, you may also want to try fabricating a multiband vertical. *The ARRL Antenna Book* (Chapter 15) has a design for an excellent two-band vertical for 10 and 15 meters that is also inexpensive to build.

Thanks to my expedition buddies (Paul, AA4XX; Joe, KD4LLV; Gerry, KD4YJV, and Howard) for helping to inspire this antenna design. Also, special thanks to my field testers, Ernie, AD4VA, and Howard, KE4RUZ.

A Paint-Pole Antenna

The old saying, "Where there's a will there's a way," certainly applies to hams who struggle with antenna restrictions. Living in a duplex town house complex, I was faced with the problem of putting up an adequate antenna for the HF bands. My first attempt was a dipole for 40 meters strung on the outside the walls of my unit in a horizontal **V** configuration. This was adequate to copy W1AW for code practice and make a few local contacts on CW. But when I upgraded to General, I wanted an antenna that would "get out" on the 20 and 17-meter bands.

I needed an antenna that could be assembled and disassembled quickly. Ideally, it wouldn't attract the attention of the neighbors or the landlord. I thought a vertical antenna would work, but the commercial verticals are not designed to be easily assembled and disassembled. As I browsed my local hardware store one afternoon, I literally bumped into the answer. There, propped in a corner, was a telescoping aluminum paintbrush extender—commonly called a "paint pole."

From Paint Pole to Antenna

The total length of the paint pole was 16 feet, which is about six inches too short for the middle of the 20-meter phone band. So, I bought a Radio Shack telescoping radio replacement antenna and clamped it to the end of the upper section of the pole. That gave me the extra length I needed. (It's a lot easier than it sounds!)

A small sheet-metal screw and washer were used to secure the center conductor of the coax at the bottom of the pole after part of the plastic handle was carved away with a hobby knife. I secured the pole to our deck fence with two pieces of Radio Shack *Superlock* Velcro fasteners.

A modest wire radial system was installed using copper wire (I used #17 wire, but almost anything will work). Part of the radial system is under the deck and part of it runs through a hedge. Four radials for 20 meters and four for 17 meters were cut to the appropriate ¼ wavelengths (16.5 feet for 20 meters and 13 feet for

Figure 1—The upper section of the paint-pole antenna (sections collapsed down). You can see the hose clamps and the copper braid I used to ensure electrical continuity between the sections. You can obtain copper braid by just removing it from an old piece of coax. Note the Radio Shack telescoping whip at the top of the antenna. It's held in place with electrical tape and a hose clamp.

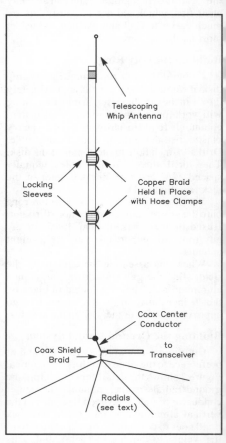

Figure 2—Construction diagram of the paint-pole antenna.

Radio Shack *Superlock* fasteners (no. 64-2360)

Quickie aluminum telescoping paintbrush extender (or equivalent): Quickie Manufacturing Company, PO Box 156, Cinnaminson, NJ 08007.

5 2-inch-diameter automobile hose clamps

Radio Shack replacement antenna (no. 270-1405)

⅛-inch sheet-metal screw and washer

2 4-inch pieces of copper braid

copper wire (for radials)

porcelain egg insulator (optional)

By Anthony J. Salvate, N1TKS
110 Prospect St
Greenwich, CT 06830

17 meters). The radials attach to the shield braid of the coax. I used a porcelain insulator as a junction point for my radials, but this is optional. A construction diagram and parts list are shown in Figure 2.

When the antenna was finished, I keyed my transmitter and measured the SWR on 20 meters. After making several adjustments to the *top pole section only*, I managed to achieve a 1.1:1 SWR. I marked the section at the locking sleeve so I'd be able to find the correct length again. I performed the same measurements on 17 meters and marked the top section accordingly. Fine length adjustments can be made by extending or collapsing the whip.

But Does It Work?

Now for the moment of truth. After listening to several conversations, I decided to call. I was ecstatic when I received a reply from a California station who gave me a 57 report. Another station in Arizona gave me a 59 report. I received a 55 from an Italian station on 17 meters, and a 59 on 17 meters from a station in Caracas, Venezuela! I had the biggest grin on my face when I heard the other hams chuckle at the story of my "paint-pole" antenna!

This antenna might not fit everyone's needs, but it's simple, effective and cheap (about $25). You can set it up and take it down in three or four minutes (Figure 3). I haven't tried the antenna on 10 or 15 meters, but it should work well, set to the appropriate length and with the appropriate radials. Have fun!

Figure 3—If you were a nonham neighbor, would this look suspicious? Probably not. You're likely to think it was a support for an umbrella. But in less than four minutes I can extend the antenna to its full height and get on the air. ᴏꜱᴛ-

Q Tony Bovee, AC6AS, asks, "I use a 100-W IC-737 transceiver and a Cushcraft R5 vertical antenna. It seems as though my station performance has decreased dramatically over the last couple of years. I'm aware that we're in the low point of the solar cycle, but I wonder if something is wrong with my radio. Is there some kind of performance test that I can use to evaluate my station?"

A The easiest way to test receiver sensitivity is with a calibrated signal generator. Determine the *minimum discernible signal* (also called the "noise floor") by feeding a signal to the radio. Tune the generator's frequency to the radio's frequency and peak for maximum response in the CW (or SSB) mode. Increase the generator output until a 3-dB increase appears at the audio output of the receiver. You can use an ac or audio voltmeter for this purpose. Compare the results to the specifications in your manual. If they're *way* off, you may have a problem with your rig.

To test the antenna and feed line, obtain an external RF wattmeter/SWR meter. Measure the power and SWR at the transmitter end with the antenna connected. Then, disconnect the antenna and replace it with a dummy load and repeat the measurements. Finally, move the meter to the dummy load end of the line and perform the measurements again. If you see a significant reduction in power at the output of the line when the dummy is connected, you probably have a bad line. If the line looks good, but you have a high SWR with the antenna connected, the antenna may be the problem. (An SWR analyzer also may be helpful.)

If you are still uncertain, you can always borrow a second receiver for an A/B comparison on the same line and antenna. Be sure to use the same signal for this test.

Q Patrick, KBØOXD, asks, "Does a packet contact count for the Worked All States award if the path between you and the other station includes an Internet 'wormhole'?"

A The Worked All States award rules require that all contacts take place *directly* from station to station, without any sort of relaying device or network. The only exceptions are contacts made via amateur satellites.

By Patrick Newton, KJ7MZ

The Droopy Loop

Decorate your roofline with an inexpensive, effective antenna!

If you're like me, your entrance into ham radio was a wondrous experience tempered by the cold reality of a snug budget. Although your resources are scarce, you need equipment that will put you on the Novice/Technician Plus subbands now, and on other bands later, as your privileges expand. The Droopy Loop fulfills those needs in grand fashion! It is a quick, easy-to-build antenna that costs very little, offers a low visual profile, and is useful on most HF bands

My introduction to the Droopy Loop came through Dave Fischer, WØMHS, who was acting as my Elmer. During the winter of 1993 I was putting together a station for Boy Scout and emergency preparedness at my church in Memphis. I needed an all-band antenna that was inexpensive and unobtrusive. Dave suggested a modification to the classic Loop Skywire. We put together a plan that called for an 80-meter square loop drooped over the top of the church (see Figure 1). We would tie down the corners with Dacron cord. Best of all, the complete set of materials cost only $50.

This first version of the Droopy Loop worked beautifully. I was able to operate on every band from 80 through 10 meters. My first contacts included the Canary Islands, Quebec, and Cuba, in addition to the West Coast states. I was sold!

I decided that if the antenna could work so well at the church, it could also work at my home in Bartlett, Tennessee. Later, I would also install one in Utah after an employer-mandated move. Because residential roofs aren't nearly as large as the roof on the church, I scaled down the 80-meter version to 40 meters for my Tennessee home. I also adapted the 80-meter version to the smaller area of my Utah residence. Both installations enabled me to realize almost the same terrific performance as the original.

Build a Droopy Loop

The Droopy Loop is a nominally horizontal loop antenna with a circumference equivalent to one full wavelength at the design frequency. Construction is straightforward and simple. The antenna is constructed from a single piece of wire laid out roughly in a square and fed by coax. As the name implies, you simply "droop" the antenna over your roof for a low-profile installation.

As you can probably guess, the Droopy Loop is intended for roofs with standard asphalt shingles. Don't try to use this antenna on a metal roof! In addition, I recommend that you run less than 100 W of power. There are points along the loop where high voltages can develop. If you attempt to run high power, there is a strong possibility of arcing and sparking.[1]

To begin, you'll need a length of 14-gauge insulated wire cut to a total length (L) in feet as follows:

80 meters: Circumference 272 feet, 68 feet on a side

40 meters: Circumference 142 feet, 35.5 feet on a side

Although the design frequency is somewhat limited by the space you have available, you can zigzag the wire on the sides that exceed the physical dimensions of your roof or yard (Figure 2). In addition, nearby trees or poles can be used to support the corners at the rear of the home, as I have done in Utah.

[1] An antenna draped over your house places you, and everyone else in the home, in proximity to strong RF fields if you're running more than 10 W or so. See Chapter 9 of the 1996 *ARRL Handbook* for more information on RF safety.

The loop can be fed by RG-58 or RG-59 coax if you operate at the design frequencies (40 or 80 meters) *only*. If you intend to use the loop on other bands in addition to 80 or 40 meters, consider feeding it with 450-Ω ladder line. No matter which feed line you choose, you're likely to need an antenna tuner to provide a 1:1

Figure 1—Can you see the Droopy Loop on this church? Don't be surprised if you can't. Most people will never notice it atop your home or apartment.

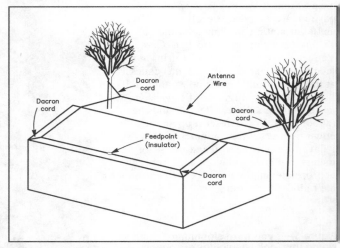

Figure 2—If your roof is big enough, you can drape the entire loop over the shingles. Otherwise, lay half of the antenna on the roof and support the other half from trees or poles in your backyard.

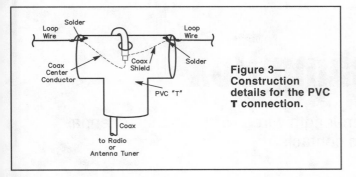

Figure 3—
Construction
details for the PVC
T connection.

SWR for your radio (you'll *definitely* need a tuner if you use ladder line).

The coax is connected directly to the loop. Mechanical support is provided by a PVC T fitting (Figure 3). Prepare the T by drilling ¹/₈-inch holes, as shown in Figure 3, to accept the antenna wire. Also drill two holes that are just large enough to let the coax pass, as shown in the figure. Feed the coax up through the bottom open end of the T, out one of the holes in the top, and back down through the other. Leave a loop of about 4 to 6 inches on the top until the stripping is done.

Strip the coax jacket, loosen the shield, and strip 1 inch of insulation from the center conductor. Pull the slack out of the coax extending from the top of the T.

Figure 4—A PVC T can be used for mechanical support at the coax/loop connection.

Pass one of the ends of the loop wire through the ¹/₈-inch holes and tie two half-hitch knots to keep it secure. The other end of the loop will be attached during installation.

Installation

You should partially construct the loop before getting on the roof. This will save time and prevent unnecessary wear and tear on your shingles. Lay out the loop on the ground. This will allow you to measure the length of each side. Mark the corners with masking tape and attach the black Dacron cords to the corners using a bowline knot. (Black Dacron is good for this purpose because of its ultraviolet resistance and low visibility.)

Connect the T and the coax to one side of the loop, leaving the other side for connection after you've pulled the loop around all the architectural features of the roof (vent pipes, chimneys and so on). When you're finished, wrap the entire antenna around a cardboard form. This greatly simplifies the task of carrying it up a ladder.

Install the antenna on the roof by drooping it over the top and tying down the corners with the Dacron cords. This work can be performed entirely on the roof, or can be done using only ladders. *Caution:* When you are on the roof be careful to tread surely and lightly. Taking a plunge from the roof is likely to limit your ability to get on the air quickly!

The corners should be secured with single Dacron lines extending away from the loop. The ends of the lines can be anchored over the edge of the roof with galvanized nails. When securing the corners use a knot that allows for easy final adjustment of

Figure 5—Install a first-class conduit system once and save time and trouble for life. Although it requires a fair amount of work to install in a roof, an electrical *weather head* is an excellent exit/entry point for feed lines.

the overall shape and tension. On several installations I slipped ¹/₂-inch PVC conduit over the wire to provide additional mechanical relief at the corners and electrical isolation at the apex of the roof when going over a metal ridge vent. You can paint the PVC flat black to reduce its visibility. Connect the free end of the loop wire to the T and coax as discussed above (Figure 4). Solder the ends, wrap them with electrical tape, and tuck the ends inside the T. After you're pleased with the overall fit of the loop, fill the T with silicone caulking to provide a watertight connection.

How Can I Get the Coax to the Radio?

At my home in Tennessee I fed the coax into the building via a hole drilled through the wall under the eaves. I then fed the coax through the attic and fished it through other holes in the ceiling above the shack. At my Utah home I installed an electrical *weather head* (Figure 5) on the roof that is connected to a surface-mount pull box in the shack with 1¹/₂-inch PVC conduit. This setup allows me to add or remove coax runs to the roof without any more drilling or trips into the attic. In addition, the pull box acts as an antenna selection center, where I can use jumpers to connect the antenna to the rig of my choice.

It's a Ball to Use!

The Droopy Loop has enabled me to operate CW and SSB as effectively as I've ever hoped for. On a recent weekend I added a multimode controller to the shack and was soon on the air with RTTY. Although putting out only 30 W, I was able to contact stations in the Virgin Islands, Quebec, British Columbia, and Mexico.

My original plan as a new ham was to build a multiband station that would fit my snug budget. My first rig was a Ten-Tec Scout, and I purchased some ancillary equipment to go with it. The Droopy Loop allows me to continue my plan, and it's a perfect fit to my Scout. This antenna may not be ideal, but it's practical and it seems to radiate well. It gives me the ability to work 160 through 10 meters on all modes. Best of all, it's a ball to use!

2667 W Midwest Dr
Taylorsville, UT 84118
e-mail patkj7mz@aol.com

By Curtis Holsopple, K9CH

The Mailbox Matching Box

Neither rain, nor sleet, nor snow, nor random-length wires will keep this antenna-matching mailbox from making its appointed contacts.

In an earlier article I described some pretty strange skyhooks for radiating a signal.[1] Few Amateur Radio operators try to make antennas out of ladders, bunkbed frames or school buses, but you never know when you'll need to load up a random wire or some other truly weird metal object. One secret ingredient in those antennas is an *antenna tuner.*[2]

The goal is to connect your 50-Ω ham rig to a 50-Ω antenna system. If the antenna doesn't present a 50-Ω load, a matching network is necessary.[3] In my previous article, I concentrated on weird antennas, mentioning my homebrew tuner in a sidebar. I received a lot of mail asking me to explain the tuner in more detail.

I'll make you a deal. I'm as allergic to math as the next guy, so this is a practical "cookbook" construction article, not an engineering discussion. I've added some footnotes at the end of this article for those who want to get a little more information. If you really want to understand these matchboxes, I recommend *The ARRL Antenna Handbook* or *Antenna Impedance Matching*, available through the ARRL.

Parts and Costs

Here is the good news! You can buy the components for a simple antenna tuner for about $35 on the surplus market. You can spend a lot more (naturally), but if you troll through the hamfest flea market tables you can probably get the parts for less.[4] It's also a good idea to ask around at ham club meetings or on the local repeaters. Someone may have a well-stocked junk box that can help you bring the cost to something less than the price of a large pizza.

When you use an antenna tuner, you also need an SWR meter or directional wattmeter to help you make adjustments. If you are using a commercial transceiver made in the last few years, you'll probably find a **REF POWER** or **SWR** position on the rig's built-in meter. Otherwise, you'll need to get your hands on a separate meter. Check the Ham Ads and commercial ads in the back of *QST*. You can get a basic new SWR meter for about $30, although fancier ones cost much more.

Don't forget to factor in the price of odds and ends, such as coax connectors, binding posts, knobs for the controls, rubber feet, clip leads and a cabinet to hold it all. Depending on how much you can scrounge or build, it is safe to factor in $10 to $15 if your junk box can't handle the situation. You can quickly go off the deep end buying a nice case, by the way. Consider alternative enclosures like my mailbox, which cost five bucks at the hardware store. Or you could try a lunch box, a Christmas cookie tin, or something soldered together with circuit board material.

The main purpose of the enclosure is safety. The matching network will operate just fine with everything hanging out in the breeze, but an enclosed case will keep you from getting zapped by exposed components or wires. Even a low-power transmitter can generate enough RF to give you painful burns.[5] Besides, you may

My Mailbox Matching Box set up outdoors on a card table with an SWR meter and my Heathkit QRP transceiver. Don't let the strange appearance fool you. With the right antenna tuner, you can get on the air from *anywhere*! In this case, the antenna tuner is directly connected to a 150-foot wire slung over tree branches about 20 feet up.

not want the fright-wig-look like Albert Einstein or Larry of the Three Stooges. A plastic or wooden box will work fine for protection, but a metal enclosure has the added advantage of providing RF shielding.

Let's Build a Mailbox Matching Box

There are several types of matchbox configurations (see the sidebar "Matchmaker, Matchmaker"). To keep costs low, I use an **L** network (Figure 1). You can use a roller inductor with a tap that moves along the spiral of wire as the coil is physically rotated. You can also use a tapped inductor like mine in the Mailbox Matching Box. This second version requires a 12-position rotary switch to select the amount of inductance in the circuit.

I mounted my coil and capacitor on a piece of wood, using the time-honored "breadboard" construction method. I cut the board to fit the mailbox with just enough room to slide it in and out easily. I also attached small wooden strips inside the mailbox to keep the breadboard in position in the bottom. This way I can safely transport the Mailbox Matching Box without the insides sloshing around.

You'll have to innovate when it comes to mounting the coil. I have a reputation for making odd wooden contraptions in my basement, and I made the hold-down brackets for the coil and capacitor on my jigsaw. Make sure that the coil and capacitor don't touch each other or the sides of the enclosure, even when the capacitor's plates are fully opened. In fact, a good rule of thumb is to maintain a distance on both sides of the coil equivalent to the diameter of the

Matchmaker, Matchmaker

My tuner is called an *L network* because the coil and capacitor are arranged like the letter **L**. The coil is in series with the feed line-to-antenna connection, and the capacitor is connected on the antenna side of the coil to ground. With one capacitor and one coil, there are four ways to lay out the components. You may need to experiment with all four arrangements if you can't get a good match the first time.

I prefer this arrangement because it allows me to ground the rotor of the capacitor, minimizing the chance for RF burns while adjusting the capacitor. Be sure to use large well-insulated knobs on the capacitor, roller-inductor and selector-switch shafts. Make sure you can't touch the set screw when grasping the knob.

If you can't get your antenna tuner to give you a good SWR reading, you may need to try reconfiguring the **L** network by moving the capacitor to the transceiver side of the coil, or by swapping the location of the capacitor and coil in the circuit.

The design I'm recommending in Figure 1 is a series-L, shunt-C on the output. Alternatives include:

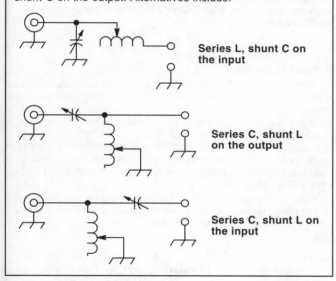

Series L, shunt C on the input

Series C, shunt L on the output

Series C, shunt L on the input

coil plus 1 inch.

You can mount the binding posts and coax connector where you want, but I chose to put them on the back end, where they'll be out of sight during normal operation. The connectors are mounted on the base by common angle brackets from the hardware store.

Grounding is Important

When using an antenna tuner of any sort, be sure to connect the rig and the tuner to a good earth ground. If you don't, you could receive painful RF burns, and you will probably experience erratic equipment operation in the shack. Even the SWR meter will probably give false and wandering readings unless you ground your station.

Good grounding is explained thoroughly in *The ARRL Handbook* and in a recent *QST* "Lab Notes" column.[6] Simply put, however, run a heavy wire (like the braid from some coax) from your rig's ground terminal outside to a ground rod driven into the earth. Keep the ground connection as short and direct as possible.

If you live on the ninth floor of a 20-story high-rise and you're having trouble getting a good ground, try a *counterpoise*. This is one or more pieces of insulated wire connected to the ground terminal on your rig. Apartment dwellers with outdoor balconies have used the metal railing as a counterpoise. It this isn't possible for you, try running your counterpoise along the baseboard of the ham shack. Try a quarter-wave wire for the lower bands (ie, 66 feet for 80 meters or 33 feet for 40 meters). Don't forget to put a piece of electrical tape on the end of each counterpoise wire. The ends can

Figure 1—Schematic of the Mailbox Matching Box. The tapped-coil version is shown at A. The roller inductor version is shown at B. Off-the-shelf prices for C1 and the roller inductor may be stiff, but you can save substantially by shopping at hamfests and surplus parts suppliers.

Values of capacitance are in picofarads (pF);
* See Text

L1—Coil, 20 turns with a diameter of 2 to 3 inches. Fair Radio Sales, PO Box 1105, Lima, OH 45802; tel 419-227-6573. The alternative is a 28-μH roller inductor (RI-28), available from Ocean State Electronics, 6 Industrial Dr, Westerly, RI 02891; tel 800-866-6626.
C1—250 pF variable capacitor. Ocean State VC-250 (see address and telephone number above)
S1—Single-pole, 12-position rotary switch. (Radio Shack 275-1385)
J1—SO-239 coaxial connector (Radio Shack 278-201)
J2, J3—Binding posts (Radio Shack 274-662)

become quite RF "hot."

The Smoke Test

In the research-and-development phase of this project, I didn't bother with the rotary switch to select the amount of inductance to be in the circuit. Initial tests were conducted using a heavy-duty clip lead instead. You may want to do the same, just to assure yourself that you have everything working properly. After using clip leads to connect all parts of the circuit, spend some time using your tuner before finalizing the connections. Experience and experimentation will reveal the arrangement and typical settings that work in your situation. Make a drawing of the connections and make permanent soldered connections if you think your antenna situation won't change very often. If you plan to use the Mailbox Matching Box at Field Day or other temporary sites, you may want to make your connections with clip leads to permit quick reconfiguration of the **L** network.

As the photos show, I used heavy-duty clip leads on this project. I didn't want to solder directly to the coil, since the wire is silver plated. The clip leads worked fine, and a package of eight costs about $4. Yes, it was painful to cut them up, but, hey, I'm strong.

What If It Doesn't Work?

In the "smoke test" phase of this project, I achieved a good match (SWR lower than 1.5:1) on all bands except 40 meters. On that band I got a definite dip on the SWR meter right as the capacitor plates became 100% meshed. Different coil-tap settings only made things worse, and my best SWR reading was around 2:1—not good enough.

The easy solution was to change the length of the antenna, so I spliced on a stray hunk of speaker wire out in the yard, bringing the total length to about 150 feet. Sha-ZAM! Instant good match

This looks like something out of a 1928 *QST*, but it's simply a variable capacitor and a coil mounted on a board. The clip leads all run to the rotary switch, mounted over the tuning shaft of the capacitor. The binding posts and coax connector are at the right.

A roller inductor from my tuner shown in the January 1996 *QST*. When I rotate the knob, the whole coil rotates. The variable tap travels along the spiral, giving me continuously variable inductance settings. Roller inductors tend to be expensive, but they make tuner design and construction much easier.

on 40 meters. Changing the length of the wire may be the simplest way to get a match on an otherwise-difficult band.

Tune-up Procedure

After connecting my transceiver through the SWR meter to the Mailbox Matching Box, I set the capacitor for about 50% mesh on the plates. Then I dragged the clip lead along the turns of the coil until the received signals reached peak loudness. (If you've already wired the switch for selecting coil taps, just spin that knob around and listen for maximum received signal strength.) If you don't hear a definite peaking in the signals as you change the coil settings, look for a wiring error.

After peaking received signals with the coil, adjust the capacitor for maximum received signal. Sometimes it's hard to hear signal peaks when turning the variable capacitor, though. You'll have to make final adjustments using the transmitter running at low power. You want to adjust the matching box so that your SWR is as low as possible. Anything lower than 1.5 to 1 is fine, and some rigs will tolerate an SWR up to 2:1.

If you've never used an antenna tuner, you'll find the extra knob-twisting annoying at first. It will soon become second-nature, however. When you first load up a new antenna using a tuner, keep a log of frequency, SWR, coil turns used and capacitor setting. Making an orderly chart of this information will save you aggravation later by allowing you to preset the tuner controls from the chart values when you come back to a favorite frequency. Then it's a small matter to put the transmitter on the air and make a few minor adjustments.

Some Final Thoughts

In more than 30 years of hamming, I've tended to use dipoles cut to the frequency I wanted to use. As long as you don't get too far away from your favorite frequencies, this approach works well. But for maximum flexibility in a temporary location, you can't beat the advantages of a random wire fed by some kind of impedance-matching device.

The components shown in the Mailbox Matching Box are "over-kill" size—they could probably handle power loads well above the typical 100-W transceiver output. I used these parts for two good reasons: they were on hand and they didn't cost much. They'd been gathering dust in my junk box for many years. You can undoubtedly get by with parts that are much smaller physically.

Don't be afraid to try and try again! Even if you don't normally need an antenna tuner, having one around will one day come in handy. A recent ice storm wiped out my inverted-**V** antenna, breaking the wires off at the feedpoint. The coax still ran out to the center insulator tied to a high tree limb, so I just loaded up the shield on the coax with the Mailbox Matching Box and went right on making contacts.

Weird? *Sure!* Fun? *Absolutely!*

Acknowledgments

Many thanks to Dave Hershberger, W9GR, for consulting with me on the technical aspects of this project. Dave and I have collaborated on projects since that electronic wolf whistle back in college—but that's another story. I also appreciate the patience of Jim Hershberger, AE4OG; Scott Brown, KF4DTX; and Maddell Reynolds, K4AAO, who listened to me think aloud on 2-meter FM as this project was under development. Initial on-the-air tests were facilitated by Bob, N4HCI; John, KBØKSA; David, N8NLZ; Les, G3AYY; and Ray, W4GOG.

Finally, thanks to my wife Edie, NG1F, and our son Jay, neither one of whom thought anything unusual was happening when I built a piece of ham gear inside a mailbox.

Notes

[1] See "Radical Radiators and Weird Wires," *QST*, Jan 1996, p 61. Be the first on your block to load up a clothesline full of wet laundry and talk to other countries!

[2] Strictly speaking, "antenna tuner" is a misnomer. If you were actually tuning the antenna, you would be changing its resonant frequency, probably by changing its physical (and electrical) length. The device commonly called an antenna tuner is used to overcome a mismatch between your transmitter's output impedance and the rest of the antenna system.

[3] According to RF design engineer Dave Hershberger, W9GR, "Your transmitter is designed to drive a 50-Ω resistive load. A resonant dipole antenna with a 1:1 SWR will have an impedance of 50 Ω at a phase angle of 0°. But your random wire antenna might have an impedance of 400 Ω at an angle of +70°, or 30 Ω at −45°, or some other screwy number. That's why they are called 'random wire' antennas—they have a random impedance and phase angle. The tuner does two things: It (1) tunes out the reactance, which brings the angle to 0°, and (2) it transforms the impedance to 50 Ω so your transmitter and receiver see the antenna impedance they were designed for." Did you follow all that? Good for you!

[4] Try Fair Radio Sales, PO Box 1105, Lima, OH 45802, tel 419-223-2196; or Antique Electronic Supply, 6221 S Maple Ave, Tempe, AZ 85283, tel 602-820-4643. They both have illustrated catalogs and they stock a lot of really interesting stuff. If you want more sources for homebrew projects, try the *Amateur Radio Mail Order Catalog and Resource Directory*, available though the ARRL.

[5] Working with random-length antenna systems can put you in proximity to strong RF fields if you're running more than 10 W or so. See Chapter 9 of the 1996 *ARRL Handbook* for more information on the potential risks.

[6] Lab Notes, "Different Grounds for Different Shacks," *QST*, Apr 1996 *QST*, p 80.

82 Brennhaven Dr
Newport News, VA 23602
e-mail curthol@beacon.regent.edu
Photos by the author

QST⌐

By Art Rideout, WA6IPD

A Simple LED SWR/Power Meter

Most analog SWR/power meters display *average* power readings. Their mechanical meter movements simply cannot react fast enough to show power fluctuations that take place in fractions of a second. When you speak into the microphone of an SSB transceiver, for example, the output power bounces up and down in sync with your voice. Maximum output occurs at split-second amplitude peaks. You'll never see these with an ordinary SWR/power meter. If you want to get a handle on the true output performance of your transceiver, you need a *peak-reading* meter.

"Oh, great—something else I have to buy!"

Not so! Why not add peak-reading capability to your existing SWR/power meter? The peak-reading LED display I'm about to describe works best when it is used to completely replace your analog indicators. (When the LED display is connected to the meter circuit, its accuracy may suffer if the analog indicators are used at the same time.) However, you can opt for a versatile combination if your analog meter features a **FWD/REF** switch. You can set the analog meter to read average reflected power while the LED meter displays peak forward power, or vice versa. They won't interfere with each other in this configuration.

I use my LED meter with a Drake L-4B linear amplifier, which has a meter that can be switched to indicate grid current, plate voltage or SWR/power. I usually monitor grid current with the analog meter and use the peak-reading LED display for SWR/power.

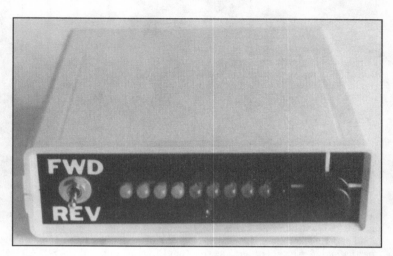

The meter works equally well with 100 W or 1500 W. The lowest power level for satisfactory operation is 15 W. The cost of parts can vary greatly, so I suggest you price shop. This project should cost under $20 to build.

Construction

As you can see in Figure 1, this is a very simple project with many parts readily available from Radio Shack. At its heart is U1, an LM3914 dot/bar display driver. I mounted U1, C1 and R3 on a Radio Shack prototyping board (Figure 2), but a printed-circuit board is

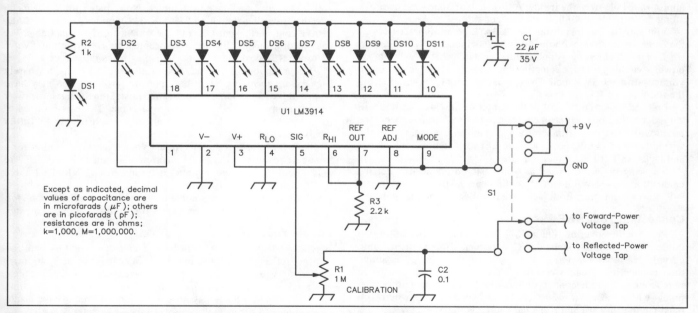

Figure 1—Schematic diagram of the peak-reading LED display. Unless otherwise specified, resistors are ¼-W, 5% tolerance carbon composition or film.

C1—22 µF electrolytic capacitor, 35 V
   (Radio Shack 272-1026)
C2—0.1 µF ceramic disc capacitor
   (Radio Shack 272-135)
DS1, DS11—Red LEDs (Radio Shack 276-041)
DS2, DS3, DS4, DS5—Green LEDs (Radio Shack
   276-022)

DS6, DS7, DS8, DS9, DS10—Yellow LEDs
   (Radio Shack 276-021)
R1—1 MΩ potentiometer (Radio Shack 271-211)
R2—1 kΩ resistor (Radio Shack 271-118)
R3—2.2 kΩ resistor (Radio Shack 271-1121)
S1—DPDT toggle switch (Radio Shack 275-1545)
U1—LM-3914 display driver (Hosfelt Electronics, 2700 Sunset
   Blvd, Steubenville, OH 43952; tel 800-524-6464)

Figure 2—Internal view of the author's LED display.

Figure 3—Why settle for one display when you can monitor forward and reflected power simultaneously? The next step for the curious experimenter is a *dual* LED display such as this one.

also available.[1] All the other components are installed on or near the panels of a plastic project box.

Ten LEDs are mounted across the front of the project box in a particular left-to-right order: The first four LEDs are green, the next five are yellow and the last one is red. When installed correctly, the LEDs will light from left to right. If the meter is used to measure reflected power, any reading past the fourth green LED indicates an SWR greater than 3:1.

I suggest that you use a straight edge and carefully mark the LED holes prior to drilling. The alternative is to create a paper template and tape it onto the front of the case as a drilling guide. Your goal is to drill a series of 10 holes in a neat horizontal row. You'll need an additional hole below the row for the **POWER** LED (DS1). Its limiting resistor, R2, connects nearby. Push each LED through its appropriate hole from the inside. A little dab of Superglue or epoxy along the rear edge will hold it in place.

You should also install the **CALIBRATE** potentiometer (R1) on the front panel, along with the **FWD/REV** switch, S1. S1 is a center-off DPDT (double-pole, double-throw) switch that is used for dc power switching and for selecting the forward or reflected source voltages from the SWR meter. Note that capacitor C2 is wired across the terminals of R1.

I placed my circuit board in the center of the box, but this will vary, depending on the type of enclosure you use. You can secure the board with epoxy, or with screws and standoffs. Placement of the wiring between the PC board and the LEDs, switch, potentiometer and jacks isn't critical.

Speaking of jacks, I used a 1/8-inch stereo phone jack for the connection to the SWR meter. A common phono plug is used for the 9-V power connector. Both jacks are installed on the rear panel.

Connecting Your SWR Meter

Remove the cover of your analog meter and look inside for two diodes. These diodes change the RF "sampled" from your coax into dc voltages for the meter(s). When you find the diodes, examine their connecting circuitry carefully. You'll discover that only one wire from each diode connects to small RF bypass capacitors. The points where these wires connect to the capacitors are where you must tap the forward and reflected source voltages.

I strongly recommend that you use a shielded cable to connect the LED display to your SWR meter. I used a two-conductor-plus-shield audio cable with an 1/8-inch stereo plug on one end. Solder the con-

ductors of the bare end of that cable to the tap points, and connect the shield braid to the meter case or circuit ground.

Calibration and Operation

Calibrating the LED meter is simple. With both the analog meters and the LED display connected in tandem, switch the LED display off (the center switch position). Place your transceiver in **CW, TUNE,** or whatever mode is necessary to achieve maximum *continuous* output. For our hypothetical example, we'll say that maximum output is 100 W. Then adjust the rig's RF power control until you measure 100 W on your analog power meter. Now, patch the LED meter into the circuit by switching S1 to the **FWD** mode. Adjust the **CALI-BRATE** control (R1) until the red LED on the far right just lights. The peak reading on the LED meter now represents 100 W output. Switch S1 to the **REV** position and you'll display reflected power.

If your analog meter reads 100 W and your LED display barely flickers, try throwing S1 to the opposite position. You may have tapped the voltage sources "backward," mistaking the forward power voltage source for reflected, and vice versa. There is no need to rewire your switch unless you've already attached your **FWD/REV** labels to the box.

SWR readings are a snap. Adjust your transceiver output for a full-scale reading in the FWD position and then switch to REV to read reflected power. Four green LEDs indicate an SWR of 3:1, three LEDs indicate 2:1, and so on.

This indicator does not automatically calibrate itself. So, *don't forget to recalibrate every time you change your transceiver output settings.*

Double Your Pleasure

The next obvious step is to build a unit that monitors both forward and reflected power *simultaneously.* We can eliminate S1 and bring both source voltages into a dual-potentiometer version of R1. Of course you need two sets of display drivers, LEDs and so forth. This time, however, another switch may have to be added to remove the analog meter completely from the circuit when the LED meter is in use.

My unit has LEDs running vertically (see Figure 3). Those on the left indicate forward power and are all green except for the top one, which is red. The LEDs on the right read reflected power. The first two are green, the second two are yellow and all the rest are red. The **POWER** LED is mounted in the center.

---

[1]A PC board for this project is available from FAR Circuits, 18N640 Field Ct, Dundee, IL 60118-9269; tel 847-836-9148 (voice and fax). Price: $3.75 plus $1.50 shipping for up to four boards. Visa and MasterCard accepted. This PC board includes mounting points for the LEDs to simplify assembly.

2235 Gum Tree Ln
Fallbrook, CA 92028
Photos by the author

QST—

Michael L. Ardai, N1IST

Build A Quickie H-T Antenna Mount

Here's a temporary antenna mount you can put together in less than one hour and use anywhere.

W hen operating portable, you often need to set up a simple antenna for your hand-held transceiver (H-T). We all know that a half-wavelength antenna works much better than the rubber dummy load that came with the radio. But walking around with a three-foot telescoping rod is rough on the H-T's antenna connector, your hand, and other people's eyes. Plus, you may need to get the antenna away from the H-T or other gear to avoid problems with nearby transceivers.

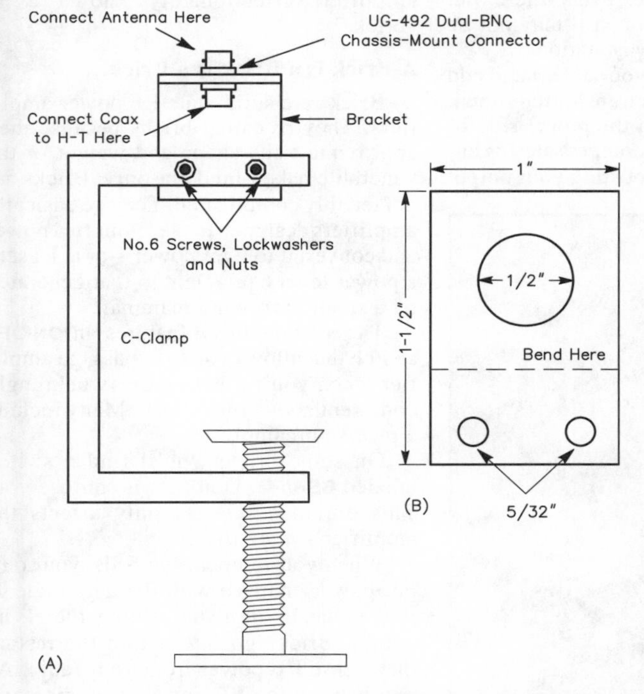

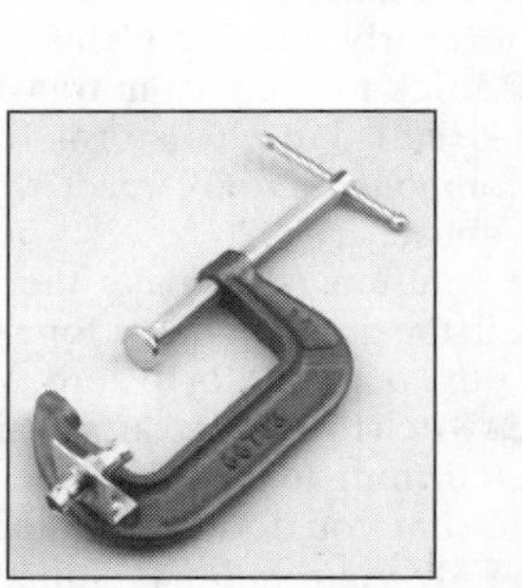

This easy-to-build temporary antenna mount uses a suitable clamp (spring clamp, **C** clamp, or even a pair of Vise-Grips) to hold a dual-BNC female chassis connector, sometimes called a UG-492 (see Figure 1A). The UG-492 resembles a double-female BNC adapter, except that it has a flange and a nut in the middle so that it can be attached to a metal panel. UG-492s are available from Ocean State Electronics, PO Box 1458, Westerly, RI 02891, tel 800-866-6626, as well as other suppliers.

Setting up and using the antenna mount is simple. Connect one end of a length of coax (with BNC plugs on both ends) to the underside of the dual-BNC connector. Connect the other end of the coax to your H-T. Your antenna of choice plugs in to the top side of the connector. Secure the clamp to a fixed object, such as a table or metal railing, and you're ready to go. I've even used the **C**-clamp version while operating railroad mobile, clamping the antenna to the curtain slide rail beneath the window of an Amtrak passenger car.

Construction

At the heart of the quickie antenna clamp is a tiny metal bracket and a couple of well-placed holes. A drill press works nicely when you're constructing the bracket, but I've also had success with a hand-held electric drill and a tapered reamer (to bring the big hole to the right size). If you have access to the proper Greenlee hole punch, all the better. Just make sure to hold the metal in a vise or with a pair of pliers while drilling. That way, if it catches on the bit and starts spinning like a saw blade, it won't shred your fingers.

Start by cutting a piece of $1/16$-inch-thick aluminum into a rectangle 1 inch by 1.5 inches (see Figure 1B). Center punch and drill two $5/32$-inch mounting holes and a half-inch hole for the bulkhead connector. Look at your clamp and figure out where to mount the metal bracket. On some clamps, like **C** clamps, bend the bracket into an **L** shape. (Use a vise or a pair of Vise-Grips to do this.) For other clamp configurations, you can leave the bracket straight. Using the bracket as a template, mark your clamp and drill one or two $5/32$-inch holes through it. Mount the dual-BNC connector on the bracket, and attach the bracket to the clamp with #6 screws, lockwashers and nuts.

When using this mount, make sure that nobody can come into contact with the antenna when you are transmitting. If you'll be transmitting with more than 5 W, it's a good idea to keep people a couple of feet away from the antenna. Also, keep the antenna at least a quarter wavelength away from metal objects that could detune it.

Figure 1—At A (not shown to scale), the quickie antenna mount shown with a common C clamp. The dual-BNC UG-492 chassis connector is installed on a small metal plate. This plate is, in turn, bolted onto the C clamp. B, a small piece of $1/16$-inch-thick aluminum is all you need to make the bracket for the dual-BNC connector.

1455 Commonwealth Ave, No. 606
Brighton, MA 02135
e-mail: ardai@maven.dnet.teradyne.com

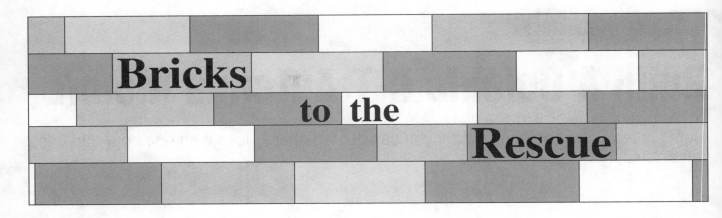

Bricks to the Rescue

If a couple of watts isn't doing the job, it may be time to turn up the heat.

By Steve Ford, WB8IMY
Assistant Managing Editor

Do you own a hand-held FM transceiver (H-T)? How about an older FM rig with only a few watts output? There's nothing wrong with running low power on VHF or UHF FM. You can accomplish a lot, especially if you have a repeater system acting as your relay.

But the day will probably arrive when you realize that you need more RF muscle. Mobile operating at the edge of a repeater's coverage area often makes this need painfully apparent. When you're trying to say something important (to you, at least), it's frustrating to know that your signal is weak into the repeater. You can bet that the folks who are listening to your transmissions are equally miffed!

"Okay, I'll say it again. Just turn right at (*scritch-scratch*) then (*ssshhhhhhh*) third traffic light, down two (bl****s until you *grrzzkqlx*). Understand?" *Right!*

Adding a mobile antenna may not solve the problem completely. Mobile antennas are more-or-less *omnidirectional*. That is, they radiate your signal in all directions at once. This is exactly what you want when you're roaming the countryside in your automobile. After all, you never know where the repeater (or any other station) may be located relative to your position. The only drawback is that your power isn't *focused* (as a flashlight beam is focused). This limits the distance your meager RF output is likely to cover.

You might encounter similar grief at home. What if you need to reach a distant repeater during an emergency? Or what if you enjoy packet, but your nearest bulletin board is 50 miles away?

With a sufficiently large *beam* antenna to concentrate your signal, your low output will go a long way. If you can't meet the challenge of a home beam, your remaining option is an omnidirectional antenna. As before, your power goes everywhere, but the gain is minimal. You still may not be able to tap those far-away stations.

If you can't rely on your antenna to add sufficient punch to your transmitted signal, you'll need to work on the *power* side of the equation. You can compensate for antenna deficiencies by boosting your output

If you can't put up a beam antenna and rotator, an omnidirectional antenna like this may be your last option. Remember that an omnidirectional antenna radiates in all directions; it can't focus your low-power signal.

to 30 W, 150 W or more. All you need is an amplifier, affectionately known as a "brick."

A Brick is a Brick is a Brick...

Bricks are solid-state RF power amplifiers. They're called bricks because they approximate the shape and weight of the venerable baked-mud masonry. Bricks are not terribly complicated. They're basically amplifiers designed to take your flea power and convert it to tiger power—or at least to a power level equivalent to that generated by a small burrowing mammal.

The average brick features an **ON/OFF** switch that allows you to bypass the amplifier when you're feeling overwhelmingly confident about your signal. Many include a receive preamplifier.

On some bricks you'll find a switch labeled **SSB/FM**. Don't let it confuse you. This ominous selector only affects the amplifier's *hang time*.

When you're operating SSB, your output power changes with the amplitude of your voice. If you're not talking, there's no output. Bricks go into action the instant they sense RF power from your radio. As you babble, the RF power is coming and going at a rapid clip. (Every time you pause to draw a breath, for example, your output drops to nearly nothing.) This causes the hapless brick to jump from transmit to receive like a toad in a hailstorm. Relays and other components don't react well to this sort of abuse.

The solution is to make the amplifier remain in the transmit mode for a second or so *after* the output falls to zero. When you flip the switch to **SSB**, the amp waits briefly before returning to the receive mode—just to make sure you don't have more to say.

On FM, your radio is supplying full output for as long as you hold down the microphone push-to-talk button. The amp stays solidly in the transmit mode until you decide to listen once again. So, you don't want the brick to hesitate before it switches to receive. Leave it in the **FM** position and the amp will bounce back to receive the instant you release the mike button. (Use the **FM** selection for packet, too.)

A Question of Power

How much output power do you really need? Thirty to 50 W is usually sufficient for mobile work. There are plenty of power amps on the market that will take 5 W or less and kick it up to 30 W. Brand new units in this power class will cost between $60 and $160, depending on how many features you want. Of course, you could run 150 W or more from your car, but I wouldn't recommend it. The intense RF is likely to drive your automotive electronics crazy.

For hearth and home, the question of power depends on what you want to do. If your goal is to put a solid signal into all the local repeaters with your omni antenna, you can probably remain at the 30-W level. But let's say you enjoy operating FM simplex and you want to expand your coverage. Maybe you've just been elected as the control station for the Klingon Language Net. This is no time to soft-peddle your signal. A jump to the 150-W class may be in order.

Of course, there is no reason why you can't combine a beam antenna with an amplifier. This is especially true of you're into satellites, contesting and so on.

Beware the urge to max your power, though. More output often means more interference to TVs, VCRs, etc. Then there is also the issue of *power supplies....*

Feeding the Brick

Bricks are hungry creatures. Most need 13.8 V pushing *lots* of current. The more power your brick generates, the more current it consumes. The average 30-W amplifier sucks down about 5 A of current. Go to 150 W and you could be talking about 22 A!

Most automobiles can supply 5 A to your brick without breaking into a sweat. Just run the amplifier's power leads directly to the battery and you'll be in business. (Make sure to use heavy-gauge wire, however.) For the intrepid souls who want

to run high-power VHF/UHF mobile, 25 A is pushing the envelope. In some cases a heavy-duty battery and alternator are required.

At home you'll need a power supply to convert 120 V ac to 13.8 V dc. This is one of the "gotchas" that pop up when you're buying a brick. A 30-W amp may seem within your budget at, say, $99, but don't forget to include the cost of a power supply if you don't own one already. You'll pay anywhere from $60 to $300, depending to how much juice you need.

When shopping for a power supply, always buy as much current capacity as you can afford. If your brick only draws 5 A, a 40-A supply may seem like overkill. Think of the future, though. If you ever decide to get a bigger amp, you'll have all the current you need. High-current power supplies are also great for running HF transceivers and other devices.

Yet Another Purchase?

An accurate VHF/UHF SWR meter is a good investment. Many amplifiers include circuits that protect them from high-SWR conditions, but why take a chance? There's nothing like the security of seeing your SWR reading every time you transmit. What if your spouse just drove a nail through your coax while hanging your mother-in-law's new portrait? Your meter will flag the problem right away. This is preferable to sitting around and wondering why no one answers your calls!

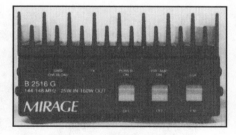

This Mirage amplifier is typical of bricks that will boost 25 W all the way to 160 W. There are other amp manufacturers as well. Check the advertising pages in *QST*.

Q **I just upgraded to General class and I'm trying to get active on the HF bands. My friends are telling me to put up a "beam" antenna, but I'm unsure. What are the advantages and disadvantages of HF beams?**

A When hams speak of beam antennas, they usually mean the venerable Yagi and quad designs. These antennas focus your signal in a particular direction (like a flashlight). Not only do they concentrate your transmitted signal, they focus your *receive* pattern as well. For example, if your beam is aimed west you won't hear many signals from the east (off the "back" of the beam).

The problems with HF beam antenna systems are size and cost. HF beams for the lower bands are *big* antennas. At about 43 feet in width, the longest element of a 40-meter coil-loaded Yagi is wider than the wingspan of a Piper Cherokee airplane. Even a 10-meter beam is about 18 feet across.

In terms of cost, a multiband (20, 15 and 10 meter) beam antenna and a 75-foot crank-up tower will set you back *at least* $2500. Then add about $500 for the antenna rotator (a beam isn't much good if you can't turn it), cables and so on. In the end, you'll rack up about $3200.

If you have that much cash burning a hole in your pocket, by all means throw it at a beam antenna and tower. The rewards will be tremendous. Between the signal-concentrating ability of the beam and the height advantage of the tower, you'll have the world at your fingertips. Even a beam antenna mounted on a roof tripod can make your signal an RF juggernaut.

In truth, only a minority of hams can afford towers these days. Those who manage to scrape together the funds occasionally find themselves the targets of angry neighbors and hostile town zoning boards. (They don't appreciate the beauty of aluminum and steel like we do!)

But do you *need* a beam and a tower to enjoy Amateur Radio? The issue isn't whether they're worthwhile (they are). The question is: Are they absolutely necessary? The answer, thankfully for most of us, is *no*. You can enjoy Amateur Radio on the HF bands with nothing more than a copper wire strung between two trees. If a beam seems out of the question at the moment, consider a dipole, loop or similar antenna. *The ARRL Antenna Book* has plenty of design suggestions.

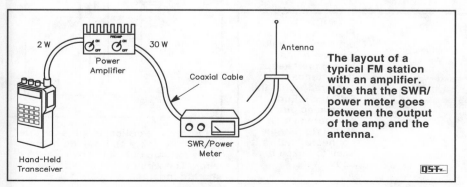

The layout of a typical FM station with an amplifier. Note that the SWR/power meter goes between the output of the amp and the antenna.

Build a Weatherproof PVC J-Pole Antenna

By Dennis Blanchard, K1YPP
143 East Rd
Hampstead, NH 03841

After you've built this antenna, you may not need anything else.

The twinlead **J**-pole antenna has been around for quite some time. It was brought into the limelight by an excellent article written by John S. Belrose, VE2CV, in the April 1982 *QST*. While John provided an excellent theoretical discussion of the **J**-pole, his article did not offer great detail on precisely how to *build* this wonderful VHF/UHF antenna.

J-poles are easy to build—which is why you see so many versions in use. (And so many articles in print!) Even so, several misconceptions exist concerning the **J**-pole. One common mistake is to assume that all you have to do is attach a piece of coaxial cable to a length of twinlead, short the bottom section and cut a notch. Not quite!

Another misconception is that once the antenna is built and tuned, you can stuff it inside a PVC tube and expect it to work flawlessly. Unfortunately for many amateurs, the PVC treatment often results in a failed antenna—unless you do it *right*.

Understanding J-Pole Construction

The **J**-pole antenna comprises two parts (see Figure 2): a ¼-wavelength matching section, which is the *entire portion below the notch*; and the radiating section, which is the ½-wavelength section *above* the notch. The portion of the antenna below the notch is most affected by the type of insulation that surrounds it. It also has the most influence on the resonance of the

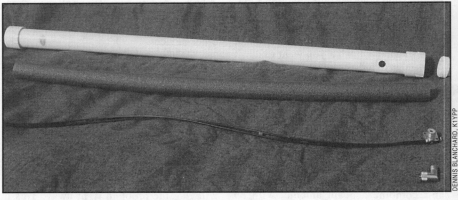

The disassembled J-pole antenna. The twinlead antenna core is shown at the bottom with the M359 right angle connector removed. It's placed within a foam insert (middle) which keeps the antenna centered within the PVC tube (top). This is the construction technique used by the JADE Products "JADE-POLE" antenna.

antenna. The radiating section is not as greatly affected by the insulation or the type of wire used. (We'll discuss this effect in a moment.)

When installed inside a PVC tube, the **J**-pole is a rugged and weather resistant antenna. If you place a **J**-pole inside PVC, however, you must *center the antenna within the tube*. One way to do this is to place the antenna inside a piece of foam insulation, preferably the type used to insulate hot-water pipes, before you slide it into the tube. If you choose a 1.5-inch PVC tube,

this insulation is often a perfect fit (see Figure 1).

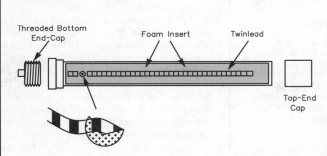

Figure 1—In this cut-away view you can see that a foam insert keeps the antenna centered within the PVC tube. End caps keep out moisture and an M-359 right-angle connector makes it easy to attach the coax.

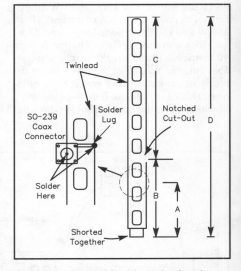

Figure 2—The critical lengths for the J-pole (see Table 1). Note the notch that's cut into one of the twinlead wires. The wires at the bottom are shorted together.

Table 1
Section Lengths (See Figure 3)

Frequency (MHz)	D, Total Length (in.)	A (in.)	B (in.)	C (in.)
50.00	160.4	3.2	48.2	112.2
51.00	157.2	3.1	47.2	110.0
52.00	154.2	3.1	46.3	107.9
53.00	151.3	3.0	45.5	105.9
54.00	148.5	3.0	44.6	103.9
146.00	54.9	1.1	16.5	38.4
222.00	36.1	0.7	10.9	25.3

Tuning Your 6-Meter J-Pole

You can use a capacitive coupling strap to easily tune your 6-meter **J**-pole for a different portion of the band. No cutting or lengthening necessary!

You can make the strap from a 1-inch wide strip of aluminum foil. Wrap the foil around the lower section of the **J**-pole and hold it in place with electrical tape. The strap doesn't connect to the antenna. It merely increases the capacitance at that point where it's positioned. By moving the strap up and down along the lower section, you'll change the resonant frequency of the antenna. This technique works best on a **J**-pole designed for 50 MHz (See Table 1).

Building a J-Pole Antenna

STEP ONE: The Decision Phase

Choose a frequency for your **J**-pole. In the case of 144 or 220 MHz bands, the antenna bandwidth is many megahertz, so this isn't a critical decision. Simply use the middle of the band, 146 MHz and 222 MHz, respectively. However, on 50 MHz the antenna will not cover the entire band without readjustment. On 50 MHz the bandwidth will be approximately 2 MHz. This means you'll need to select a frequency that corresponds to your favorite portion of the band.

Table 1 gives you the cutting lengths for the antenna sections. But before you can start cutting, you need to consider the *velocity factor* of the twinlead you're using. Despite what you may have heard, RF energy does not flow through a cable at the speed of light in a vacuum. The wire and even the insulation act to slow the speed of the wave. So, the time required for the signal to travel through a length of cable is *longer* than the time required to travel the same distance in free space. This means that the full wavelength of the signal exists in a physically *shorter* length of cable. If you cut the cable for the wavelength of the signal in free space, you'll be off the mark!

Cable manufacturers test for the velocity factor and specify it as a decimal percentage of the speed of light. The lengths shown in Table 1 are based on windowed 300-Ω twinlead with a velocity factor of 0.85. If other twinlead is used, you may need to increase or decrease the lengths proportionally. For example, if a section length is 16½ inches long and you're using TV twinlead with a typical velocity factor of 0.83, reduce the length by 2%, to 16³/₁₆ inches. (A velocity factor of 0.83 is roughly 98% of 0.85. Putting it another way, it's 2% *less* than 0.85.)

Next, decide how the antenna will be used: indoors or outdoors, fixed station or portable. If the antenna is to be used indoors, weather sealing will not be needed. If you're going to use it outdoors, apply a sealant to cover the exposed metal (the coaxial cable connection and the copper wire in the twinlead).

To limit possible RF absorption, use schedule-40 PVC. Make sure it is ultraviolet resistant as well.

Applying a sealant directly to the twinlead will change the resonant frequency of the antenna. At first this may seem a bit odd. But, believe it or not, the sealant *does* affect the velocity factor of the twinlead. If the velocity factor changes, the resonant frequency of the antenna changes. Usually it will be lower than calculated. For example, an antenna cut for 146 MHz may resonate at 142 MHz after the exposed conductors are coated with sealant—a 4% change!

STEP TWO: Cutting the Wire

Select a good grade of 300-Ω twinlead, one that is tough and will withstand abuse. Avoid TV-grade twinleads that tend to crack easily. Windowed 300-Ω twinlead is available from several *QST* advertisers.

Measure a length of twinlead that is approximately 10% longer than the amount needed. Measure it so that the notch will be cut where there is insulation all the way across between the two conductors, not at a "window."

Cut the notch. Cut only one wire; the other will run the full length of the antenna. The notch can be a small **V** or square. Make it at least a ¼ inch long. Measure from the notch to the bottom of the antenna cut off the excess wire. Strip about ¼ inch of insulation off each of the wires at the bottom. Take a small piece of bare wire and wrap several turns between the two exposed wires at the bottom. Now measure from the bottom to the top of the antenna and cut off the excess. Using a razor knife or other sharp knife, remove the insulation where the coax will be connected.

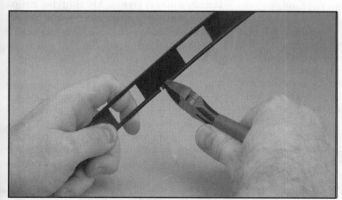

Cut the notch in only *one* of the twinlead wires. The twinlead shown in these photographs is 450 Ω. However, the same techniques apply to 300-Ω twinlead.

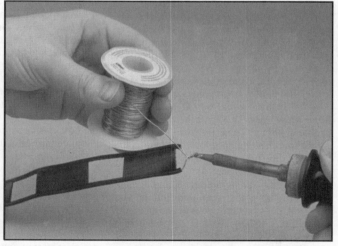

Strip the insulation from the end of the twinlead and twist the conductors together. A little solder ensures a good electrical connection.

STEP THREE: Connect the Coax

You have two choices: You can solder the coaxial cable directly to the twinlead, or install a UHF or BNC coaxial connector. A connector is highly recommended because it allows quick connections and disconnections. It also provides some strain relief, so the connection is less likely to break.

If you decide to use a connector, first file a slot in the center conductor of the connector and set the antenna wire into the slot. For the other connection, mount a solder lug on one of the holes on the connector. Wrap the lug around the wire, or slot the lug and slip the wire into it. Solder both conductors. One word of caution: Make sure the center conductor is connected to the wire that runs the full length of the antenna and that the braid side of the coax is connected to the notched side.

After you install your **J**-pole in a PVC tube, an M-359 right-angle coax connector comes in handy. It makes it much easier to bring the coax connection outside the tube. You can create a flat spot on the tube with a heat gun. Heat the PVC carefully until it softens, then press down with a narrow piece of wood. By creating this flat surface and using a small rubber gasket, you'll have a waterproof seal for the coax connector.

STEP FOUR: Test the Antenna

You can tune the antenna with an SWR analyzer, if you have one, or just an accurate SWR meter. The resonant frequency of your **J**-pole is where you'll find the lowest SWR. The 144 and 220-MHz versions have

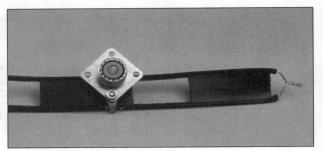

The center pin (not shown) of the SO-239 coaxial connector is soldered to the wire that runs the full length of the antenna. You can use a file to notch the pin. This will make it easier to solder. Then, attach a solder lug to the exterior of the SO-239 using the appropriate screw and nut. Strip away enough insulation to expose the wire on the opposite side of the twinlead and solder the lug in place.

a bandwidth almost twice as wide as the bands themselves, so tuning should not be necessary. The 50-MHz version may require minor tuning to make it resonant at the correct frequency (see the sidebar, "Tuning Your 6-Meter **J**-Pole"). Place the antenna in the foam core and PVC *before* you check for resonance.

If you find that you need to tweak your **J**-pole, make the matching section at the bottom slightly longer. Usually this will not be necessary.

STEP FIVE: Installation

You can install your PVC **J**-pole on a mast, or against a flat nonconductive wall. Plastic clamps for 1.5 and 1.0-inch PVC are available from JADE Products, PO Box 368, East Hampstead, NH 03826. Consider drilling a tiny hole in the bottom of the tube to allow any water to escape.

Conclusion

In his original work, VE2CV recommended placing a choke near the coaxial connection. To fashion a simple choke, take a cylindrical ferrite (Amidon 2X-43-251) and attach it to the coax at the feed point.

The **J**-pole antenna does not need radials, so it has a very narrow profile and low wind resistance. This is particularly important if you live in an area where icing is a problem. If the PVC enclosure has a threaded bottom, the antenna can be attached to a short piece of mating PVC and mounted above surrounding surfaces. **QST**

Q Can you use open-wire feed lines for VHF and UHF? If you can, why don't more hams do so?

A Yes, you can use an open-wire feed line on VHF and UHF. Although this type of line is not as efficient as it is on HF frequencies, the losses are still low.

The two wires that make up a VHF/UHF open-wire feed line must be spaced very close together in order to eliminate feed line radiation. See pages 18-2 and 24-13 in the 17th edition of *The ARRL Antenna Book*. You'll see that the impedances for such close-spaced homemade open-wire lines are lower than the typical 600 Ω seen for HF home brew lines. This isn't the most serious problem, though. The transition from balanced line to unbalanced coax down in the shack is the tricky part. You'll need some sort of balun transformer, and/or a VHF/UHF antenna tuner—an item rarely found in most stations. After going to all this trouble, you may find that you were better off using one of the newer low-loss flexible coaxial cables offered by several *QST* advertisers or Hardline. The benefit of open-wire feed lines at VHF and UHF is probably not worth the hassle.

Q Radios, antennas and other products made for UHF and above often use Type-N feed line connectors. Why?

A One of the primary tasks of any coaxial connector is to maintain a constant impedance at the point where the cable joins the radio, antenna or whatever. If the impedance changes at the connector, you have what some call an *impedance bump*. This translates to an elevated SWR and increased signal loss (transmit and receive).

The connector found on most HF and VHF transceivers is the so-called "UHF" connector (one of the worst misnomers in radio!). Although a UHF connector isn't the best choice for providing a constant impedance, any loss it causes at HF and VHF frequencies isn't worth worrying about. When you start dealing with frequencies above the 222-MHz band, however, the loss caused by a UHF connector can become significant. This is especially true if you're involved in weak-signal work or similar activities, where you need every bit of signal energy you can get.

Type N connectors are far superior when it comes to maintaining a constant imped-

ance. That's why they're preferred among hams who operate at 420 MHz and above. Type Ns have an added advantage over UHF connectors: they make watertight connections.

Q Hal Dietz, WA8ZYH, asks, "I'm hearing static that sounds for all the world like a loose antenna connection, but it occurs with several different antennas and receivers. My S meter drops about 10 dB whenever the noise appears. Could this be power line interference?"

A Power line problems can make the static sounds you describe, but your S meter would normally go *up*, not down. The fact that the S meter drops when you hear the noise does indeed sound like a loose connection. Was there anything in common between the different antennas and receivers you tried? An SWR meter? Antenna switch? Were you using the same piece of coax cable, or the same connector?

Look for this type of "commonality." If it is a loose connection is the culprit, you can often find it by wiggling and moving things about.

A "Universal" VHF/UHF Antenna

When considering your antenna options, don't overlook the discone!

By Dave Miller, NZ9E
7462 Lawler Ave
Niles, IL 60714-3108

Everyone would like to own a *universal* antenna. It would cover all VHF/UHF bands in a reasonably small package and wouldn't require special tuning. Does such an antenna exist? As a matter of fact, it does—and it's not a high-tech, only-available-to-the-military device.

As the song goes, "Everything Old Is New Again" and the venerable *discone* antenna is no exception. It's been reassessed, simplified and built to withstand the elements more successfully with the passage of time. The one that I purchased is made of stainless-steel radiating elements, mixed with aluminum and other rust-resistant hardware. This design should guarantee a long life even in bitter Chicago winters. Check the advertising pages of *QST* and you'll find discone antennas sold by several manufacturers.

Like many discones, the one I'm using is marketed primarily to scanner enthusiasts for receiving use. Even so, chances are good that the discone you've found will function as a transmitting antenna, too. My antenna is also rated at 200 W for *transmitting* on all ham bands between 50 and 1300 MHz. This makes it a natural for the VHF/UHF FM crowd.

Dissecting the Discone

The name discone comes from the antenna's basic appearance: a disk with a cone beneath it. In its modern versions, the disk is replaced by spikes formed in a circular pattern around the top. More spikes are added at steep angles, making up the "skirt" or cone around its base. (Birds love this design. It gives them an incredible number of places to sit.)

The standard discone exhibits about the same gain as a ground-plane antenna. It's vertically polarized and it performs over a very broad frequency range.

The completed discone is very light (around 2 pounds), and quite compact in size (about 34 inches in diameter at the widest part of the skirt, and 58½ inches tall). For the amount of spectrum it covers, it's a featherweight champion!

My antenna came with a type N coaxial connector at its base, but can be adapted to a UHF connector (for use with a PL-259) if desired. Other discones may be equipped with SO-239 connectors. Using a constant-impedance N connector is still the best choice, however.

I've found that my antenna is usable on all amateur bands from 50 to 450 MHz (which are the limits of my present transmitting capabilities). I've routed the coax from my discone through a five-position coaxial cable switch in the shack. The first four switch positions are used to connect the antenna to my transceivers. Discones are also terrific receive-only antennas for VHF/UHF scanning, so the fifth position connects the antenna to my 60 to 905-MHz Yaesu FRG-9600 scanner. All in all, I've ended up with a double-duty "universal" antenna for my time and effort! As another song asks, "Who could ask for anything more?"

The Importance of Transmission Line

A broadband antenna like the discone

Peter Budnik, KB1HY, examines construction of discone antenna.

may not exhibit a low SWR on all frequencies within its range. If the SWR happens to be somewhat above 2:1 on your frequency of choice, you can still operate effectively—as long as you use low-loss transmission line.

Low-loss transmission line is always a good investment. You can write that one in stone! Many hams shy away from these low-loss cables, partly because of the cost, but also due to the fact that low-loss cable is usually more difficult to work with. Even if only half of your total cable run is comprised of low-loss line, that's still preferable to using higher-loss coax throughout. Because feed-line losses increase with frequency, the losses from "regular" cables can become very high indeed.

In real terms, what does this mean? Well, even the low-loss cables (those that are readily available to the average ham), dissipate about 2.5 dB of your signal per hundred feet of line at 400 MHz. This means that your 10-W, 450-MHz signal is reduced to about 5 W at the antenna. This presumes that you're using 100 feet of coax between the radio and the antenna, and that the SWR at the input of the coax is 1:1.

But consider this: If you use RG-8X cable instead (which shows a much higher loss at these frequencies), only *1.5 W* reaches the antenna under the same 100-foot assumption. If the SWR is something other than 1:1—which it could be with a discone—the loss becomes even worse!

A similar amount of loss occurs on *received signals*. Transmitter power loss can often be compensated with an amplifier in the shack, but it's not nearly that easy to make up for received signal loss. A preamplifier is one prescription for the problem, but you must install it at the antenna. In addition, you must be able to automatically bypass it whenever you transmit; not always an easy task. Dollar for dollar, you're much better off buying decent coax than sinking your money into RF amplifiers and preamps.

Conclusion

There's little doubt that if you spend all of your time on a single band, you're probably better off with a single-band antenna. But if you want the flexibility to explore the other parts of the spectrum available to you, consider the newly found-again discone.

Build Your Own 2-Meter Beam!

All you need is a few dollars and a couple of hours to build this simple directional antenna.

By Dale L. Botkin, NØXAS
13421 Polk St
Omaha, NE 68137
e-mail: dbotkin@probe.net

NEW HAM COMPANION

If you're like most new hams, you probably own a 2-meter hand-held FM transceiver (H-T) that came equipped with a flexible "rubber duck" antenna. These antennas are fine for many portable and mobile applications, but they often perform like rubber dummy loads when you need greater range. If you live far from your favorite repeater, like I do, you probably have to use your H-T's highest power setting to reach it—assuming you can reach it at all.

The solution is a better antenna, but what kind? I wanted to chat with a friend who lives in another town. Not only was my rubber duck completely inadequate, my homebrew **J**-pole antenna didn't help, either. What I needed was an antenna that would focus my H-T's meager output in a particular direction. In other words, I needed a *beam*.

Too Difficult?

Like most people, I had always assumed that beam antennas were tricky to build and tough to tune. I also figured that any beam with less than three or four elements wasn't worth my time. Most of the ads and plans I saw were for big, 9 to 22-element antennas with tons of gain.

You can certainly spend a lot of time designing, building, and optimizing a large beam antenna from scratch. (You'll at least save some money!) But I discovered that a smaller, simpler beam offers more than enough performance for casual operating. The big antennas are great if you're trying to work 2-meter SSB, satellites and so on. To expand the range of your FM voice or packet station, however, this easy *quad* antenna is just the ticket!

After finding plans in the *ARRL Antenna Book* for a two-element quad antenna, I made a quick trip around the house to see what materials I had on hand. Because we had recently completed a new deck, I had lots of scrap wood, including some pieces that were about 1¹/₂×³/₈ inches and a little under two feet long. They were perfect for the job. I did have to make a trip to the hardware store for some #12 copper wire (I removed the insulation from #12 electrical wiring). You could use #8 aluminum wire instead (clothesline wire), but it is much

more difficult to solder. Using larger wire, or insulated wire, will affect the resonant frequency of the antenna. The dimensions described in the text are for #12 bare wire.

Construction

Cut one piece of wire to 85¹/₂ inches in length. This will become the *reflector* element. Make a 90° bend in this wire 10⁵/₈ inches from one of the ends, then measure 21³/₈ inches from this bend and make another 90° bend. Measure another 21³/₈ inches and make another bend, another 21³/₈ inches, another bend. You'll eventually wind up with a square 21³/₈ inches on each side (see Figure 1). Solder

the ends of the wire together to complete the square.

Now cut another piece of wire to 81¹/₂ inches in length. Bend it as I've just described, but use 20⁵/₈ inches for each side. Start 9⁷/₈ inches from the end to make sure you wind up with the ends in the middle of one side, just like the other loop. You'll wind up with a gap of an inch or so between the two ends (see Figure 1). *Don't* solder the ends together! This is the driven element and the gap is the point where we'll attach the coaxial cable.

Now for the supports. Lay one wood support across each loop (see Figure 2) and mark the points where the wires cross. Cut

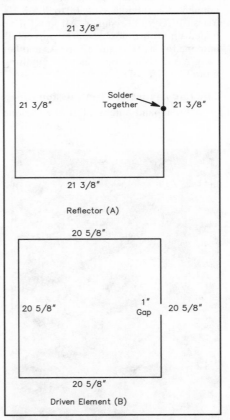

Figure 1—When you're finished bending the reflector wire, you should have a square 21³/₈ inches on each side (A). The driven element is 20⁵/₈ inches on each side with a small gap (B).

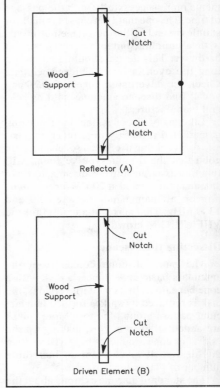

Figure 2—Lay the wood supports on top of the wire loops and draw lines where the wires cross the supports. Cut deep notches along the lines and use epoxy cement to glue the wires into the notches.

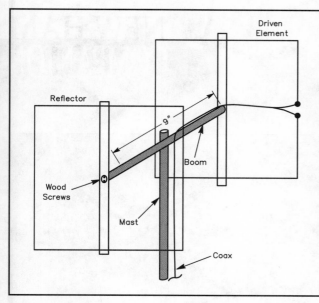

Figure 3—The finished quad should look like this. The boom is attached to either support with two small wood screws. (Other methods can be used as well.) The coaxial cable is routed along the boom and down the mast. The mast can be metal, wood, PVC or whatever suits your fancy.

Parts List

3 1¹/₂×³/₈×24-inch wood supports
#12 copper wire (no insulation)
Epoxy cement
Coaxial cable
Small wood screws
BNC connector (Use a PL259 connector [or a BNC-to-PL259 adapter] if you intend to use the antenna with a mobile or base radio.)

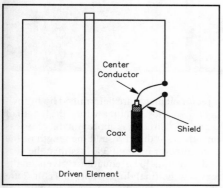

Figure 4—Strip the end of the coaxial cable to expose the center conductor and the shield braid. Solder the center conductor to one side of the driven-element loop and the braid to the other.

notches in the supports and slide the wires into the notches. Center the supports in both loops. For the driven element, make sure the wood support is *parallel* to the side where the coax will attach. Use epoxy cement to hold the wires in the notches.

When the glue dries, the loops can be attached to the boom (the third piece of wood stock). Secure the driven element (the open loop) at one end with screws or glue (Figure 3). Tack the other loop onto the boom about 9 inches behind it. Use small tacks, tape or some other means to hold this loop in place temporarily. You may need to move it soon. (More about this in a moment.)

All that's left is the feed line. Strip back the outer insulation from the last couple of inches of coax and separate the center conductor and shield braid. Solder the shield to one side of the driven element and the center conductor to the other side (Figure 4). Install a BNC connector on the other end of

the coax, and connect the coax to your H-T.

SWR Adjustment

If you can get your hands on a VHF/UHF SWR meter that's capable of making measurements at low power levels, take a few moments to adjust your quad. Set up the antenna away from nearby metal objects. Transmit at 146.52 MHz and check the SWR. If the SWR is 1.5:1 or less, secure the reflector loop permanently and leave the antenna alone. If not, move the reflector loop in one direction or the other, stopping to make more measurements. As soon as you reach the 1.5:1 SWR point (or lower), stop. You're ready to fly!

Many factors affect the resonant frequency of an antenna, especially at VHF. The dimensions I recommend were developed using antenna-modeling software, verified by testing in the ARRL Lab. However, your mileage may vary. The type of wood, the way the antenna is attached to the wood and the size of the wire can affect the tuning. The dimensions are fairly critical; a ¹/₄-inch error will change the resonant frequency by about 500 kHz. Most H-Ts are very tolerant of high SWR, so the antenna will work even if it is not perfect. If you do use an SWR meter to measure the antenna's performance, you may want to adjust the length of the driven element slightly to achieve resonance in the part of the band you use most. Lengthen the antenna by ¹/₄ inch to lower the resonant frequency; shorten the antenna to raise the resonant point.

Bear in mind that the signal direction will be toward the driven element. In other words, you want the loop with the coaxial connection to point toward your target. The other loop is called the reflector, because it does just that—it reflects RF energy toward the driven element.

Results

The first time I tested my new antenna, I simply held it over my head and aimed it roughly west from my office. My target was Fremont, Nebraska, where my friend Joe lives. It's about 25 miles distant, over hilly terrain, and my office is in a depression surrounded by paging-system towers, a police station, a fire station, and business-band radio antennas! I've never been able to raise the Fremont repeater with my H-T, even with a J-pole (and it's a struggle even with my 15-W mobile rig).

Dialing in the frequency of the Fremont repeater, I pushed the PTT switch and announced my call. I heard the repeater squelch tail loud and clear! Another ham answered! But wait—I had the frequency wrong! This wasn't the Fremont repeater on 146.76 MHz. I had hit the Lincoln machine, about 20 miles farther out, on 146.67 MHz! I changed frequencies and tried the Fremont repeater. Even at my H-T's lowest power setting, I hit the repeater loud and clear.

If you install the antenna outdoors, treat the supports with a wood preservative or several coats of spar varnish. You'll want to use a secure means to attach the supports to the boom if you expect the antenna to survive high wind gusts. Use low-loss coax if you install the antenna more than 20 feet from your station.

You can point the quad in the direction of your favorite repeater and leave it. If you want to reach stations at other points of the compass, you'll need an antenna rotator. An inexpensive TV antenna rotator is more than adequate for the job. You'll find used rotators selling at hamfest fleamarkets and elsewhere for peanuts.

Conclusion

I've been really impressed with the performance of this little antenna, all the more so since it was so incredibly easy and cheap to build. If you're tired of being the weak signal on the band, or if you want to try to see just how many repeaters you can hit, it's a joy. You can also use it for simplex contacts over a much greater range than you'd ever think possible. It's just amazing what a couple of watts of VHF FM can do with the right antenna! QST.

A Five-Element Quad Antenna for 2 Meters

By Jim Reynante, KD6GLF
PO Box 27856
San Diego, CA 92198

NEW HAM COMPANION

If your station is located on the fringe of the repeater's coverage area, you've come to the right place. Why not build a 5-element quad antenna? It may be just the thing you and your radio need to provide a reliable communication link with the outside world.

My own location provides me with spotty coverage to the local repeater, and I knew that I needed a beam antenna to establish solid communication. I had seen designs for quad antennas in various books including *The ARRL Handbook*, yet I wondered how easily and inexpensively I could put one together for 2 meters. I chose low cost and simple construction as the main design goals. As a result, I ended up with an effective antenna that has the following features:

❏ A forward gain of at least 11 dBi

❏ An SWR of 2:1 or better throughout most of the 2-meter band

❏ Total construction time under two hours using simple hand tools

❏ Total cost less than $8 (depending on where you purchase your materials)

"What, Me Build a Beam Antenna?"

I made sure that building this antenna would be simple. In so doing, I practically guaranteed that I'd be able to complete the project! (I'm the last person that should be building an antenna. I'm typically "all thumbs" when it comes to construction practices.)

As you can see from the photograph, the antenna uses wood for the boom and dowels for the wire spreaders. It's oriented in the classic diamond configuration. The all-wood design allowed me to use simple hand tools for its construction, and the total cost for materials was just under $8 (see Table 1).

Construction

Before beginning construction, you must first determine the physical dimensions of each of the antenna's elements. The five elements of this quad antenna are the reflector, a driven element and three directors. The reflector is at one end of the boom, followed in order by the driven element and the first, second and third directors. Maximum radiation is along the line of the boom, in the direction of the third director.

Because the director element is arranged into a square loop one wavelength long, the actual length varies from the naturally resonant length. The lengths of the reflector, driven, and first director loop elements can be computed using the following formulas:

If you want an 11-dBi-gain beam antenna for less than $1 per dB, here it is!

$$L_{Reflector} = 1071 / F_0$$
$$L_{Driven} = 998 / F_0$$
$$L_{Director1} = 973 / F_0$$

where:

$L_{Reflector}$ = Length of the reflector element (in feet)

L_{Driven} = Length of the driven element (in feet)

$L_{Director1}$ = Length of first director element (in feet)

F_0 = Center frequency (in MHz)

The lengths of the second and third director elements are determined by following a 3% series. In other words, the length of the second director is approximately 3% less than the first director, and the length of the third director is about 3% less than the second director. [The equations given in the text and the final dimensions in Table 2 are based on an optimized design for this antenna modeled at ARRL HQ with the *NEC2* computer program.—*Ed.*] Table 2 shows the element lengths, spreader lengths, and element spacings.

With the element dimensions in hand, it's time to get started. Begin by preparing the boom. I decided to use wood for construction because of its low cost, wide availability and ease of use. When building antennas using wood, be sure to select pieces that are well-seasoned and free of knots or damage.

Start with an 8-foot section of 2×2. Cut a 2-foot section from one end. (Don't discard it. It'll be used to make a "shorty" mast section.) Starting from 2.5 inches from one end of the boom, carefully measure and mark the locations for each of the spreader

Table 1
Materials List

Quantity	Description	Typical Cost
1	2×2×8-inch wood piece	$1.99
10	⅝-inch dowels, 30 inches long	$2.10
34 feet	#10 AWG bare copper wire	$3.06

Table 2
Lengths and Spacing

Element	Element Length (inches)	Spreader Length (inches)	Spacing from end of boom
Reflector	88	31.25	2.5 inches
Driven	82	29	19.5 inches
1st Director	80	28.5	32.5 inches
2nd Director	78	27.75	48.5 inches
3rd Director	76	27	67.5 inches

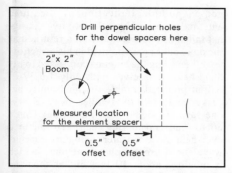

Figure 1—Close-up look at the boom shows mounting the hole offsets used for the dowel spacers.

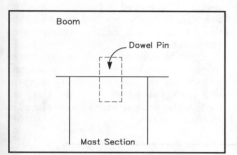

Figure 2—Use a 1-inch scrap piece from one of the dowels as a joint pin to secure the boom to the "shorty" mast section.

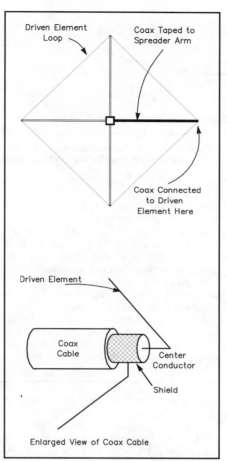

Figure 3—Feed the side corner of the driven element for vertical polarization.

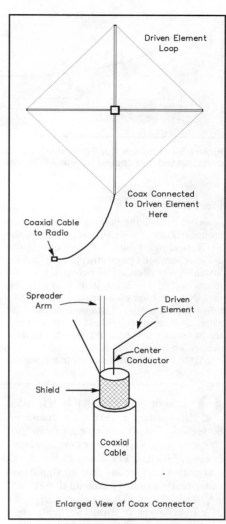

Figure 4—Feed the bottom corner of the driven element for horizontal polarization.

arms. Each element requires two dowels to form the cross-arm assembly, so offset the hole locations by ¹/₂ inch (see Figure 1). A drill press is ideal for drilling the holes, but an acceptable job can be done with a power hand drill. Be sure to mark which end is the reflector end and which end is the director.

Now carefully measure and mark the wood dowels that are used for the element spreaders. Use the dimensions in Table 2. You'll need two dowels cut to the same length for each element. After cutting the dowels, mount each pair into the appropriate hole locations on the boom, but don't glue them yet! Visually inspect the location of the spreaders on the boom. If everything's in place correctly, you should see the spreaders taper in length from the reflector end to the director end. Once you've verified the placement of the spreaders, you can secure them to the boom. Use a weather-proof glue or epoxy that is nonsoluble. Use a small saw or hobbyist's motor tool to carefully notch the ends of the dowels. These notches will be used to secure the wire elements.

Mount the boom to the remaining 2-foot length of 2×2. I used a simple butt-end joint reinforced by a small 1-inch long wood pin fashioned from a piece of scrap material from one of the dowels (Figure 2). Simply drill a small hole in the top of the mast about ¹/₂-inch-long and the same diameter as your doweling. Drill a corresponding hole in the boom. Glue or epoxy the pin into the mast and boom to form the joint. For further reinforcement, you could also fashion gusset plates made from triangular pieces of ¹/₄-inch plywood and attach them to both sides of the boom.

That completes the construction of the main antenna structure. Now, carefully measure and cut the wire used for each of the five elements. *Do not* use insulated wire! (Or at least remove the insulation.) Once the wire elements have been cut, it's time to mount them to the spreader arms to form the closed loops.

The reflector and director elements are strung around their respective element spreaders and held in place by soldering the ends together. At this point, you must decide whether to use horizontal or vertical polarization. The feedpoint of the driven element determines the polarization. Use corner feed on the side if you want vertical polarization (Figure 3), or attach the transmission line to the bottom corner for horizontal polarization (Figure 4). I opted for vertical polarization since I wanted to use it for FM and repeater work. If you want to try your hand at SSB and CW work, choose horizontal polarization. Attaching the transmission-line to the driven element may prove to be a little tricky, so an extra pair of hands

may help. I found it useful to tape the transmission-line spreader arm to hold it in place while I soldered it to the driven element.

I used RG-8X for my setup since I only had a short run (less than 20 feet) to my shack. For installations with longer runs, I recommend using standard RG-8 coax or better to deliver every dB you can to the antenna. Apply a silicone or similar sealer to the exposed end of the coax to prevent the possibility of moisture seeping into the line. The wood surfaces should also be varnished to help protect them from the weather.

This five-element quad is a real performer. If you build the antenna as shown, the computer model predicts 11 dBi gain and a front-to-back ratio of 20 dB. ARRL Lab measurements confirmed the computer-predicted antenna pattern.

You may wish to read further about tuning adjustments in *The ARRL Handbook*. It describes how to check the antenna with a field-strength meter, or by using a separate receiver in conjunction with a dipole antenna.

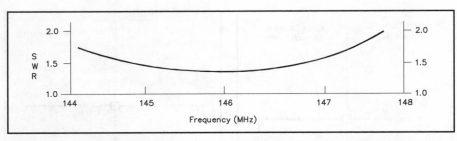

Figure 5—Here are the SWR readings the author obtained. When the antenna was constructed and tested by the ARRL Lab, even better SWR results were obtained.

Field Results

After connecting the quad to my radio, I rechecked the SWR. Figure 5 shows the SWR readings I obtained throughout the 2-meter band. It's interesting to note that the lowest SWR occurs just below the center frequency of 146 MHz. This is due to the fact that I cut the elements a little long to allow for trimming. I suggest you do the same. Shortening the wires is simply a matter of cutting off the extra length and then deepening the notches in the dowels.

After I had established contact with a friend on the local repeater, we decided to try the quad by switching to simplex operation. (In the past, he and I were unable to communicate directly.) I punched in 146.535 MHz on my radio and rotated the quad toward his station. I nervously called him. After waiting for what seemed like an eternity, I heard his answer! We proceeded to carry on a casual ragchew discussing antennas, current events and so on without tying up the local repeater. (The joys of simplex!) Before signing off, I slowly rotated my quad while he talked in order to

get an audible indication of the quad antenna's side and back directivity. His signal faded as expected, and then returned as the quad once again pointed in his direction.

When using the antenna connected to my hand-held transceiver with only 1.5 W of output power, I'm able to consistently access repeaters 40 to 50 miles away. Everyone says my signal is full quieting. That's not too bad, considering I had been unable to even hear those repeaters using my quarter-wavelength ground-plane antenna—which is mounted about 10 feet higher than the quad.

Summary

I've been enjoying this antenna for the past few months without any problems whatsoever. I've logged a couple of hundred contacts, both simplex and via repeaters. I've also used it with equal success for operating packet.

Don't be disheartened if you happen to live in a community with difficult antenna restrictions. In addition to being inexpensive and simple to construct, this quad antenna is also compact enough to be placed in an attic! — QST-

---

Q Carolyn Sullivan, KE4CHI, asks, "I'm using a vertical antenna on 80 meters. I'm able to communicate just fine over long distances, but my local coverage is lacking. The hams in the North Carolina ARES net say that my signals are consistently weak. What could cause this?"

A The difficulty may be in the type of antenna you're using. Vertical antennas feature *low-angle* radiation patterns. This is ideal for long-distance communications, but nearby contacts may suffer. Your signal may be skipping over the local hams.

As an experiment, string up a horizontal wire dipole antenna between a couple of trees about 30 feet off the ground. Check into your net again and see if you receive better signal reports. A dipole has a higher-angle radiation pattern than a vertical. Perhaps your local communication coverage will improve with the dipole. The alternative is to increase the strength of your signal by using a linear amplifier.

Q George Alich, WØLNT, asks, "I have a strange problem with my 10-meter Yagi antenna. I recently moved my TV antenna to within 15 feet of the Yagi and now I hear an annoying hum on 10 meters. The hum is especially loud at 16-kHz increments throughout the band. When I rotate my Yagi, the interference changes. It stops altogether when I turn the TV off. Any ideas?"

A It sounds like your 10-meter Yagi is picking up signals from your television. The signal you hear every 16 kHz is probably the TV's horizontal sweep oscillator at 15,750 Hz. This problem is more common

on 80 meters than 10. There are a couple of things you can try.

Install a high-pass filter (Radio Shack 15-579) at the antenna input of your TV set. It may work in reverse to prevent the signals radiated by your television (those below 54 MHz) from appearing on the TV antenna feed line.

If you're using coaxial cable to feed your TV antenna, wrap several turns around an FT-240-43 toroid core to create a common-mode choke. As with the high-pass filter, do this at the antenna input of your TV.

The last, most obvious, suggestion is to move your TV antenna away from your Yagi. If possible, try doubling the distance (mount it 30 feet away). For more helpful suggestions, see the ARRL book *Radio Frequency Interference: How to Find It and Fix It*.

Q A strange thing is happening with my antenna tuner. I'm running it with an open-wire feed line and using the built-in 4:1 balun. On some bands it's fine. On others, I notice that the SWR increases slowly while I'm transmitting. Any advice?

A Yes—when you see that slowly rising SWR, stop transmitting! It sounds like the core of your 4:1 balun is heating up. The SWR is probably quite high on the band in question, and some hefty RF currents are present in your feed line as a result. For the sake of compact design and cost savings, some tuners use relatively small 4:1 baluns to provide an interface between the open-wire line and the tuner's matching network. A small balun can't dissipate much heat. Under high SWR conditions, its tiny ferrite core saturates. The temperature increases

and the electrical characteristics of the balun change (that's when you see the rising SWR reading). If you keep transmitting, the insulation on the wires that surround the core can melt.

Contact your tuner manufacturer to see if you can replace the balun with a larger one. If a larger balun isn't available from the manufacturer, you can make one yourself. Several *QST* advertisers sell 4:1 balun kits. Be careful, though. You're looking for an *internal* 4:1 balun, not the type that you install at the antenna.

Q Steve Heimerl, KF9KH, asks, "When I use the repeater autopatch to call my wife at work, I'm often placed on hold. Her company uses 'music on hold' and, as a result, music is transmitted over the repeater while I'm waiting. Is this legal?"

A It is illegal to transmit any kind of music on Amateur Radio frequencies. Even so, the FCC takes the issue of intent into account in situations like these. A question similar to yours appeared several months ago, but with a somewhat different spin. (It involved music heard in the background during transmissions from a special-event station.) In your instance as well as the previous one, it appears that the music was not being transmitted intentionally.

The FCC expects us to avoid incidental music transmissions, but they recognize that this isn't always possible. The next time you call your wife's workplace, ask them not to put you on hold. If they do, and she doesn't come to the phone soon, terminate the autopatch and try again later.

Two 2-Meter Antennas

◆

Try these simple, effective antennas for home or portable use. Build them yourself for less than $20!

◆

By Chester S. Bowles,
AA1EX
RFD 2, Box 335L
Sharon, NH 03458

So you've purchased your first 2-meter hand-held transceiver (or "H-T," as they're often called). Congratulations! By now you've learned how to program its memories with frequencies, repeater splits, CTCSS tones and so on. You've also learned how to use most of those nifty features your H-T includes. I'll bet you've even followed Joel Kleinman's advice on improving your signal with a better H-T antenna. (see "Better than a Rubber Duck," *QST*, March 1993.)

Now you want to use your radio at home. You'd like to hit some of the more distant repeaters and enjoy simplex conversations with your friends. It won't be long, however, before you discover that your H-T antenna doesn't do the job when it comes to covering a wide area. To improve your range, you need a permanent *outdoor* antenna—one with performance and gain that exceeds even the best rubber ducks.

No doubt you've looked at the various base-station antennas on the market. They're great, aren't they? Most commercial antennas are well-made, have excellent performance characteristics and are very durable. But they have a big disadvantage: They can be very expensive. Don't be discouraged, though. VHF antennas are easy and inexpensive to build. Building your own antenna also gives you an opportunity to put some of your textbook theory to practical use.

You'll find that antenna theory is a favorite topic of conversation among hams of all ages. I've often discussed antennas with my brother-in-law, Pete, WA1FEU (now a Silent Key). In fact, Pete formulated the concepts for the antenna designs you're about to see. I simply polished the ideas a bit and tested them in the field. The results are a couple of inexpensive and easy-to-build antennas!

Start with a Base-Station Antenna

The base-station antenna is essentially a vertical dipole using PVC pipe and stiff wire. Its somewhat *stealthy* design offers excellent performance without attracting too much attention from neighbors! (It also pleases spouses who object to highly visible antennas.)

I recommend ¾-inch PVC pipe for this antenna because of its inherent strength, and because it's large enough to accept any coaxial cable you're likely to use. Unfortunately, PVC pipe is only available in 10-foot lengths in many areas of the country. I say "unfortunately" because you will need less than half that length for the antenna. On the other hand, you'll have plenty left over to make a second antenna for a friend. You will also need a ¾-inch PVC **T** connector.

I used 10-gauge galvanized wire for the dipole elements. Galvanized wire may not have the best electrical characteristics, but it is weatherproof and is easy to work with. Copperweld is another obvious choice, but I didn't happen to have any of it lying around. Some of your ham friends may have suitable wire they'd be happy to give you.

The only other materials required are the ⅛- × ⅝-inch nuts and matching bolts to secure the dipole elements to the PVC pipe. You'll also need PVC cement for gluing the pipes together. You may want to have silicone caulking or coax sealant to make the antenna weatherproof.

The first step is to cut and form the dipole elements. Using the formula for determining the length of a dipole (468/f MHz), and assuming 146.0 MHz as the center frequency, I determined that the total length should be approximately 38-39 inches. To make sure you end up with enough material, start with two pieces of wire, each 21 inches long.

Straighten each wire as much as possible. Then, form a loop at one end. The loop should be just large enough to fit over the ⅛-inch bolts.

Prepare the coaxial feed line by separating the braid from the center insulator and stripping about ¾ inch of insulation from the center conductor. It's helpful to solder lugs onto the coax braid and center conductor. These lugs should be sized to allow them to fit over the ⅛-inch bolts (see Fig 1).

Dipoles are most effective when the feed

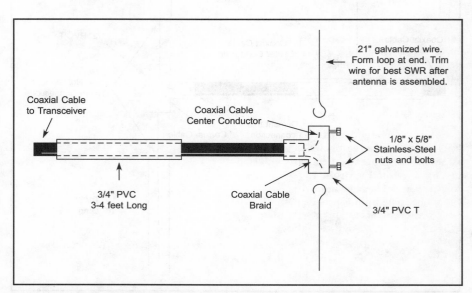

Fig 1—Construction diagram of the 2-meter base-station antenna. Note the loops at the ends of the radiating elements. These attach to the braid and center conductor of the coaxial cable through the use of stainless-steel nuts and bolts.

In the figure:
- Coaxial Cable to Transceiver
- Coaxial Cable Center Conductor
- 21" galvanized wire. Form loop at end. Trim wire for best SWR after antenna is assembled.
- 1/8" x 5/8" Stainless-Steel nuts and bolts
- 3/4" PVC 3-4 feet Long
- Coaxial Cable Braid
- 3/4" PVC T

line runs perpendicular to the radiating elements for at least ½ wavelength. This means our vertical dipole needs to have a perpendicular run of at least three feet. For my installation, I cut a piece of PVC piping four feet in length. This allowed sufficient perpendicular length and it also provided a solid connection to the eave of my house. The coax should be fed through the PVC pipe at this time, but *do not* glue the pipe to the **T** connector yet.

Drill two mounting holes through the top of the PVC **T**. These holes should be about ½ inch from each end at the top of the **T**. The dipole wires are fed through the ends of the **T** and are attached using the bolts and nuts.

The next step is the most difficult. One of the coaxial cable wires and one of the dipole wires must be attached to each of the ⅛-inch bolts. This connection must be made *inside* the **T**. It is not easy to get the solder lugs and the dipole wires to fit over the bolts—much less attach and tighten the nuts—in such a confined space. Perseverance is the only answer. But, once you are done, the entire assembly can be sealed with silicone caulking or coax seal to render it weatherproof.

Once the mechanical connections are made, the four-foot length of PVC piping can be glued to the **T**. I was concerned about insects or moisture getting into the antenna assembly. So, as an added precaution, I

caulked the cable-entrance end of the pipe.

The final step is to tune the antenna. Use a VHF SWR/power meter of known accuracy. Trim both ends of the dipole in *very* short increments until you reach the lowest SWR point at 146 MHz. Be careful! Even a quarter inch can make a *big* difference!

After my antenna was tuned, I mounted it on the eave of my house using galvanized clamps and screws. You may want to try a similar installation. My antenna has been in use for more than a year. It has proven to be very effective and has weathered the winter ice and snow extremely well.

When You Need Something Portable...

Once the base antenna was up and working, Pete and I turned our discussions to lightweight, portable antennas for H-Ts. Of course, there are countless examples of collapsible vertical whips on the market, but we wanted a full-length antenna that avoided the use of loading coils. We also wanted to avoid the mechanical strain that long vertical antennas place on standard H-T antenna connectors.

Using the same concepts employed in the vertical-dipole base antenna, I developed a portable version using smaller and lighter materials. For the portable antenna, I chose ½-inch PVC pipe. Strength is not an issue in this case. Also, the smaller diameter is perfect for RG58/U coax.

Construction is extremely simple and re-

quires *no connecting hardware*. Starting with a 12-foot length of coax, prepare one end by separating the braid from the center insulator and then stripping about ½ inch of the insulation from the center conductor.

Next, cut two 20-inch lengths of wire to serve as the radiating elements of the antenna. I chose 14-gauge stranded automotive wire, but most any wire will work. The key point is that it needs to be flexible and lightweight. Solder one of these wires to the center conductor of the coax. Solder the other wire to the coax braid.

Once the wires are soldered, feed them through a ½-inch PVC **T** connector. The coax must enter the **T** from the bottom opening and one radiating element must exit from each side of the connector. I used silicone caulking to hold the wires in place inside the connector. Straighten the wires and check the SWR at 146 MHz. Do whatever trimming is necessary to lower the SWR as much as possible.

Cut three 18-inch lengths of ½-inch PVC pipe. Thread the coax through one of the pipes. Attach this pipe to the bottom of the

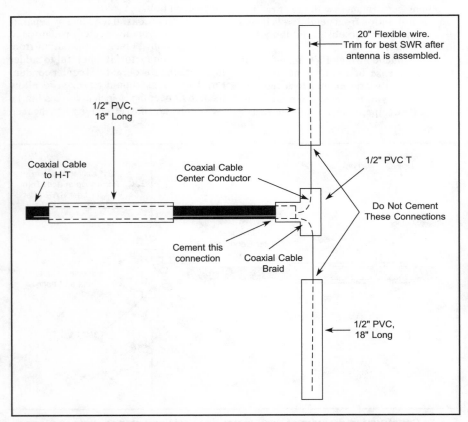

Fig 2—Construction diagram of the *portable* 2-meter antenna. The radiating elements are supported by two lengths of PVC pipe. These pipes detach easily for packing.

A carved wooden owl is all that's necessary to hold this portable 2-meter antenna on the author's deck railing.

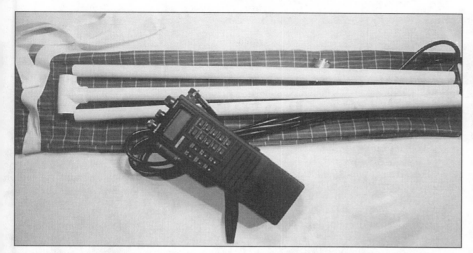

Fig 3—Here is the portable antenna completely disassembled and ready to go! It collapses to a package just 18 inches long and 3 inches wide. (*photos by the author*)

packing in my carry-on bag or my back pack. My wife was kind enough to make a small pouch for storing the antenna, which makes packing even neater (see Fig 3).

Best of all, this portable antenna works extremely well. It takes just seconds to assemble and can be temporarily mounted almost anywhere. I carry a small roll of tape so I can attach the antenna to the windows or balconies of hotel rooms. When hiking and camping, the antenna can easily be supported by tree branches, rocks, or even the ridge pole of a tent.

Conclusion

Total construction cost for my two antennas, including coax and connectors, was less than $20. Construction time was about 45 minutes for the base antenna and about 30 minutes for the portable antenna.

It is certainly obvious that these two projects do nothing to further antenna theory. However, they prove once again that antennas do not need to be complex or expensive to work well. Of course, I built my antennas for 2 meters, but the design will work equally well on UHF. Enjoy!

QST

T connector using PVC cement. Slip the radiating elements through the other two pipes as shown in Fig 2, but *do not cement these pipes to the T.* Simply push them into the openings for a snug fit. Keeping them loose allows you to disassemble the antenna when traveling.

My antenna folds to a package 18 inches long and 3 inches wide. It weighs just 13 ounces. This is a perfect size for

---

Radio Tips: Mobile Grounding

Any part of your vehicle that is electrically connected to the negative terminal of the battery is said to be *grounded*, or at *ground potential.* Knowing how to achieve proper ground is extremely important for mobile operating. If you're powering your radio from the car's electrical system, the negative voltage wire *must* attach to ground.

Finding a good ground connection in older vehicles is pretty straightforward. Most older cars are made almost entirely of metal and each piece is firmly interconnected. If you install an antenna on a metal bumper, for example, you can be reasonably certain that the bumper is at ground potential. The same is true inside the car. If you find a metal screw under the dashboard, you can often use that screw to ground the negative voltage wire from your radio.

With modern cars, it's a new ballgame. Most new cars have exteriors of high-strength plastic or other nonconducting composite materials. The roof or trunk may be metallic, but they're often not electrically connected to the chassis of the car. In some cases, even the chassis isn't a solid metal structure. To make matters more difficult, the interior of the car is usually made of plastic or synthetic fiber.

By using a volt-ohm meter, or

VOM, you can determine which parts of your car are really at ground potential. You need to measure the *resistance* from the negative terminal of the battery to your chosen ground point. (You may need to use a long, insulated wire to connect the negative probe of the meter to your negative terminal of your car battery.) If you measure a resistance of less than 10 ohms, you can be reasonably certain you've found a ground connection.

When installing radios, many hams take the extra step of routing two heavy-gauge wires directly to the battery (see Fig 1). This assures a reliable, direct connection for the positive *and* negative voltage leads. The wires are routed through existing openings in the firewall and carefully

threaded around the engine to the battery. If you choose this approach, take care to keep the wiring well away from any electronic components in the engine compartment. This reduces the possibility of interference to the electrical systems in your car.

Some antennas require a nearby ground connection as well. If you can't find a grounded bolt or screw, you may have to install your own. The trick is to find a ground point that's close to the antenna (no more than a few inches away). Once you've found a suitable ground location, drill a small pilot hole and install a sheet-metal screw of the appropriate size. After you connect the ground wire, it's a good idea to apply a rust-inhibitive compound over the screw.—*WB8IMY*

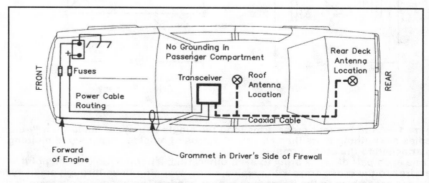

Fig 1—A typical wiring diagram for mobile installations.

The Repeater Eater

A 2-meter indoor directional antenna that will reach every repeater in sight, and maybe even farther.

I recently retired. To the average radio amateur, retirement can be defined as finally having the time to do all the things you can no longer afford. In my case, one of those things was to get back on 2 meters, but because of the second part of the definition I've been too cheap to do anything about it.

This changed a short time ago when an electronics store chain advertised its own brand of 2-meter hand-held radios for sale at about half the price of any of the lowest-priced "Big Name" models. This, together

By George Murphy, VE3ERP
77 McKenzie St
Orillia, ON L3V 6A6
Canada

with a senior citizen discount, constituted an offer I couldn't refuse. So I bought one, using funds from my "Someday I May Go on a DXpedition to Las Vegas" account.

But alas! Upon returning home, I discovered that I couldn't access even the closest repeater using the radio's ducky little rubber antenna. I dauntlessly decided that the meager 7.2 V in the NiCd battery wasn't enough, so I hooked the radio up to my 12-V portable emergency battery power supply.[1] I still couldn't trip the repeater. Being adventurous by nature, I figured I may as well go for broke and fire it

up with a few other voltages from my triple-output variable-voltage regulated all-purpose utility power supply.[2] I still couldn't excite the repeater, even with 13.8 V (full-blast 6-W output from the handy).

The Sherlock Holmes trait deep within me immediately deduced that a 150-mm (6-inch) rubber ducky antenna wasn't efficient to reach even the closest repeater, 30 km (approximately 18.6 statute miles) from my operating position—inside my dwelling, on a reclining easy chair within an arm's length of the refrigerator.

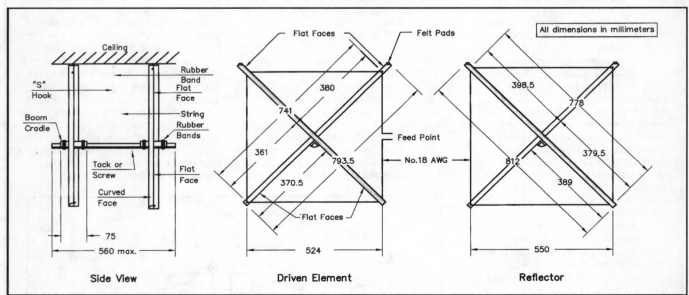

Figure 1—A total of four cross arms (and the single boom) are made from ³/₄-inch quarter-round wood molding. The boom cradles are nothing more than two short pieces of outside corner wood molding. The cradles hold the boom in place when it's attached to the cross arms.

Glue each pair of cross arms to each other. Glue a boom cradle at the point where each pair crosses in the center. Attach the wires to the cross arms with staples, or by wrapping them through small eye screws. Fasten the driven element and reflector assembles to the boom with rubber bands. (The boom simply rests in the grooves provided by the cradles.) Adjust the spacing between the driven element and the reflector for minimum SWR. Feed the antenna with 50-Ω coax lashed to the boom with wire ties.

The Problem

My quandary could be easily solved by installing a proper outdoor 2-meter rotating directional antenna. This wasn't possible because of the following inescapable factors:

❏ I'm too cheap to buy a tower, or even a mast, let alone a commercial, rotating 2-meter antenna.

❏ Because of the construction of my house and the opinion of my wife (not necessarily in that order), there's no way I can run a feedline from an exterior antenna to the refrigerator.

❏ Even if I could overcome the first two items, I'm too old, fat and lazy to even consider the work involved.

The problem boiled down to this: I needed an indoor rotating directional antenna that could be hung from the ceiling of my refrigerator room, which my wife refers to as the "kitchen." (It couldn't even be an attic antenna because my personal dimensions exceed the dimensions of our attic access hatch).

The Solution

After consultation with a Renowned Authority on Weird Antennas,[3] I decided that my antenna would be a quad, hung from the ceiling and rotated by the Armstrong method.[4] From this point onward, the project was clear sailing.

The Design

The design of the antenna was easy. I didn't have to do a single calculation because I used the latest version of a computer program called *HAMCALC*, which I got free through something I read in *QST*.[5]

Most published design data for quad antennas determine the length of the elements by dividing an empirical number (usually in the order of 1005 or thereabouts) by the frequency in MHz to arrive at the length of the element in feet. *HAMCALC* makes more precise calculations that result in a quad that doesn't require pruning and can be fed directly with 50 to 75 Ω coax with no baluns, stubs or matching-line sections. Matching is accomplished simply by

adjusting the spacing of the elements for minimum SWR.

The drawings in Figure 1 show the configuration for a vertically polarized antenna. If you want horizontal polarization, feed the driven element at the center of the bottom horizontal leg instead of halfway up one of the vertical legs.

Installation and Operation

The antenna is suspended from a hook in the ceiling by string and elastic bands. They prevent it from turning by pulling it up against the ceiling. To rotate, pull the antenna a few centimeters (or fewer inches) away from the ceiling, point it where you

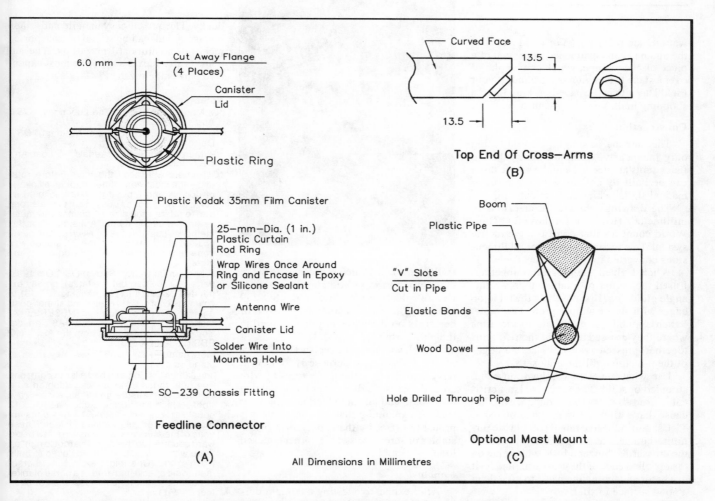

Figure 2—Detail of the feed-point assembly is shown at A. The entire assembly is enclosed in a Kodak 35-mm film canister. The top ends of the cross arms are shown at B. Note the felt pad at the end of the cross arm. The pad helps hold the antenna in position against your ceiling, and protects the ceiling as well. If you prefer a mast mount, you make one easily with plastic pipe (C).

Table 1
Metric to Feet/Inches Conversion

Use this table to convert the metric dimensions in Figures 1 and 2 to feet and inches.

(If you use cubits, you are on your own.)

Metric dimensions in Figures 1 and 2	Feet/Inches
6 mm	1/4"
13.5 mm	17/32"
75 mm	2 15/16"
361 mm	1' 2 7/32"
370.5 mm	1' 2 19/32"
379.5 mm	1' 2 15/16"
380 mm	1' 2 31/32"
398.5 mm	1' 3 11/16"
389 mm	1' 3 5/16"
524 mm	1' 8 5/8"
550 mm	1' 9 21/32"
560 mm	1' 10 1/16"
741 mm	2' 5 3/16"
778 mm	2' 6 5/8"
793.5 mm	2' 7 1/4"
812 mm	2' 7 31/32"
0.31 meter	1' 7/32"
0.51 meter	1' 8 3/32"
2.095 meters	6' 10 15/32"
2.2 meters	7' 2 5/8"

A closer view of the *Repeater Eater* cross arms and boom cradle.

The *Repeater Eater* antenna secured to the ceiling and ready for action.

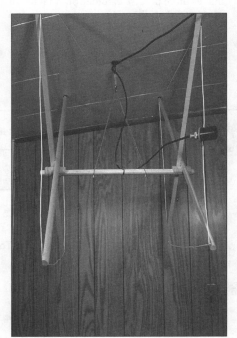

want it, and release it.[6] For Field Day use, the antenna can be attached to the end of a piece of plastic pipe, which can be placed over a stake driven into the ground. If your Field Day site is the paved parking lot of a shopping mall, you're on your own.

Construction

The antenna is simple to build, using only inexpensive common materials. No fancy tools are needed and the whole thing can be built by anyone with my level of manual skills, which is practically nil.

The drawings show all dimensions in millimeters. However, for those few Third World countries that don't use the metric system, I've included a table of all dimensions converted into feet.[7] (See Table 1.)

When I glued the crossarms together, I used the corner of a tabletop as a right-angle gluing jig, first covering the tabletop edges with plastic wrap to protect the table. I then applied hot-melt glue to the arms where they crossed and held the two arms together, pressed against the corner edges of the tabletop until the glue set.[8]

Use whatever wire you have on hand, stranded or solid. The wire size isn't critical. I used #18 stranded house wiring because that's all my neighbor had on hand.

Use self-adhesive felt or soft plastic furniture bumpers as pads at the top ends of the crossarms. Smear a little white glue on the bevelled ends of the crossarms and let it dry before attaching the pads, to give them a good surface to stick to.

The only tiddly bit about the antenna is the feedline connector (see Figure 2). If you use stranded wire, the stripped ends should be twisted and tinned by flowing a little

solder on them to make it easier to wrap them around the plastic curtain-rod ring. Before soldering the wires to the SO-239 chassis connector, clamp some sort of heatsinks on the wires to prevent melting the plastic ring.

The plastic film canister isn't really necessary. Its only real purpose is to prevent nosy hams from noticing the turns of wire around the plastic ring and pointing out that they could add unwanted inductance. I got tired of explaining that this inductance is probably offset by the capacitance of the staples or screw eyes at the corners of each loop.

Conclusion

After exhaustive testing one night during a TV commercial, when I happened to be at the refrigerator anyway, I'm firmly convinced that under virtually all conditions, this antenna will outperform a rubber

ducky. The quad is easy to build and, when disassembled, can be stored or transported nicely in a cardboard pizza box. The antenna is also inexpensive. The most expensive part is the pizza.[9]

Notes
1. G. Murphy, VE3ERP, "The Lunchbox," *QST*, Aug 1987, p 28.
2. G. Murphy, VE3ERP, "Super ACadapt," *QST*, Dec 1985, p 25.
3. G. Murphy, VE3ERP, "Aerials—A Lost Art," *QST*, Jul 1986, p 20.
4. Old-timers will recall the days before rotators—the mast was rotated through a linkage of pulleys and ropes to a crank located as close to the shack as possible. It took a strong arm to rotate a full-sized 4-element 40-meter beam, hence the name "Armstrong" for this method. Usually by the time you got the beam pointed at the DX signal, the DX station was gone and the band had shut down for the night.
5. "Free Ham Software," Strays, *QST*, Oct 1993, page 23. You can get the latest, greatly expanded version (8.1) by sending $5 (US) to cover the cost of disk, mailer and airmail postage to George Murphy, VE3ERP, 77 McKenzie St, Orillia, ON L3V 6A6 Canada. You can also download it from the ARRL HQ BBS (203-666-0578).
6. Short hams in tall hamshacks may need to stand on a box.
7. King James I of England had a large right foot. The heel-to-toe distance was adopted as a standard of measure imaginatively called a "foot," which was further subdivided into 12 equal parts called "inches." History does not record whether the King had 12 toes. These units of measure are still in use in a few backward countries to this day. The foot is right up there with the cubit, which was used to build Noah's Ark. (One might expect that horsemen could specify the area of a horse blanket in hand-feet, but no such use has yet been found—*Ed.*)
8. Time this operation carefully. Invariably, just as you get everything held in place, the phone will ring.
9. Most people don't bother reading footnotes. Thank you for your attention.

Recycle Those Rabbit Ears

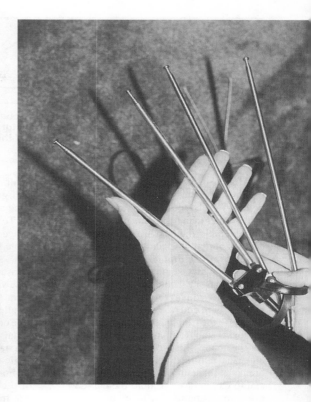

How many pair of rabbit ears do *you* have lying around?

By Al Brogdon, K3KMO
Managing Editor

My 2-meter rubber ducky, used inside my apartment, wouldn't reach a couple of local repeaters with a full-quieting signal. I needed a simple, inexpensive, indoor antenna that would radiate a little better signal than did the rubber ducky. Rummaging around for suitable antenna materials, I found two pair of TV rabbit ears in my junk box. You can adjust the length of each of the two extendible whips to 19 inches, a quarter-wavelength at 2 meters. Two quarterwave whips make a half-wave dipole. *Ta-da!*

You always get a pair of rabbit ears when you buy a TV (and sometimes with a VCR). Hams being the natural packrats that they are, the rabbit ears never get thrown away. You don't believe me? When I showed my new dipole to Steve Ford, WB8IMY, I asked him how many pair of rabbit ears *he* had. Even without going home to check, he could think of three pair that he had. What a packrat!

I first thought that I could take the easy approach and just replace the short piece of twin lead on the rabbit ears with a short piece of RG-58, and make no other mechanical changes. *Wrong!* The twin lead was attached to a pair of little metal clips via crimped tabs, which I don't trust to deliver a low-

impedance RF connection. I disconnected the twin lead and connected the RG-58 to the crimp tabs, and then tried to solder the connections. Oops! the metal clips wouldn't accept solder. So much for that idea!

So I disassembled the rabbit ears, kept the two extendible whips, and threw the rest of the parts away. I bummed a small piece of clear plastic from the ARRL Lab (thanks to Mike Gruber, WA1SVF) to use as the mounting block and center insulator for the

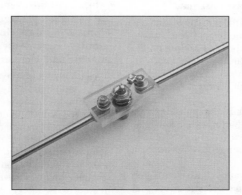

Figure 1—The center block of the dipole. Instead of solder lugs, you can use short pigtails of #20 tinned solid wire between the coax connector and the whips.

dipole, and went back to my junk box for the BNC connector and the rest of the small hardware (three solder lugs and some 4-40 nuts and bolts).

I drilled a hole in the middle of the plastic block and mounted the UG-657 BNC connector in the hole, placing a large solder lug under the nut. This was a solder lug made to go on the shaft of big old 1950s potentiometers, to be used to ground one lug of the pot via its shaft. If you can't find one of these lugs at a ham flea market, you can just put a loop of #20 tinned solid wire under the nut, with a short pigtail to reach to and around the bolt that secures the antenna element to the center insulator.

Then I drilled two smaller holes and mounted the two extendible whips to the plastic block, using 4-40 hardware. Again, I used solder lugs under the nuts to make the connections between the two halves of the dipole and the center conductor and ground of the BNC connector, but short pigtails of wire work just as well.

Figure 1 shows the center block of the dipole, and Figure 2 shows how the two halves of the dipole are wired to the coax connector on the center block.

Note that I am not giving you blow-by-blow details for making the antenna. Just use whatever insulating material you can

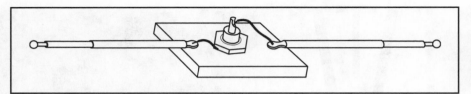

Figure 2—Wiring the dipole to the connector consists of making one connection from one whip to the center pin of the connector, and making a second connection from the other whip to the shell of the connector.

find for the center mounting block, and keep the inside ends of the whips fairly close together. Here's your chance to experiment a little, rather than following detailed instructions! That's the best way to learn things. The accompanying photo shows the center insulator of my dipole, to give you an idea of how it was assembled.

You can substitute a UHF connector for the BNC, if you prefer. Or you can just connect the bare end of a piece of coaxial cable right into the dipole feedpoint, with no connector. If you do that, provide strain relief for the connection, so you don't subject the electrical connections to strain and possible breakage. A simple nonconductive cable clamp can be used to hold the cable to the block that supports the antenna.

The whips from my rabbit ears each collapse to a length of $11^1/_2$ inches and extend to a length of $39^3/_4$ inches, so that the overall length of the dipole can be adjusted from 24 inches to $80^1/_2$ inches. Plugging this into the familiar formula that relates frequency to dipole length tells us that the dipole can be adjusted to be a half wavelength from about 70 to 234 MHz. Thus it can be used as a half-wave dipole on two ham bands—144 MHz and 220 MHz. (If you want to build a dipole like this for 6 meters, a pair of Radio Shack's 270-1408 replacement rod antennas, each $71^3/_4$ inches long, will get you down to 6 meters, where you need a 112-inch dipole.)

To adjust the completed dipole to resonance on 2 meters, connect 50-Ω coaxial cable from the connector on the dipole to a VHF SWR meter or wattmeter, and from the measuring device to your rig. Hang the dipole vertically. You can hang it by a string from the ceiling, or attach it to a broom handle or the edge of a wooden door with tape or a rubber band—just keep it away from metal objects and other antennas. Run the coaxial cable away from the dipole at a right angle for about three feet, for best results.

For starters, adjust the length of each half of the dipole to 19 inches. (Keep in mind that the two halves of the dipole should be adjusted to the same length—whatever it turns out to be—so the dipole is fed at its center.) Set the rig to an unused frequency near your desired operating frequency, so as to avoid causing interference to other hams while you're tuning up. Press the push-to-talk switch and check the SWR. If it's more than about 2:1, adjust the length of each whip to be about ¼ inch longer and try again. If the SWR is *lower* than your first try, you're adjusting the length in the correct direction; if the SWR is *higher*, you went the wrong direction, and you need to adjust the length of the whips slightly *shorter* as you continue the adjustment process. And please sign your call sign when you begin these test transmissions and when you finish them, so as to follow legal (and good) operating practice.

After a few adjustments and measurements, you will find the dipole length that gives you an SWR near 1:1 at your favorite frequency. Remember to make a final physical measurement of the lengths of the two halves of the dipole, to be sure that they are the same.

After I had adjusted my dipole to the desired resonance point, I used a small file to score a mark around the center rod of each extendible whip to indicate how far it was pulled out of the next piece of tubing, so I can collapse it for travel and then easily reset it to the correct length.

That's it! If you don't believe my claim that the dipole will work better than your rubber ducky, make some comparison checks with another ham on simplex, first trying the rubber ducky, then the dipole. If, in fact, your dipole doesn't outperform the rubber ducky, you better recheck your dipole to find out what's wrong with it.

If you can't find the problem, ask some old-timer with good technical skills to help you. He would probably be flattered that you value his expertise, and would be happy to help you find the problem *and* to teach you some things that would help you in your future ham ventures. **QST**

Q My new car has a plastic roof, so a roof-mounted ¼-wavelength vertical for 2 meters is out of the question. Do you have any opinions on on-glass antennas?

A Some hams report excellent results. Others are less than enthusiastic. There are two things to remember if you want to use this type of antenna. First, mount it as high as possible on the glass, so that the radiating element is as far above the heads of your passengers as possible. This may not be all that important if you are running just a few watts, but at high power it becomes a safety issue.

Second, check the glass for tinting. Some windshields use a thin metal layer as a sun screen. Other manufacturers use a similar approach for defrosting systems. This layer will definitely reduce the performance of your glass-mounted antenna, if it does not ruin it completely!

And don't count out that roof-mounted vertical just yet. If you can get underneath the *headliner*—the cloth or plastic cover that comprises the interior ceiling of your car—you may be able to mount a thin aluminum sheet or glue heavy-duty aluminum foil to the underside of the roof. This makes a fine ground plane for a vertical ¼-wavelength antenna.

Q Sam Woodley, KF4EPG, asks, "I recently replaced the rubber-duck antenna on my H-T with a telescoping whip. The improvement was remarkable! Everyone commented on how good my signal sounded into the repeater. With this in mind, I'm wondering if my telescoping whip would provide a similar improvement to my marine band H-T? The VHF marine and 2-meter amateur frequencies are fairly close."

A You've discovered the "secret" of so-called rubber-duck antennas: They're poor performers! (An RF engineer of my acquaintance once referred to them as, "Air-cooled dummy loads.") Your telescoping antenna is a vast improvement.

As far as your marine H-T is concerned, a telescoping antenna designed for ham frequencies can be partially collapsed to a shorter length that corresponds to a quarter-wavelength at the desired marine frequency, and be used to the same advantage. Even a 2-meter quarter-wave ham antenna whose length cannot be adjusted will likely outperform the rubber-duck antenna that was supplied with your marine H-T. Most H-Ts are designed to work into the high SWRs presented by various "attachable" antennas, so your marine H-T probably won't balk at working into a ham whip.

Packet
Without
Computers

By Fred Wolf, N3CSL
946 West Fairway Dr
Lancaster, PA 17603-5902
Photos by the author

One of the best-kept secrets about packet radio is that you don't need a computer to get started!

Have you heard this before?

"QSL Fred, and thanks for the info. I'd like to discuss this with you further. Do you have a packet address?" Or, "Hey, Fred! Any idea when ZS8MI was on last? Can you check it on the *PacketCluster* for me?"

For years my answer was an emphatic "No." I didn't own a computer. Therefore, I couldn't have a packet station; or so I thought! Then, in a totally unrelated conversation, someone let the cat out of the bag: You don't need a full-blown megabuck, megabyte computer to try packet. Incredible as it sounds, it's true. It's possible to have an effective packet station *without a computer* if you are willing to make a few concessions, and give up some frills.

All you really need is a used *dumb terminal*. These terminals are available for anywhere from $5 to $50, depending on the condition of the unit and the features it offers. That's quite a bit less than you'd pay for a computer of any age…unless it's in pieces! Sound interesting? If so, read on! Assuming that you already have a 2-meter FM transceiver and an outside antenna, you're halfway there already.

Figure 1—A Liberty Electronics "Freedom" terminal with a separate keyboard and a green monitor. Total cost on the used market: $35!

What Do I Look For?

Before you go shopping for terminals, you must purchase your packet *TNC* (terminal node controller). That's the device that connects between your transceiver and your terminal (or computer). The TNC is the heart of your packet station. It takes digital data from your terminal and configures it for transmission according to the AX.25 packet protocol. The TNC then converts the data packets into audio tones for your transceiver. The TNC also takes the received audio and processes it back into data that you can read on your terminal.

Check the advertising pages of *QST* for TNC manufacturers. Write or call to make sure their models will work easily with dumb terminals. By the way, the term "dumb" refers to the fact that the terminal usually has no memory and can't accept a program contained on a disk. (There's no disk drive to put it in!) These terminals were made for use in conjunction with *host* or *mainframe* computers in large businesses.

If you get the go-ahead from the TNC manufacturer, it's time to start searching for a terminal. Get on your local repeater and ask if anyone

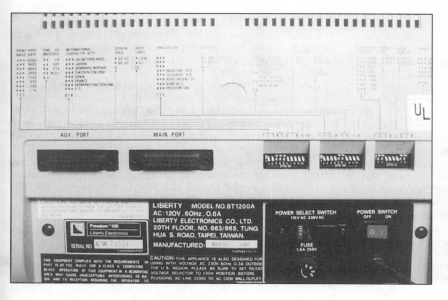

Figure 2—Rear view of the Liberty Electronics terminal showing the port connections and the DIP switches. The TNC connects to the MAIN PORT.

Figure 3—A typical packet station configuration using a terminal. The transceiver can be virtually any 2-meter FM rig—even a hand-held!

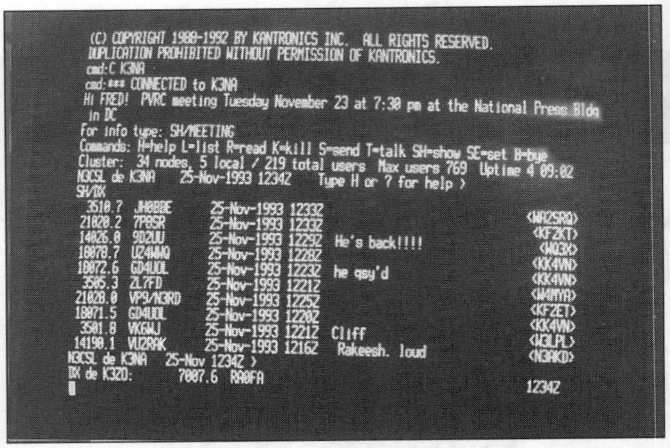

Figure 4—When the TNC and terminal are talking to each other, you're ready to get on the air. This is an actual screen shot from one of my terminals. At the top you can see the sign-on message from the Kantronics KPC-3 TNC. As soon as I saw the sign-on, I sent the command to connect to the K3NA *PacketCluster* and asked for a list of the latest DX spots.

has a terminal for sale. If you find one, ask the owner if he is using it for packet, and what kind of TNC he has in his station. Is it the same one you hope to buy? If not, is it compatible?

If you come up empty, go to the next hamfest and walk around. You'll often see plenty of terminals, depending on the size of the 'fest. Tell the seller exactly what you want to do and, if possible, ask him to plug it in and demonstrate that it works.

Here's where you need to be a little careful. If the TNC is going to communicate successfully with the terminal, there are certain parameters you must adjust. These parameters are the *baud rate*, *parity*, *data bits* and *stop bits*. It isn't necessary at this point to understand what these terms mean. Just make sure that you can change them, either through small DIP switches on the terminal, or by an on-screen menu contained in the terminal *firmware* (software that exists on chips inside the terminal). If there is a manual with the terminal, so much the better. Scan through it before you open your wallet.

The available space at your operating position will determine the type of terminal you need. You may want a model with the keyboard attached directly below the screen, or one that has a separate keyboard connected by a coiled cable (see Figure 1). Screens come in black and white, amber, or green. Beware of screens that have a "burned-in" appearance. If you notice shadowy lines on the screen before the terminal is even turned on, you're looking at a model with a lot of mileage! Don't waste your money.

How Do I Hook it Up?

On the back of the terminal there should be at least one RS-232 connector (see Figure 2). On some models there may be as many as three separate connection points. These connectors have 25 pins, but in most cases you'll only need three of them to make the terminal "talk" to the TNC. In fact, there are some terminals that won't work if you connect them to the TNC with a standard DB-25 cable.

If you're lucky, you may be able to pick up an RS-232 serial cable from Radio Shack and patch the terminal and TNC together right away. If this doesn't work for one reason or another, you'll need to make your own cable. This isn't as difficult as it sounds. You only need to connect pins 2, 3 and 7 on the terminal data port to the TNC. Pin 2 is **Transmit Data**, pin 3 is **Receive Data** and pin 7 is **Signal Ground**. Please note that the terminal's **Transmit Data** line must connect to the TNC's **Receive Data** line. By the same token, the TNC's **Transmit Data** line must connect to your terminal's **Receive Data** line (see Figure 3). There are usually directions included in the TNC owner's manual to guide you.

Use the information in your TNC manual to set the terminal DIP switches for the parameters we discussed previously. When you've

connected your cable, it's time to power up the equipment and see if you're getting readable text from the TNC. This will usually take the form of a *sign-on* message telling you the version of the TNC software, the manufacturer's name and so on (see Figure 4).

If you get a screen full of gibberish, don't despair. At least the TNC and the terminal are "talking"—they just don't understand each other! Recheck the DIP switch settings on the terminal. If you find one that isn't set correctly, *turn off the terminal*, change the DIP switch, and turn the terminal back on. (Most terminals will not accept changes with the power on.)

You must establish communication between the terminal and the TNC before you even think about hooking up your transceiver. Get the bugs worked out between the TNC and the terminal prior to making up a cable for your radio. After all, there's no need to worry about attaching a rig to the TNC if you can't get information to appear on the screen!

Once you're getting readable text on the screen, you can practice *connecting* to your own TNC *mailbox* and reading the "HELP" menu contained in the TNC's memory. Your TNC manual will tell you how to do this easy off-air test. We don't have enough space in this article to describe the cable that connects your transceiver to the TNC. They're all different, but you can make them yourself or purchase them from some suppliers ready-made.

It's Worth the Effort

There is a certain amount of experimenting to be done with various terminals, but with a little patience—and maybe some help from local hams—you'll succeed. Don't be discouraged. Think of the money you're saving!

I am currently using a so-called *smart/dumb* terminal with an 8-page memory capacity. It's attached to a small printer so that I can save messages of interest. My TNC is a Kantronics KPC-3. In addition to this terminal, I own two others that work equally well. One cost $25 and came with a separate keyboard and monitor. The other one was free!

I'd like to thank the following amateurs for helping me get started in packet radio, and for telling me the "big secret" about data terminals: Fred Althouse, KE3FV; Ron Bouder, KA3CNT; Randy Miller, N3FOG; and Brad Thomas, WA3TBG.

Fred Wolf, N3CSL, was licensed in 1982 to the General class. His late father worked for the RCA "Super Power" tube division, so Fred was exposed to electronics from an early age. He enjoys DXing and recently achieved DXCC Honor Roll status. His packet radio station plays a central role in DXing and other activities.

Quick and Easy
CW
With Your
PC

See, hear and send CW using a simple interface and your PC.

By Ralph E. Taggart, WB8DQT
602 S Jefferson
Mason, MI 48854

Most multimode communication processors (MCPs) on the market include CW along with RTTY, PacTOR, AMTOR and other modes. Their CW functions allow you to send perfect Morse code from your computer keyboard. The MCPs do a fair job of decoding received CW, too.

But what if you're not interested in the other modes? What if you want CW *only*? Buying an expensive MCP seems a waste if you only want one mode.

Here's an excellent alternative. With a $50 hardware interface and *free* software, you can transform your computer into a Morse machine that's a full-function CW keyboard *and* a receive display terminal.

My interface works with any IBM-compatible PC and uses the printer port to communicate with the computer (see Figure 1). The interface should set you back less than $50 in parts, and a printed-circuit board is available to make construction easier. An experienced home brewer can have the project finished in a single evening while a rank beginner might need a few evenings. Either way, it's easy to build and simple to align.

Construction

A PC-board pattern and parts overlay for this board are available from the ARRL.[1] You can use them to make your own PC board, or as a guide for wiring the circuit using perf-board. An etched and drilled PC board, with a silk-screened parts layout, is available from FAR Circuits.[2] Assuming you use a PC board or the perf-board equivalent, the required mainframe wiring is shown in Figure 2. The circuit board has all the part outlines and values silk-screened, so it's easy to get everything properly positioned.

The most economical approach to obtaining the needed parts is to order them from one of the larger mail-order suppliers. Most parts are also available at well-stocked Radio Shack outlets or local parts distributors, although the cost will tend to be a bit higher.

Any cabinet that can accommodate the circuit board can be used. The **POWER** switch and **POWER** and **CW LED** indicators are the only front-panel items. J2 (**KEYED LINE**), J1 (**AUDIO IN**), J3 (**+12V DC POWER**), and P1 (**COMPUTER**) are all on the rear apron.

Power Supply Options

The interface requires +12 V, +5 V, and –9 V, all at relatively low current. The simplest solution is to use a wall-mount power transformer/supply (200 mA minimum) to provide the +12 V. A 7805 voltage regulator chip produces +5 V from the +12 V bus for the 74LS TTL ICs. Since the –9 V current requirements are very low, I use a 9 V alkaline transistor battery. The battery is switched in and out using one set of contacts on the **POWER** switch and will last a long time—unless you forget to turn the unit off between operating sessions! Alternatively, you can use a multivoltage power supply module or a dc-dc converter to produce the negative voltage for the op amps (anything from –8 to –12 V will do). The suggested power supply option is simple and inexpensive and also assures that there are no hazardous voltages present in the interface unit.

The Computer Connection

This project is designed to connect to the PC parallel printer port, normally implemented with a DB-25F connector on the rear of the computer. You would expect to see a similar DB-25F connector on the interface rear apron with a standard parallel data cable (DB-25M connectors at each end) to connect the interface and computer.

That's what you'd *expect* to see, but DB-25 connectors need an odd-shaped mounting hole, which is difficult to make with standard shop tools. We can simplify construction since we only need the four conductors normally found in a parallel cable: ground, printer data bits 0 and 1, and the strobe data bit.

Connections are made at the interface end using a common 4-pin microphone chassis mounting connector. This connector mounts in a standard ⅝-inch round hole that doesn't take long to make, even if you have to file it by hand. To interface to the computer, we need a cable with a 4-pin microphone plug at one end and a DB-25M connector at the other. The DB-25M connector is actually fabricated from a standard male connector and a plastic DB-25 shell, both of which are widely available. The microphone plug and chassis connectors can usually be found at the same distributors who sell the DB-25 hardware.

For our cable, any lightweight cable with at least four conductors will do just fine. Jacketed 5-conductor TV rotator cable will work very well, but so will a range of available intercom or speaker cables. The following interconnections between the microphone plug and DB-25M connector are required:

Function	Microphone Plug	DB-25M Connector
Ground	1	25
Printer data 0	2	2
Printer data 1	3	3
Printer strobe	4	1

If you've wired the microphone connector on the interface rear apron properly, there are no voltages or signals that can harm your parallel port. You should take reasonable care in wiring the cable, however. If you make an error, the interface simply won't function when you run the software.

If you have the facilities (or the patience) to use a DB-25 connector on your interface, use a DB-25F connector and wire I/O points 1-4 to the connector, following the pattern indicated for the cable. Connection to the computer would then be made using a standard "parallel cable" with DB-25M connectors at each end.

Keying Options

If your equipment uses a positive, low-voltage keying line, point **K** on the board can be connected directly to the keying jack. In this case, you will not need the reed relay and one of the 1N4004 diodes. Since all my CW work is done using low-voltage QRP gear, I used this option for the operational version of my interface. If you might use a wider range of transmitting equipment, use the keying relay. The circuit board does not accommodate the relay (a wide range of relays can be used), but you can mount the relay anywhere in the cabinet using a dab of silicone adhesive or a piece of double-sided foam mounting tape. If you will be operating at relatively high power, I would also suggest the use of the ferrite beads at all wires connected to the rear-apron connectors.

Alignment

There are only three alignment adjustments, all of which are associated with the receive interface. Most selective CW receivers have a very pronounced peak for the beatnote, somewhere in the 400 to 1000-Hz range. In the case of my ARK-30 transceiver, this peak occurs at 700 Hz. I will use this as an example, but you would use a frequency appropriate to your receiver.

Switch the receiver to a dummy antenna to eliminate any interfering signals and tune the receiver to a strong signal from your frequency calibrator or other stable signal source. Carefully adjust the receiver for peak audio output. The audio input to the interface can be a data output port from the re-

ceiver, or you can interface to the external speaker line using a **Y** connector. Connect a pair of headphones or other audio-monitoring option to the junction of the 0.1-μF capacitor and 10-kΩ resistor at the output of U3. Adjust the **TUNE** (R1) control on the PC board for the loudest signal. The filter is sharp, so make the adjustment carefully.

Set the PC board **LEVEL** pot (R2) to midrange and adjust the **VCO** pot (R3) until the **CW** LED comes on. Decrease the **LEVEL** setting slightly (adjust the control in a counterclockwise direction) and readjust the **VCO** pot, if required, to cause the **CW** LED to light.

Continue to reduce the **LEVEL** setting in small steps, refining the **VCO** setting until you reach the point where operation of the **CW** indicator becomes erratic.

Now advance the **LEVEL** control clockwise to just past the point where the LED comes on with no sign of erratic operation. The **LEVEL** threshold setting is critical for best operation of the receive demodulator. If the control is advanced too far, the LED will trigger on background noise and copy will be difficult. If you reduce the setting too far, the interface will trigger erratically, even with a clean beat note. If you have a reason-

ably good CW receiver (CW bandwidth crystal filters and/or good audio filtering), you can back down the **LEVEL** control until the LED stops flickering on all but the strongest noise pulses, but where it will still key

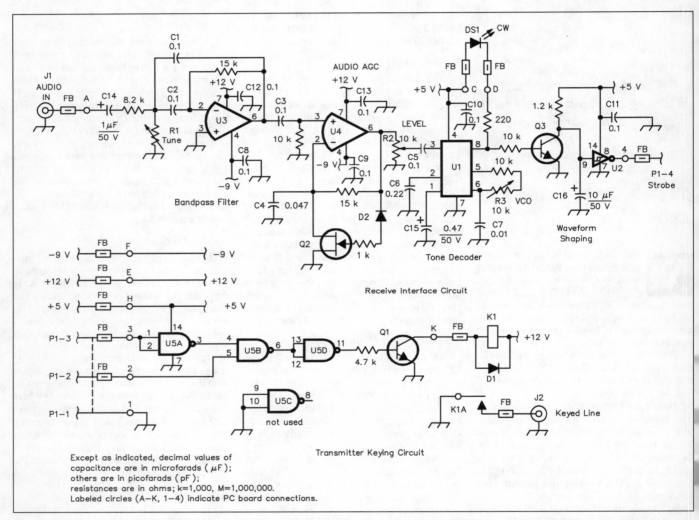

Figure 1—Schematic of the CW interface. All fixed value resistors are ¼ W, 5%-tolerance carbon film. Capacitance values are in microfarads (μF). IC sections not shown are not used.

C1-C3, C5, C7-C13—0.1 μF monolithic or disc ceramic, 50 V
C4—0.047 μF Polypropylene (dipped Mylar), 50 V
C6—0.22 μF Polypropylene (dipped Mylar), 50 V
C14—1 μF Tantalum or electrolytic, 50 V
C15—0.47 μF Tantalum or electrolytic, 50 V
C16—10 μF Tantalum or electrolytic, 50 V
D1,D3—1N4004
D2—1N270 germanium
DS1—Green panel-mount LED (Radio Shack 276-069)
DS2—Red panel-mount LED

FB—Ferrite beads (11 total)
K1—12 V dc SPST reed relay (Radio Shack 275-233)
J1, J2—RCA phono jacks
P1—4-pin microphone jack (Radio Shack 274-002)
Q1, Q3—2N4401
Q2—MPF102
R1—1 kΩ (TUNE)
R2, R3—10 kΩ (LEVEL and VCO)
U1—NE567CN PLL tone decoder (8 pin)
U2—74LS14N hex Schmitt trigger (14 pin)
U3, U4—LM741CN op amp (8 pin)

U5—74LS00N quad NAND gate (14 pin)
Miscellaneous
4-pin microphone plug (Radio Shack 274-001)
DB-25M Connector (Radio Shack 276-1547B)
DB-25 Shell (Radio Shack 276-1549)
Coaxial power connector (Radio Shack 274-1563)
8-pin DIP IC sockets
14-pin DIP IC sockets
DPDT miniature toggle switch

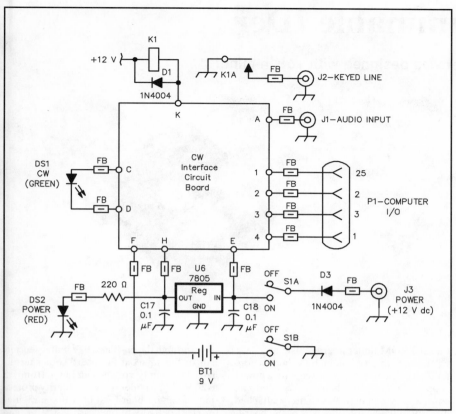

Figure 2—Mainframe wiring, assuming the use of a printed circuit board or perf-board equivalent. J3 is a panel-mounting coaxial power jack to match your wall-mount/ transformer power supply. BT1 is a 9-V alkaline battery. See text. C17 and C18 are 0.1 μF, 50 V monolithic or disc ceramic bypass capacitors. The +5 V regulator chip should be mounted to the grounded wall of the cabinet. Off-board components are duplicated in this diagram (J1, J2, P1, the CW LED indicator, and K1). The CW and POWER indicators are panel-mounting LED indicators. I used red for POWER and green for CW. FB indicates optional ferrite beads used to prevent RF interference with the interface circuits. As noted in the text, if you only intend to use the interface with transmitters with a positive, low-voltage keying line, point K on the board can be connected directly to J2, eliminating K1 and the 1N4004 spike-suppression diode. The break-out points for connections to the circuit board are positioned for clear illustration and do not correspond to the actual locations of these points on the PC board.

reliably on a properly tuned CW signal.

Software Installation

The MORSE.EXE program is available at no cost from either the ARRL BBS, 203-666-0578, or my own WSH BBS, 517-676-0368. You'll also find it in CompuServe's *HamNET* forum, library 7.

The distribution file (MORSE.ZIP) includes MORSE.EXE, a sample set-up file (CW.DAT), a sample logging file (LOG.DAT), the HELP text file (CWHELP.DAT), and the program Quick-BASIC source code (MORSE.BAS).

Most of the program structure is built around the many CW keyboard functions, most of which are initiated with single-key-strokes.

❏ *SPEED*—Select your transmitting speed from 5 to 60 wpm. The program autocalibrates to your computer clock speed and transmitting speeds are accurate to within 1%. On receive, the system automatically tracks the speed of the station you are copying from *very* slow up to somewhere between 50 and 60 wpm.

❏ *YOUR CALL*—The program stores your call sign so you never have to type it in routine exchanges. The call can be changed at any time if you want to use the program for contests, special events, or any other situation where you will be using another call.

❏ *OTHER CALL*—If you enter the call of the station you are working (or would like to work), all standard call exchanges at the beginning and end of a transmission can be accomplished with a single keystroke.

❏ *CQ OPTIONS*—The program supports two CQ formats. The "standard" format is a 3×3 call using your call sign. The program also lets you store a custom CQ format which is useful for contests and other nonstandard activities.

❏ *MESSAGE BUFFERS*—The software supports two message buffers that can be implemented with a single keystroke.

❏ *SIDETONE*—If your transmitter doesn't have its own sidetone circuit, you can toggle a sidetone function on or off, letting the computer generate the tone for you. The frequency of the tone can be set between 400 and 1200 Hz.

❏ *WEIGHTING*—Weighting can be adjusted from 0.50 through 1.50.

❏ *DEFAULT SETUP*—All the information discussed up to this point can be saved into a default disk file (CW.DAT) so that you preset all functions whenever you boot the program. The setup can be saved at anytime with a single keystroke.

❏ *LOGGING*—The program supports a range of logging functions that are too numerous to outline here, but one feature is worthy of note. When you first key in the call of a station, the computer will check the log and let you know if you have worked that station before. If you have fully implemented the logging options, it will even tell you the operator's name and QTH.

❏ *HELP FILES*—The program is simple and completely menu-driven. If you forget how to use a function or are using the program for the first time, you can call up on-screen HELP files that explain every function.

Notes

[1] A PC-board template package is available free from the ARRL. Address your request for the TAGGART CW INTERFACE TEMPLATE to: Technical Department Secretary, ARRL, 225 Main St, Newington, CT 06111. Please enclose a business-size SASE.

[2] A circuit board is available for $5 (plus $1.50) from FAR Circuits, 18N640 Field Court, Dundee, IL 60118.

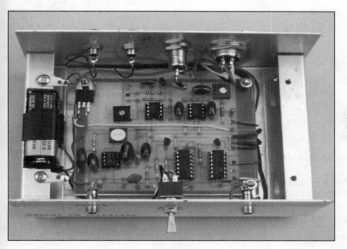

An internal view of the CW interface.

A User-Programmable IDer

This flexible, feature-packed IDer was designed with *you* in mind!

By Robert Silva, WB2OXJ
341 Wicomico Rd
Stevensville, MD 21666

Although there have been many CW identifiers (IDers) featured in the ham magazines over the last few years, those I've seen require the ID message to be programmed into PROM by the author/designer and make it difficult (or impossible) for the user to reprogram. This IDer is different. Its message is stored in a serial EEPROM, which means *you* can program the IDer. No fancy equipment is required. To change the message, all you need is something you probably already have in the shack: a PC-AT-compatible keyboard. (If you don't have one, check with your neighbor's kid.) I dubbed this project the WB2OXJ Ultimate IDer.

Description

At the heart of the IDer is a Microchip MTA81010, known as the PICSEE. The PICSEE (a trademarked name) is identified by the manufacturer as a "28-pin MCU with Serial EEPROM Multi-Chip Module." I chose the PICSEE because it contains—in one IC—an 8-bit high-performance PROM-based microcontroller and a 1024-bit serial EEPROM. The IDer's program occupies nearly the entire 512-byte PROM. A user-entered message (of up to 127 characters) is stored in the 1024-bit serial EEPROM. Reprogramming the serial EEPROM will eventually wear it out, but it can be programmed a minimum of 100,000 times. (Please—let me know when you wear out the EEPROM under average use...)

A compact $2^1/_4 \times 2^1/_8$-inch PC board[1] contains all of the IDer's parts except for a power supply. As the title photo shows, that can consist of a common 9-V battery attached directly to the board by means of the board-mounted snap-on connectors.

Description and Operation

Refer to Figure 1. Power is applied to the IDer through the on-board 9-V battery terminals or the adjacent PC-board solder terminals. The supply voltage can range from 7.5 to 20 V. D1 provides reverse-polarity protection and an on-board 78L05 voltage regulator (U2) delivers the necessary 5 V to feed the IDer and AT compatible keyboard. If the switches for the LED (S1-6) and piezo speaker (S1-7) are off, the IDer's current consumption is a mere 3.5 mA. The dual-colored LED (DS1) and piezo speaker (LS1) are normally on, but if battery operation is required, they can be turned off to prolong battery life.

S1-4 and S1-5 control the timer functions. The timer is off if S1-4 and S1-5 are both off. The IDer plays its message only if the **PLAY/PROGRAM** button is pressed, or the ID terminal is grounded. When the timer is off, the IDer spends some of its time in sleep mode, reducing its current requirement from 3.5 mA to 2.5 mA. If S1-4 and S1-5 are both on, the IDer continuously plays the message. When S1-4/S1-5 are off/on or on/off, the 5 or 10-minute timer is selected. These timers cause the IDer to play its message every 5 or 10

---

[1] Parts are available from the author (410-643-1581) and from Maryland Radio Center, 8576 Laureldale Dr, Laurel, MD 20724, tel 800-447-7489, 301-725-1212. A complete kit (PC board and PC-board-mounted parts), $30; PC board (double-sided, masked and silk-screened), $8; MTA81010 IC programmed and tested, $12; piezo transducer, $1.50. Shipping and handling for orders from the US, Canada and Mexico, add $4; overseas orders add $8.

Table 2
S1 Control Settings

WPM	5	7.5	10	13	15	18	20	25
S1-1	off	off	off	off	on	on	on	on
S1-2	off	off	on	on	off	off	on	on
S1-3	off	on	off	on	off	on	off	on

TIMER	OFF	5 Min	10 Min	Continuous
S1-4	off	off	on	on
S1-5	off	on	off	on

S1-6—DS1 on/off
S1-7—Speaker on/off

PC-Board Connections

ID—A momentary ground on this terminal causes the IDer to play its message; same as pressing the **PLAY/PROGRAM** pushbutton.

PTT—An open-collector output which goes to ground 250 ms before the CW output occurs. This output is used to place radio in transmit mode and is monitored by the red LED.

KEY—An open-collector output that goes to ground during CW keying. This output is monitored by the speaker and the yellow LED.

Table 1
PICSEE I/O Control Line Use

Port	Direction	Use
RA0	output	Piezo speaker
RA1	output	Key
RA2	output	PTT
RA3	input	Pushbutton / ID
RB0	output	Serial EEPROM clock
RB1	input/output	Serial EEPROM data
RB2	input	wpm select
RB3	input	wpm select
RB4	input	Keyboard clock
RB5	input	Keyboard data
RB6	input	Timer select
RB7	input	Timer select
RTCC	counter input	wpm select

minutes. If the **PLAY/PROGRAM** button is pressed, an ID input occurs, or the timer times out, the message plays, then resets the timer.

The timer's period is measured from the end of the last message played to the start of the next message. S1-1, S1-2, and S1-3 select the speed at which the CW message is sent. The eight available speeds are 5, 7.5, 10, 13, 15, 18, 20 and 25 wpm. Sound is produced by a piezo speaker that is controlled by S1-7. The speaker is driven by a square wave with a frequency of approximately 600 Hz. The square-wave harmonics give the sound a higher pitch than normal because the speaker's response at 600 Hz is poor. Like most piezo speakers, the one I use is non-

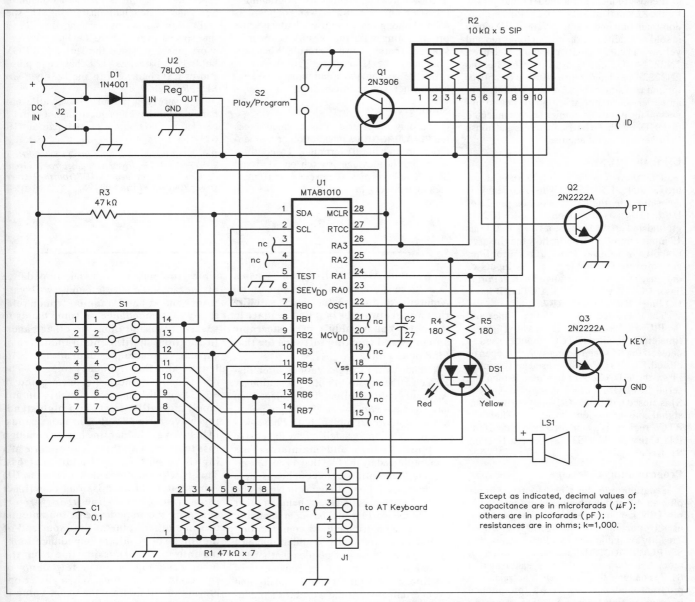

Figure 1—Schematic of the WB2OXJ Ultimate IDer. All resistors are ¹/₈-W, 5%-tolerance carbon-composition or film units. Equivalent parts can be substituted. Part numbers in parentheses are Digi-Key (701 Brooks Ave S, PO Box 677, Thief River Falls, MN 56701-0677, tel 800-344-4539, 218-681-6674, fax 218-681-3880).

C1—0.1 µF, 25 V (P4887-ND)
C2—27 pF, 25 V (P4842-ND)
DS1—Two-colored LED, red/yellow (P509-ND)
J1—5-pin standard-size DIN PC-board-mount female socket (CP-2350-ND)
J2—PC-board-mount 9-V battery clips (male, BSPCM-ND; female, BSPCF-ND)
LS1—Piezo speaker (available from the author; see Note 1)
Q1—2N3906 (2N3906-ND)
Q2, Q3—2N2222A or PN2222A (PN2222A-ND)

R1—47 kΩ 7-resistor common-terminal SIP (Q7473-ND)
R2—10 kΩ 5-resistor isolated-terminator SIP (Q6103-ND)
S1—7-position SPST DIP switch (CT2067-ND)
S2—Miniature SPST pushbutton (P8011S-ND)
U1—Microchip PICSEE MTA81010 serial EEPROM, see Note 1 (MTA81010-RC-P-ND)
U2—78L05, positive 5-V, 100-mA regulator (AN78L05-ND)

IDer Specifications
Supply voltage: 7.5 to 20 V dc
Current requirements with LED, speaker and timer off: 2.5 mA
Current requirements with LED, speaker off and timer on: 3.5 mA
(When on, each LED draws 17 mA; the speaker draws 15 mA)
PTT and KEY outputs off: <40 V; on: <500 mA
CW speed: 5 to 25 wpm
Audio tone: square wave, approximately 600 Hz
Size: 2¹/₄×2¹/₈ inches

polarized, but has polarity markings to indicate phasing. For some reason, the piezo-speaker volume is louder when the positive (+) terminal is connected to the microcontroller port and the negative (–) lead to +5 V. The bicolored LED (DS1) is controlled by S1-6 and monitors the **PTT** and **KEY** outputs.

I chose to use red for the **PTT** and yellow for the **KEY** indicators because yellow is more dominant than red. (Actually, the LED I used is sold as green and orange, but looks red and yellow.) The **PTT** and **KEY** outputs each use a 2N2222A (Q2 and Q3). In its off state, the 2N2222A can handle up to 40 V on its collector and can sink 500 mA when saturated. In an RF environment, it's a good idea to bypass all the input and outputs leads connected to the IDer with 0.01-μF capacitors and house the IDer in a metal enclosure.

Using the PICSEE

The microcontroller's clock runs at approximately 1.57 MHz. This frequency is determined by the RC network on pin 22 of U1 that consists of a 27-pF capacitor (C2) to ground and a 10-kΩ resistor to +5 V. U1 has 12 input/output (I/O) ports; how they're used is shown in Table 1. These I/O control lines are software selectable to act as inputs or outputs. The lines are arranged so that Port A has 4 I/Os: RA0 through RA3. Port B has 8 I/O lines: RB0 through RB7.

The IDer needs 13 input/output lines, but the PICSEE has only 12. Here's how the real time clock counter (RTCC) input is used to detect if the S1 speed-select switch is open or closed. The RTCC input is used as a counter. First, the RTCC count is cleared, then the serial EEPROM's clock is toggled. Only if S1 is closed will the RTCC input see the clock signal and increment its count. Then the RTCC register is tested for a zero state. If the RTCC register is 0, S1-1 is open; a 1 means S1-1 is closed.

Programming a Message

Programming the IDer is easy. Simply plug an AT-compatible keyboard into the 5-pin DIN keyboard jack. (If your keyboard uses a 6-pin mini-DIN connector, you'll need a readily available adapter.) Press pushbutton S2 (**PLAY/PROGRAM**) and hold it closed for more than two seconds. If speaker switch S1-7 is on, you'll hear a beep. You're now in program mode. If you hear a low-pitched beep when you release S2, that means no keyboard was detected and you're returned to play mode.

Once in program mode, key in your message. (In program mode, the **PTT** and **KEY** outputs are disabled.) With each typed character, the IDer's sidetone plays the corresponding CW character at 20 wpm. If you enter an incorrect character, use the backspace key to erase it and retype. When you've completed your message, press the **Enter** or **Escape** key.

A few CW prosigns are available and are entered by using the function keys: **F1** = /$\overline{SK}$, **F2**= /$\overline{AR}$, **F3** = /$\overline{AS}$, **F4** = /$\overline{BK}$ and **F5** = /$\overline{BT}$. Since the **Shift** keys are disabled, use the tilde

(~) key to enter a question mark (?), and the opening square bracket ([ ) key to enter a colon (:).

Battery Life Considerations

With the keyboard LEDs off, some AT-compatible keyboards draw only about 2 mA, but most draw about 40 mA. Battery operation was not intended for programming the IDer unless a low-power keyboard is used. Although you can use a battery while programming with the 40-mA keyboards, shortened battery life is the result. When programming the IDer using battery power, make the session quick and unplug the keyboard when you're finished.

Summary

To play the IDer's message once, press the **PLAY/PROGRAM** pushbutton or momentarily ground the **ID** terminal. To continuously play a message, switch on S1-4 and S1-5. To play a message every 5 or 10 minutes, selectively turn on S1-4 or S1-5 (see

Table 2). S1-1, S1-2 and S1-3 select the playback speed (see Table 1). S1-6 turns on the LED that monitors both the **PTT** and the **KEY** output. S1-7 turns on the speaker.

I developed this IDer because of a need for an easily programmable unit. Using a PC keyboard was about the easiest method I could think of! In addition to its use with repeaters, this unit is ideal for transmitter hunts and amateur balloon tracking. The special call or suffix can be changed easily for that special event. There's even room for a short message, since the serial EEPROM holds 127 characters (127 characters plus 1 end-of-text character fills the 128-byte-size SEEPROM.

I'm sure you'll find this versatile unit handy. If you have any questions about it, I'll be glad to QSO on the twisted pair at 410-643-1581.

Bob Silva has been a ham for 25 years. He is currently self-employed as an electronic circuit designer. Bob obtained his BET from the University of Central Florida in 1981.

Q David McDaniel, AB5UE, asks, "Are there any plans to put up an Amateur Radio geostationary satellite that would always be in the same place in the sky? You wouldn't need steerable antennas and tracking software for that kind of satellite."

A The AMSAT organizations often discuss the possibility of a geostationary Amateur Radio satellite. The project even has a name—*Phase 4*. As you might guess, the most serious problem with Phase 4 is cost. Geostationary satellites are expensive to build, launch and maintain. This is complicated by the fact that a geostationary satellite positioned over our hemisphere would be useful only to hams in North and South America. As a result, hams in other areas of the world would be understandably reluctant to contribute to its construction.

But amateur satellite builders haven't given up on Phase 4. One idea that's been kicked around is a *drifting* geostationary satellite. Such a bird would be positioned over certain areas of the world for a predetermined time, then moved so that it can "see" a different part of the globe. My guess is that you won't see Phase 4 until well into the next century. Phase 3D is likely to keep satellite-active hams busy for at least a decade.

Q Tom Wood, KB5QLT, asks, "I recently put up a multiband dipole fed with 450-Ω ladder line. My antenna tuner loads up fine on all bands except 40 meters. What can I do to fix this?

A You have selected the simplest multiband antenna. It is not without its pos-

sible problems, though. The impedance of the antenna wire element will vary from band to band, ranging from a relatively low impedance on some bands to several thousand ohms on other bands. In addition, it will contain inductive or capacitive reactance, depending on its length and the frequency in use. The 450-Ω ladder line is not terminated in 450 Ω on all bands (or possibly on any band) and will operate at a high standing-wave ratio (SWR) on most bands. (This is okay; ladder line has low enough loss to begin with that it can operate at a high SWR without much additional loss. This is why the antenna works so well!) A mismatched transmission line will act as a transmission-line *transformer*, changing the impedance at the antenna to some other value at the input end of the line. The resultant impedance looking into the transmission line from the tuner can range from a few ohms to several thousand ohms. When you're operating on 40 meters, the exact value is outside the matching range of your antenna tuner.

Although the SWR on the ladder line does not change materially along its length, the exact impedance *does* change with distance. The easiest fix is to change the length of the feed line. I suggest you add a $\frac{1}{8}$-wavelength piece (this is about 15 feet on 40 meters). This will probably change the impedance enough to make your antenna system load up fine on 40 meters. Unfortunately, this could simply move the problem to another band, so be prepared to experiment a bit with different configurations.

By Steve Ford, WB8IMY

DX *PacketClusters*

The time-saving solution for busy DXers and contesters!

I'd love to spend hours trolling the HF bands. I really would. With a hot cup of coffee at my side, I could spend these chilly winter evenings searching for DX on my favorite bands. And then there are the contests. You can burn through several hours hunting for that last state, section, country or whatever.

In truth, however, I'm typical of most middle-aged and younger hams—the majority of the ham population today. Our evenings and weekends are filled with school or family activities. We have to squeeze Amateur Radio into those few precious moments when we can park ourselves in front of our radios.

So how do you reconcile the desperate need to pursue DX or contests, and still find time to meet all your other commitments? Wouldn't it be nice if someone could at least do the hunting for you? That's the most time-consuming part. With the reports of their "reconnaissance" in hand, you could choose which "prey" you wanted to stalk.

But who would be crazy enough to volunteer for such a job? As it turns out, there are thousands of such "volunteers" throughout the nation…and thanks to some nifty software developed by Dick Newell, AK1A, they're connected to *DX PacketClusters*!

As Close as your TNC

If you have a packet radio setup (a 2-meter FM transceiver, terminal node controller [TNC] and a computer or data terminal), you're ready to enjoy the advantages of *PacketClusters*. A *PacketCluster* is a network of relaying nodes devoted to contesting and DX hunting. Some *PacketCluster* networks are small, single-node systems with a dozen users or so (see Figure 1). Other networks are vast, with many nodes interconnected using VHF/UHF or Internet links (see Figure 2).

Regardless of its size, a *PacketCluster* exists for one fundamental purpose: *sharing information*. When a ham sends a piece of information to a *PacketCluster* node (the appearance of a rare DX station, for example), the node relays it to everyone connected to the network. If you're on the network, you share the "profits."

Busy hams like me can connect to their nearest *PacketCluster* nodes and, within seconds, receive lists of all the most recent DX sightings. In the blink of an eye I can see which bands are hot at the moment, and which DX stations are on the air (and at what frequencies). And if I'm the lucky guy who stumbles across a DX signal first, I can post the information for everyone else to see. (Share and share alike!) If I'm dabbling in a contest, I can connect to the *PacketCluster* and determine where to find the stations I need to boost my score.

The Basics

You connect to a *PacketCluster* in the same way you'd connect to any other packet station. However, the information you'll receive will be very different!

The secret of using a *PacketCluster* is knowing the various commands. The most common ones are shown in Table 1.

My routine is to connect to my nearest node and immediately ask for a list of the latest DX sightings using the **SHOW/DX** command (Figure 3). Then, I take a peek at solar conditions by sending **SHOW/WWV**. By sending these two commands, I receive a capsule summary of band conditions and DX activity.

If I'm tuning through the bands I might stumble on a DX station worthy of a *spot* on the cluster. Let's say I hear SV3AQR on

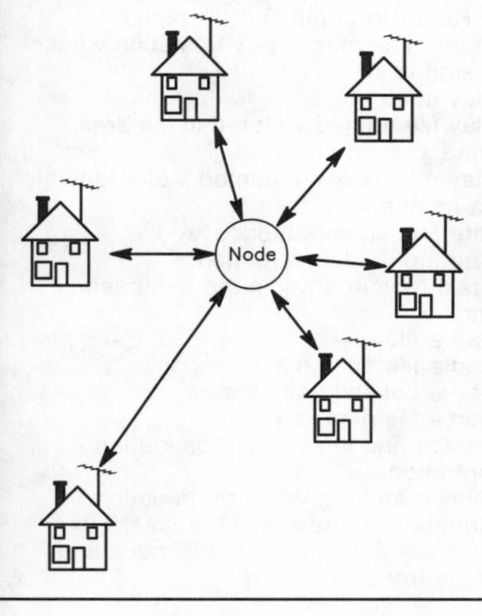

Figure 1—A small *PacketCluster* may be comprised of a single node. Everyone who connects to the node shares the same DX or contest information.

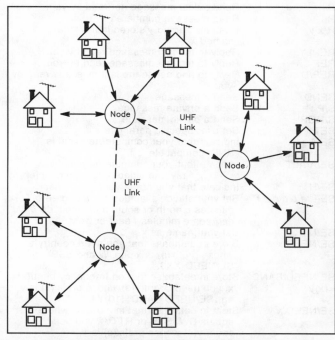

Figure 2—Other *PacketCluster* networks are huge, covering entire states or regions. The individual nodes often use UHF radio links or Internet connections to exchange information.

Table 1

Common *PacketCluster* Commands

Command	Description
ANNOUNCE	Make an announcement.
A x	Send message x to all stations connected to the local node.
A/F x	Send message x to all stations connected to the cluster.
A/x y	Send message y to stations connected to node x.
A/x y	Send message y to stations on distribution list x.
BYE	Disconnect from cluster.
B	Disconnect from cluster.
CONFERENCE node.	Enter the conference mode on the local
CONFER node.	Enter the conference mode on the local
	Send <CTRL-Z> or /EXIT to terminate conference mode.
CONFER/ F	Enter the conference mode on the cluster. Send <CTRL-Z> or /EXIT to terminate conference mode.
DELETE	Delete a message.
DE	Delete last message you read.
DE n	Delete message numbered n.
DIRECTORY	List active messages on local node.
DIR/ALL	List all active messages on local node.
DIR/BULLETIN	List active messages addressed to "all."
DIR/n	List the n most recent active messages.
DIR/NEW	List active messages added since you last invoked the DIR command.
DIR/OWN	List active messages addressed from or to you.
DX	Announce DX station.
DX x y z	Announce DX station whose call sign is x on frequency y followed by comment z, eg, DX SP1N 14.205 up 2.
DX/a x y z	Announce DX station whose call sign is x on frequency y followed by comment z with credit given to station whose call sign is a, eg, DX/K1CC SP1N 14.205 up 2.
FINDFILE	Find file.
FI x	Ask the node to find file named x.
HELP or ?	Display a summary of all commands.
HELP x	Display help for command x.
READ	Read message.
R	Read oldest message not read by you.
Rn	Read message numbered n.
R/x y	Read file named y stored in file area named x.
REPLY	Reply to the last message read by you.
REP	Reply to the last message read by you.
REP/D	Reply to and delete the last message read by you
SEND	Send a message.
S/P	Send a private message.
S/NOP	Send a public message.
SET	Set user-specific parameters.
SE/A	Indicate that your computer/terminal is ANSI-compatible.
SE/A/ALT	Indicate that your computer/terminal is reverse video ANSI-compatible.
SE/H	Indicate that you are in your radio shack.
SE/L a b c d e f	Set your station's latitude as: a degree b minutes c north or south and longitude d degrees e minutes f east or west.
SE/N x	Set your name as x.
SE/NEED x	Store in database that you need country(s) whose prefix(s) is x on CW and SSB. eg, SE/NEED XX9.
SE/NEED/BAND =(x)y	Store in database that on frequency band(s) x, you need country(s) whose prefix(s) is y, eg, SE/NEED/BAND=(10)YA.
SE/NEED/x y	Store in database that in mode x (where x equals CW, SSB or RTTY), you need country(s) whose prefix(s) is y, eg, SENEED/RTTY YA.
SE/NEED/x/BAND	Store in database that in mode x (where

Command	Description
=(y)z	x equals CW, SSB or RTTY) on frequency band(s) y, you need country(s) whose prefix(s) is z, eg, SE/NEED/RTTY/BAND =(10) ZS9.
SE/NOA	Indicate that your computer/terminal is not ANSI-compatible.
SE/NOH	Indicate that you are not in your shack.
SE/Q x	Set your QTH as location x.
SHOW	Display requested information.
SH/A	Display names of files in archive file area.
SH/B	Display names of files in bulletin file area.
SH/C	Display physical configuration of cluster.
SH/C x	Display station connected to node whose call sign is x.
SH/CL	Display names of nodes in clusters, number of local users, number of total users and highest number of connected stations.
SH/COM	Display available show commands.
SH/DX	Display the last five DX announcements.
SH/DX x	Display the last five DX announcements for frequency band x.
SH/DX/n	Display the last n DX announcements.
SH/DX/n x	Display the last n DX announcements for frequency band x.
SH/FI	Display names of files in general files area.
SH/FO	Display mail-forwarding database.
SH/H x	Display heading and distance to country whose prefix is x.
SH/I	Display status of inactivity function and inactivity timer value.
SH/LOC	Display your station's longitude and latitude.
SH/LOC x	Display the longitude and latitude of station whose call sign is x.
SH/LOG	Display last five entries in cluster's log.
SH/LOG n	Display last n entries in cluster's log.
SH/M x	Display MUF for country whose prefix is x.
SH/NE x	Display needed countries for station whose call sign is x.
SH/NE x	Display stations needing country whose prefix is x.
SH/NE/x	Display needed countries for mode x where x equals CW, SSB, or RTTY.
SH/NO	Display system notice.
SH/P x	Display prefix(s) starting with letter(s) x.
SH/QSL x	Display QSL information for station whose call sign is x.
SH/S x	Display sunrise and sunset times for country whose prefix is x.
SH/U	Display call signs of stations connected to the cluster.
SH/V	Display version of the cluster software.
SH/W	Display last five WWV propagation announcements.
TALK	Talk to another station.
T x	Talk to station whose call sign is x. Send <CTRL-Z> to terminate talk mode.
T x y	Send one-line message y to station whose call sign is x.
TYPE	Display a file.
TY/x y	Display file named y stored in file area named x.
TY/x/n y	Display n lines of file named y stored in file area named x.
UPDATE	Update a custom database.
UPDATE/x	Update the database named x.
UPDATE/x/ APPEND	Add text to your entry in the database named x.
UPLOAD	Upload a file.
UP x	Upload a file named x.
UP/B x	Upload a bulletin named x.
UP/F x	Upload a file named x.
WWV	Announce and log WWV propagation information.
W SF=xxx, A=yy, K=zz,a	Announce and log WWV propagation information where xxx is the solar flux, yy is the A-index, zz is the K-index and a is the forecast.

21.250 MHz. I can add this information to the network by sending: **SV3AQR DX 21.250.**

Within seconds the spot will appear on the screens of everyone else who is connected to the network.

One question that comes up often is, "How do I know if a DX station is worthy of an announcement on the *Cluster*?" After all, what's choice DX to one ham is garden variety to another. My advice is to observe the activity on your network before you start posting spots of your own. On some networks, anything goes. Other networks, however, concentrate on rarer contacts. You might receive a sarcastic response if you post a spot for, say, a French station on 20 meters from the east coast. (A contact with France is not rare DX to most hams.)

In either case, make your spots accurate. Be sure you've entered the call sign and frequency correctly. If the DX station is working split, say so. Just a brief comment such as "LISTENING UP 30" is sufficient.

If there is a hot contest in progress, you'll know right away when you connect to the *PacketCluster* (see Figure 4). Just the nature of the spot listings will tip you off. In addition, the node may send a sign-on message telling you that the network is in the "contest mode." This means that certain *PacketCluster* functions are disabled during the contest. Generally speaking, you should only post information about contest contacts when the network is in this mode.

Above and Beyond

PacketClusters have other useful features. You can use the **DIR** command to see a list of bulletins just as you would on a packet BBS. Using the **R** (READ) command will allow you to read any bulletin you wish. Unlike packet bulletin boards, however, *PacketClusters* can relay bulletins and messages only within the networks they serve.

As I'm watching the *PacketCluster*, I see a spot for a DXpedition on Sable Island. Hmmm... I could use that one! I wonder what bands would provide the best propagation from my location to Sable Island? Why not ask the *PacketCluster*? All I have to do is send: **SHOW/M CY0.**

"M" stands for *maximum usable frequency* (or *MUF*) and CY0 is the call sign prefix for Sable Island. Here's how the *PacketCluster* responds:

Sable-Is Propagation: Flux: 137 Sunspots: 90 Rad Angle: 29

Table 2
Additional SHOW Commands

Note: Some of these commands may not work on your local *PacketCluster* network.

Command	Definition
SHOW/BUCKMASTER	Buckmaster US call-sign list
SHOW/RUMORS	Anything and everything!
SHOW/OBLAST	Russian oblast information
SHOW/PREFIX	Listing of countries and zones by prefix
SHOW/ALLOC	ITU allocation table
SHOW/STARS	Planetarium data
SHOW/BAND	Frequencies available for each class of license
SHOW/ZONE	Listing of countries and zones by prefix or zone
SHOW/DXNODES	Database of known DX *PacketCluster* nodes.
SHOW/BUREAU	World and Russian Oblast QSL bureau addresses
SHOW/CONTEST	Calendar and info on DX-related contests
SHOW/COORD	Longitude and latitude of US/DX locations
SHOW/DEALER	Amateur Radio dealer telephone/FAX directory
SHOW/DXCC	ARRL DXCC Country List
SHOW/FCC	FCC Field Office Directory and FCC Info Guide
SHOW/FLUX	Historical sunspot/solar flux data and glossary
SHOW/IRC	Required IRCs for QSL returns and IRC/postal info
SHOW/NCDXF	Information on the Northern California DX Foundation
SHOW/PUB	Directory of Amateur Radio publications from various countries
SHOW/QSLREC	Information on QSL cards received by users
SHOW/RULES	FCC Rules and Regulations Part 97
SHOW/IOTA	Islands on the Air (Award)
SHOW/TODAY	Did you know? Events of yesteryear!
SHOW/COUNTY	Directory of US counties
SHOW/EXTRA	Element 4B Extra Class Q&A
SHOW/INFO	International Q Signals, ARL Messages
SHOW/MIC	MIC wiring data prepared by KC4LWI
SHOW/LADDER	*PacketCluster* DXCC "Ladder of Success"
SHOW/SWL	Shortwave Listeners Guide

Figure 3—When I connect to my local *PacketCluster* node (KC8PE), I usually ask for a list of the most recent DX spots. I follow up with a request for WWV solar activity reports.

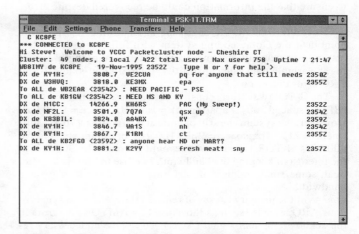

Figure 4—Here's a snapshot of my local *PacketCluster* network during the 1995 ARRL November Phone Sweepstakes. Notice that several spots have been posted for "rare" sections.

Dist: 995 km   Hops: 1

MUF (90%): 9.0 (50%): 10.7 (10%): 13.1

The MUF calculations tell me that propagation to the island is most reliable at 9 MHz (90%), but drops rapidly as the frequency increases. The 30-meter band (10 MHz) would be the best bet.

DX PacketClusters also allow you to chat with other stations in the network. You can send a simple greeting by using the **TALK** command:

TALK KX4V Hello, Rick. Nice job working 5U7M!

If Rick wants to talk to me at length, he can use the same TALK command to establish a link between our stations. The *PacketCluster* will continue to show us new DX sightings as they appear, but everything we type will be sent to each other.

If you want to see how the *Cluster* network is configured and who's connected to it, just send the **SHOW/C** (show configuration) command. The *PacketCluster* will respond with a complete list of every station connected to the network grouped by the node they're using. Here's a typical example:

PacketCluster Configuration:

Node	Connected stations
KC8PE	N1API KS1L K1WJL KC1SJ WB8IMY
W1RM	(WB1AIU) NT0Z KA1BSA AB1U KB1LE N1JBH N1GLA KG1D-1 (NJ2L) (NA1I) KB1HY K1FRD NX1L KB1BE W1CKA KB1CQ (W1GG) K1ZJH WB1GUY K1KI
K2TR	KA2EXB (K2QE) N2JJ NJ1F K2VV (KB2HUN) K2ONP KQ2K WK2H KA2HTU WS2U N2EKU

You can send TALK messages, or enter into a conversation, with any ham on the list. The only exceptions are call signs in parenthesis. These hams are connected to the *Cluster*, but they're away from their keyboards temporarily. How does the system know this? Actually, it doesn't—unless you tell it. (Yes, there is a command for this, too!) And like packet bulletin boards, you don't need to send the full command every time. Instead, you can use the abbreviated form such as **SH/DX** rather than **SHOW/DX**.

There are many other functions available, depending on the sophistication of your local network. See Table 2 for some of the more versatile and interesting SHOW commands.

Where's My *PacketCluster*?

There are *PacketCluster* networks in most urban areas, and even in some lightly populated regions of our country. Ron Rueter, NV6Z, maintains a list of active *Cluster* networks, but it's too large to publish here. If you have Internet access, you can obtain the list from the ARRL InfoServer. Simply address an e-mail message to: **info@arrl.org**. Leave the subject line blank. In the body of your message enter the following on separate lines:

SEND CLUSTER.TXT

QUIT

The server will send you the complete list right away. You'll also find CLUSTER.TXT on the ARRL *Hiram* BBS at 860-594-0306. List updates can be found at the following Internet ftp site: **pinsight.com** in the directory /pub/K6PBT.

And what if there are no *PacketClusters* in your area? Consider starting your own! You can obtain more information about *PacketCluster* software from the manufacturer: Pavilion Software, 8 Mount Royal Ave, Marlborough, MA 01752. Enclose a self-addressed, stamped envelope.

Q Can you give me the real nitty-gritty about G-TOR? I know it's a form of HF digital communication, but I'm coming up short on how it works and what sort of equipment is required.

A G-TOR is an acronym for *Golay*-coded *T*eleprinting *O*ver *R*adio. Golay coding is the error-correction system created by M. J. E. Golay and used by the *Voyager* spacecraft. Sending billions of bytes of data across the solar system required a scheme to ensure that the information could be recovered despite errors caused by interference, noise, and so on.

To create G-TOR, the engineers at Kantronics Corporation combined the Golay coding system with full-frame data interleaving, on-demand Huffman compression, run-length encoding, a variable data rate capability (100 to 300 bit/s) and 16-bit CRC error detection.

The G-TOR waveform consists of two phase-continuous tones (BFSK) spaced 200 Hz apart (mark = 1600 Hz, space = 1800 Hz). However, the system can still operate at the familiar 170-Hz shift (mark = 2125 Hz, space = 2295 Hz). The optimum spacing for 300-bit/s G-TOR transmissions would normally be 300 Hz. In the interest of keeping the bandwidth as close to 500 Hz as practical, some small amount of performance is traded-off to save bandwidth.

One of the primary causes of reduced throughput on synchronous ARQ signals (such as those used by AMTOR) is errors in the acknowledgment signal (ACK). To reduce unnecessary retransmissions due to faulty ACKs, G-TOR uses *fuzzy* ACKs. This system allows receiving stations to tolerate a small number of errors in an ACK signal, rather than ignoring it completely and automatically resending the data. If you want the details of this complex protocol, I suggest you read "G-TOR: A Hybrid ARQ Protocol for Narrow Bandwidth HF Data Communication" by Phil Anderson, WØXI, in the May 1994 *QEX* (the ARRL experimenter's magazine).

As this issue went to press, G-TOR was available in only one multimode TNC: the Kantronics *KAM Plus*. MFJ has announced that G-TOR will be available in the MFJ-1278 controller very soon.

If you have an SSB transceiver that will switch from transmit to receive in less than 100 ms (most will), you should be able to use it for G-TOR with little difficulty. You can operate G-TOR in direct FSK or AFSK. Most G-TOR operators are using AFSK, however. No special software is required other than a terminal program to interface with the TNC.

Q James Nichols, KQ4YC, asks, "I'm operating a VHF/HF packet gateway station. I've been asked to leave it on continuously, but what happens if, say, a codeless Technician licensee accesses the gateway when I'm not there?"

A It's perfectly legal for codeless Technicians to use your packet gateway to access the HF subbands specified in 97.221 (b), whether you're present or not. This is not a remote-base situation. Instead, your gateway is operating automatically. The distinction is important. Unlike a remote base, your gateway users cannot perform control-operator activities (such as changing frequencies). Instead, they simply connect on VHF and your station relays the data on the appropriate HF frequency. They're operating their stations legally and so are you.

By Donald Cox, AA3EK

ACARS: Packet for Airplanes

A new digital communication mode for commercial airliners and business jets

Do you remember the flight attendant on your last airline flight reading off the list of connecting gate numbers as you prepared to land? That information was most likely passed to the flight crew using a new digital communication link called *ACARS*—Aircraft Communications and Reporting System. As complex as it may sound, it's similar in many respects to amateur packet radio.

Until a decade ago, almost all radio links between the ground and commercial aircraft used voice communication to relay weather, position, aircraft performance and departure/arrival reports. The airlines supported the creation of an organization, Aeronautical Radio Inc (ARINC), to run a network of ground stations with which to communicate with airliners anywhere in the world. VHF, HF and satellite links were used to stay in touch with aircraft.

The expansion in air traffic, reduction in the size of flight crews, and the automation of aircraft cockpit and control systems generated the need for a faster and more efficient system for handling communication with aircraft aloft. The result was the creation of ACARS, a digital data link system designed to use existing ground station and aircraft radio equipment, and to enhance air-ground-air communication.

The Heart of ACARS

On board the aircraft, the heart of the ACARS system is a computer that receives data from the cockpit or other aircraft systems and passes it to the VHF radio for transmission to the ground. In the cockpit, the pilots have their own terminal and keyboard to display incoming messages and to compose outgoing requests and reports. A printer provides the crew with a hard copy of the messages.

The ACARS computer can also be linked to other on-board avionics systems. When tied to these systems, the ACARS system can automatically pass aircraft and engine performance data to the ground. Many airlines and aerospace firms routinely collect performance data that is passed to their engineering staffs for analysis and early identification of problems or performance improvements.

ACARS messages currently carry weather reports, arrival and departure time reports and aircraft system data dumps. Plans call for ACARS-derived systems to be used eventually to handle most of the air traffic control messages. Instead of a controller on the

ACARS Hardware, Software and Resources

Decoders and Demodulators

A number of commercial demodulators are available to receive VHF-band ACARS messages, including several under $99. All use the audio output of any VHF receiver/scanner capable of covering the 129 to 132-MHz AM aircraft bands.

AEA ACARS, produced by Advanced Electronics Applications, is an IBM PC-compatible serial-port decoder and DOS-based software system. A 386 or higher CPU is recommended. A software-only version of the system is also available to use with AEA PK-900 or DSP-232 multi-mode controllers, or AEA FAX decoders. The software includes options to suppress the display of messages received with parity errors, write messages to disk, print them, change screen colors, and review and manage log files. A 132-page manual documents ACARS message formats and the extensive reference information necessary for understanding the messages.

The AEA ACARS serial decoder and software package is available from many AEA product distributors, or from AEA, PO Box C2160, 2006 196th St SW, Lynnwood, WA 98036; tel 206-774-5554. AEA ACARS software for PK-900, DSP-232 or AEA FAX product owners is also available separately.

Lowe Airmaster 2.0 is distributed by Lowe Electronics and uses the same basic DOS software as the AEA system, but a different serial-port decoder. Like the AEA software, message fields are broken apart and displayed separately and there are message printing and logging options. It comes with a 24-page manual.

Universal Radio's M-400 is a stand-alone hardware reader that decodes ACARS messages and displays them in the raw, transmitted format. Their M-1200 PC card and M-8000 hardware systems also receive ACARS and display it in the same manner. Universal's product line also includes the ACT-1 PC serial port decoder and DOS-based software system. It comes with a 33-page manual and a copy of the book *Understanding ACARS*. The ACT-1 software includes several message displays and filtering options and displays message fields individually. Universal Radio M-400, the M-1200 PC card, ACT-1, and the M-8000 are available from Universal Radio, 6830 Americana Parkway, Reynoldsburg, OH; tel 800-431-3939.

Books

Understanding ACARS by Ed Flynn, third edition, published in 1995 by Universal Radio. 92 pages.

Complete technical details on the ACARS message format and system architecture is documented in a series of ARINC technical publications, available for $65 to $80 from ARINC Document Section M/S 5-123, 2551 Riva Rd, Annapolis, MD 21401-7465; tel 410-266-4117; fax 410-266-2047.

ARINC Characteristic 724B-2: Aircraft Communications Addressing and Reporting System (ACARS), November 1993. A follow-up to ARINC Characteristic 597-5 covering second-generation ACARS units.

ARINC Characteristic 620-2: Data Link Ground System Standard and Interface Specification, December 1994. Complete technical reference on ACARS message formats.

ARINC Characteristic 635: HF Data Link Protocols, August 1990. Technical reference on HF ACARS system design, message and data link formats.

Cyberspace

Web sites with ACARS information include **http://barbie.epsilon.nl/~bart**, **http://web.inter.nl.net/hcc/Hans.Wildschut**, **http://www.u-net.com/~morfis/acars.htm** and **http://www.arinc.com**.

Table 1
ACARS Message Types

Label	Message Type
:;	Data transceiver autotune
5D	ATIS request
5P	Temporary suspension of ACARS
5R	Aircrew initiated position report
5U	Weather request
5Y	Aircrew revision of previous ETA or diversion report
5Z	Airline designated downlink
7A	Aircrew initiated engine data/takeoff thrust report
7B	Aircrew entered miscellaneous message
10-49	User-defined functions
51	Ground GMT request/GMT update
54	Aircrew initiated voice contact request/voice go-ahead
57	Alternate aircrew initiated position report
80-89	Aircrew addressed downlinks
C1	Printer message
F3	Dedicated transceiver advisory
H1	Optional auxiliary terminal message
Q0	Link test
Q1	Departure/arrival report
Q2	ETA report
Q3	Clock update advisory
Q4	Voice circuit busy
Q5	Unable to deliver uplinked message
Q6	Voice to ACARS channel changeover
Q7	Delay message
QA	Out/fuel report
QB	Off report
QC	On report
QD	In/fuel/destination report
QE	Out/fuel/destination report
QF	Off/destination report
QG	Out/return in report
QH	Out report
QK	Landing report
QL	Arrival report
QM	Arrival information report
QN	Diversion report
RA	Command/response uplink
RB	Command/response downlink

3C01 POSWX 1722/18

Table 2
ACARS Message Examples

Message label: RA GATE ASSIGN UA837 EWRSFO GATE 82 FREQ 129.5 EON 1844 APU OFF	Translation: United flight 837 from Newark to San Francisco will arrive at gate 82 at 1844 GMT. The aircraft is to turn off its auxiliary power unit upon arrival and contact United operations on129.5 MHz.
Message label: C1 Flight ID: DDAA 2 Message content:- 10012 FROM ^D39 13 13 AN N41063/GL IAD- WX RADAR SHOWS TSTMS DVLPG ALNG THE SOUTH SHORE OF L.I. ALSO ONE LG CELL TO FL600 OVE HUO MOVG SE-20KTS.	Translation: weather advisory message from ground to American Airlines aircraft N41063 near Washington, DC, advising of thunderstorms near Long Island.
Message label: QF Flight ID: CO1854 Message content:- DTW1646EWR	Translation: Departure message from Continental flight 1854, which departed Detroit at 1646 GMT for Newark.
Message label: 40 Flight ID: 0023 Message content:- ARR ORD ARR M20 BAG IAB DEST GATE DALLAS/FT W H6 DENVER H15 KANSAS CITY K15 LOS ANGELES H1	Translation: Message from ground with list of gates for connecting flights at Chicago. The flight will arrive at gate M20.
Message label: 80 Block ID: 7 Msg. no: 1553 Flight ID: DL1722 Message content: KDFW/KLGA .N922D /POS OTT /OVR 2214/ALT 370/FOB 0132/SAT 61 /WND 246025/MCH 746/TRB SMOOTH / SKY CLEAR	Translation: Delta flight 1722 from Dallas to NY is over Nottingham, MD (OTT) at 2214 GMT, flying at 37,000 feet, with 13,200 lb of fuel on board, air temp of −61 deg, wind from 246 deg at 25 kt, speed Mach 0.746 with a smooth ride and clear sky.
Message label: 40 Flight ID: 0023 B Message content: HX TO ORD 28JUL/1745Z POSN-07B KWRD-SEAT ARM-6847007H TRAY TABLE WILL NOT RETRACT/	Translation: aircraft advising ground maintenance that the tray table in seat 7B is broken.
Message label: 5Z Block ID: 4 Msg. no: 1846 Flight ID: US0065 Message content:- /ENG/0938/350/248/740/ 432/M19/M44/199/ 199/860/850/454/433/ 855/880/2750/2700	Translation: a data dump from USAir flight 65 showing it at 93,800 lb of fuel, 35,000 feet altitude, 248 kt speed, Mach 0.74, true airspeed 432 kt, indicated & true outside temp of −19 and −44 degrees C. Pairs of data for the plane's two engines follow: EPR of 1.99/1.99, N1 = 86.0/85.0%, EGT = 454/433 deg C, N2 = 85.5/88.0%, fuel flow = 2750/2700 lb/hr.

ground talking to the flight crew via voice radio, the controller will transmit a digital message to the flight crew to tell them to climb or turn. Most new commercial aircraft are equipped with ACARS systems, as well as a significant number of private business jets. Airlines are already experimenting with the use of in-flight satellite communication links and HF links to carry ACARS messages. This would allow global coverage and would reduce the need for an extensive network of ground stations.

You Can Receive ACARS

Most commercial receivers and scanners capable of receiving the VHF aircraft-band AM transmissions can receive the 129 to 132-MHz ACARS frequencies. A growing number of modern Amateur Radio 2-meter transceivers can also cover this band. ACARS frequencies in the US include 131.550, 130.025, and 129.125 MHz; in Europe, 131.725 and 131.525; in Asia, 131.450; and Air Canada has used 131.475 MHz. The 131.550-MHz frequency is considered the primary channel in the US. ACARS-like transmissions on HF have been observed on 6.646, 10.027 and 13.339 MHz on flights traveling the North Atlantic routes.

VHF ACARS reception is easiest for most hams. All you need is an ACARS demodulator connected to the speaker output of your scanner or transceiver and your computer. The demodulator translates the ACARS audio tones into data your computer can understand. Specialized software running on your PC displays the ACARS information on your monitor. See the sidebar, "ACARS Hardware, Software and Resources."

Depending on where you live, a simple omnidirectional antenna such as a ground plane or J-pole is perfectly adequate. An outdoor antenna is best, but even an indoor antenna can bring you plenty of action. Some have also reported success using only telescoping whips and rubber-duck antennas, but they're the options of *last* resort.

You can expect to receive ACARS transmissions from high-altitude aircraft 150 to 200 miles away. If you're lucky enough to

```
Message content:-
3401/08 KATL/EDDM .N172DN
60 MINUTE OUT TEST CHEC
K OK ON ENGINE 2330Z

[08/06/1996    19:30]
ACARS mode: 2  Aircraft reg: .N915DL
Message label: Q8  Block id: 3  Msg. no: 3043
Flight id: DL0635
Message content:-

[08/06/1996    19:30]
ACARS mode: 2  Aircraft reg: .N912DL
Message label: 80  Block id: 3  Msg. no: 3118
Flight id: DL0439
Message content:-
3701 INRANG 0439/08 KATL/KIAD .N912DL
/ERT 2243
```

```
<PgUp> = scroll back        <* AEA ACARS *>        Data->
```

AEA ACARS software decodes received data and displays the results on your monitor.

```
File  Search  Log  *Filter  Options                        Help
Seq.   Date     Time     M  ADDR  ML B  MSN  FID   MESSAGE

0016  11/08/95  18:16:59 2 ..N791N  Q8 6  1650 PI1897
0017  11/08/95  18:17:06 2 .N779AU  52 7  1656 US1041  /IR BWI
0018  11/08/95  18:17:11 2 QQq791N  Q0 J  N)50 P)N79w  ~W~
0019  11/08/95  18:17:11 2 .N904DE  Q0 J  NHLG  ;3NOLH  !\0
0020  11/08/95  18:17:40 R QQQq 1U  _^ 7  Mm1> 8,0P/q  !         v
0021  11/08/95  18:17:58 2 ...NSN>    G  M7A  ,7000 !P( PA T(J - 5 H Em    zC
0022  11/08/95  18:18:00 R Q115J*>    5  18:8 U=0Bn0 !   RD   ~)c_UR
0023  11/08/95  18:18:11 J QqJJyUA  _^ K  N7Oh UA0FN/
0024  11/08/95  18:18:11 r QQ-N31U  nK 0  2rY> 8,P0OA WM~ >8q4P 2N(7K2u7J,US -PQT
                                                       >,x__) P_?,TC  Q>Wx~** ~?
0025  11/08/95  18:18:19 2 ...NS U  _^ q  :4P> 8,00DN
0026  11/08/95  18:18:26 2 .N653UA  H1 2  D005 UA0946 #DFB/PIREPUA.E22C246530946KIA
                                                       DEHAM11 8952318CL  122 DATA N
                                                       OT AVAILABLE   38.9713 -77.46
                                                       3223 9  1450  0.2286 22    39.
                                                       1175 -77.50512312  6482-
0027  11/08/95  18:18:32 2 .N779AU  52 8  1903 US1041  /IR BWI
0028  11/08/95  18:18:33 2 .N653UA  H1 3  D006 UA0946 #DFB12.8296 30   39.1102 -77.
                                                       16662316 11517-19.8296 31
0029  11/08/95  18:18:35 2 ...N31U  _^ 3 -L=  8P0000  12h
```

```
ACT-1 1.01
```

The *ACT-1* ACARS software from Universal Radio displays the data in a column format.

live near an airport, you might be able to receive ACARS ground-to-air uplink messages.

Understanding ACARS Messages

The VHF ACARS frequencies carry a large volume of traffic between aircraft and ground stations. The types of information in the transmissions varies widely. It can range from simple arrival or departure reports, to lengthy downlinks of navigation, engine and performance data. Messages might include weather observations and forecasts; departure clearances and checklists; flight plans; navigation positions; aircraft and engine performance data; arrival, departure and delay reports; equipment malfunction reports; crew reports; and connecting gate lists.

Like amateur packet, ACARS transmissions are very short, burst-type signals that last only a fraction of a second. Each message is broken up into a number of subfields. The seven-character address field contains the registration number of the aircraft. The registration number is the official number assigned to the aircraft by the government. International agreements dictate a letter prefix indicating the country of origin. For US aircraft, all registration numbers begin with "N." Shortwave radio listeners and ham radio operators will notice the similarity between these letters and the radio call sign allocations for the same countries. The following give some examples of registration numbers for airliners from several countries: N14245, USA; C-FDSN, Canada; G-BNLR, Britain; D-AIBE, Germany; JA8097, Japan; HB-IGC, Switzerland; and PH-BFH, The Netherlands.

A number of references and computer databases have compilations of registration numbers for aircraft around the world. These can be used to quickly identify the type of aircraft sending an ACARS message, the aircraft operator and other related information.

A series of two-character message labels have been defined to designate the type of message being sent. These include a number of fixed-format messages with key information like arrival/departure times (so-called on/off times) and fuel loaded, as well as a number of labels with variable formats that can be defined by the aircraft operators. These labels are crucial to understanding the type of information in the message; they are frequently the entire extent of the message themselves. For example, if the message label is "51," the aircraft is requesting the ground to update its on-board clock. A short list of these labels is shown in Table 1.

Several examples of ACARS communications between the ground and aircraft are shown in Table 2. ACARS messages use a shorthand style of abbreviations and a good reference is necessary to fully understand the message contents.

Give It a Try!

ACARS monitoring is a fun and relatively inexpensive addition to your ham activities. By following the message traffic, you'll gain an educational insight into airline operations, how flights are planned and flown, the types of daily challenges they experience, and much more. Best of all, you'll quickly appreciate the complexity and sophistication of today's airlines and air traffic control systems.

PO Box 11130
Washington, DC 20008-0330
e-mail 74507.3446@compuserve.com

QST~

Q Dr Alan Kelley, KC7EIE, asks, "I often do relief work in Third-World countries in Africa and Asia and I would like to use Amateur Radio to communicate with friends at home. Since I prefer digital communication, I've been looking into the packet satellites. Do you think they would be appropriate—especially for portable operation in rural areas?"

A If you want a reliable Amateur Radio link to your hometown from Asia and Africa, satellite packet at 9600 baud is probably the way to go. No matter where you are in the world, you would enjoy several useable satellite passes each day. The same would be true for the folks at home.

In addition to a 9600-baud compatible VHF/UHF FM transceiver and a laptop computer, you'll need a 9600-baud TNC. The good news is that most of these hardware items are compact and easy to transport. And since you'll be operating from areas with relatively few amateurs, "signal competition" should be almost nil. That being the case, simple omnidirectional antennas should be sufficient to reach the birds.

If we were having this discussion in the year 1999 or 2000, I'd suggest that you try one of the robust HF digital modes such as CLOVER, G-TOR or PACTOR II. Band conditions by that time should support reliable HF links over great distances on most days. With sunspots few and far between in 1996, however, a portable HF amateur station might have a tough time spanning the distances you require.

One caution: check on licensing before you go. Not all countries permit amateurs to use the satellite frequencies you will need.

Q Vernon Beck Jr, N3JWP, asks, "What is the proper procedure to join a net that's already in progress?"

A If the net you wish to join is a *directed net* managed by a net-control station (NCS), the standard procedure is to wait until the NCS asks for additional check-ins. On voice nets, the NCS may simply say, "Are there any additional check-ins for the net? Please call now." That's your cue to speak your call sign. On less formal nets, you may have to assert yourself by saying "check in!" between transmissions.

On CW nets, the NCS will usually ask for check-ins by sending QNI at the appropriate time. As with voice nets, this is your opportunity to send your call sign and join the net.

By Donald Cox, AA3EK

Explore HF/VHF Digital and Image Modes on the Cheap

Use software to "try before you buy."

If you are new to ham radio, or are a seasoned veteran just curious about the many digital and image signal modes heard on the HF and VHF bands, you can take a peek at these modes for just a few dollars before committing to the purchase of a full-featured multimode controller or TNC.

The key to this exploration is the vast array of software that has been developed by hams and other creative individuals. Coupled with an IBM PC-compatible computer, programs like *HamComm*, *JVFAX* and *PKTMON* will allow you to explore Baudot RTTY, ASCII, CW, AMTOR, SSTV, WEFAX, or HF/VHF packet modes using a simple serial-port decoder that costs less than $10 to build (see Figure 1)!

You don't need a souped-up computer to run these programs. A PC with a 386 CPU, VGA graphics and color monitor, and *DOS* 3.0 will suffice. Better-quality graphics capabilities will produce improved pictures for SSTV/WEFAX image modes. If you don't already own one, these computers can be found at hamfests, garage sales, or used computer stores for $200 to $350. Used 486 PCs with better graphics and later versions of DOS are widely available now for only a bit more.

The interface used by all of these programs is a simple 741 op-amp limiting circuit that can be built from a few parts available from stores like Radio Shack. The circuit conditions the receiver's audio output signal and feeds it to the PC via a serial port. Several diodes and capacitors are used to draw and filter power for the interface from the serial port. Assembled commercial versions of the interface are also available, including the MFJ-1213.

The digital and image signal modes all use frequency-shift keying (FSK), where different tone combinations are used to represent various characters or picture colors. The computer software uses the internal computer clock to measure the frequency of the audio signal and convert the tones into data. Details on the structure of digital- and image-mode signals can be found in *The ARRL Handbook*.

The decoding software can be found on a number of computer bulletin boards, Internet sites, on-line services, and some ham

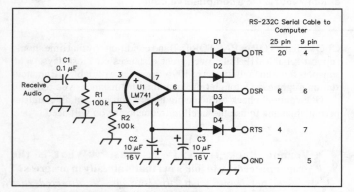

Figure 1—The *HamComm*-style receiver interface. Note that the serial-cable pin numbers differ between the 25-pin and the 9-pin cables. Use a piece of audio coaxial cable to connect the interface to the audio output of your receiver.

C1—0.1 µF ceramic disc (Radio Shack 272-135)
C2, C3—10 µF electrolytic (Radio Shack 272-1013)
D1, D2, D3, D4—1N914 (Radio Shack 276-1122)
R1, R2—100 kΩ, ¼ W (Radio Shack 271-1347)
U1—LM741 op amp (Radio Shack 276-007)

Finding Shareware

Shareware is the name given to software programs that are shared by the developer with the potential users, usually at no initial cost. If the users find the software useful and run it regularly, they are encouraged to send a small registration fee to the developer. In exchange, the developer typically sends the user a program manual and offers future upgrades. Shareware programs occasionally have some features disabled, limitations on how long it can be run, or logos superimposed on the output.

Since they are not commercial software products, you usually can't find shareware at regular computer stores. Almost all of it is downloaded by users from computer bulletin board systems (BBSs) or World Wide Web ftp sites, or it can be found on ham radio shareware CD-ROM disks, or in the libraries of on-line services such as Compuserve's "Hamnet" forum. The software mentioned in this article has been widely distributed to many BBS and ftp sites. Two prominent locations are the ARRL *Hiram* BBS, at 860-594-0306, and on the World Wide Web: (for *HamComm* and *JVFAX*) **ftp://oak.oakland.edu/pub/ hamradio/arrl/bbs/programs/** and (for *PKTMON12*) **ftp:// oak.oakland.edu/pub/hamradio/dos/digital/utils/**.

Shareware usually comes in compressed (ZIP or LZH) formats for faster downloading from BBSs or Web sites. For *HamComm* and *JVFAX* you'll need *PKUNZIP.EXE* to decompress the files. For *PKTMON12* you may need *LHA.EXE* (unless you can find it elsewhere in ZIP format). You will find *PKUNZIP.EXE* everywhere, but *LHA.EXE* is less common. To download *LHA.EXE* on the Web, check **http://www.ami. com.au/bbs/local.html**.

Each shareware program has a file that contains the program documentation or manual. Print it out and read it over to discover all of the program setup and configuration options.

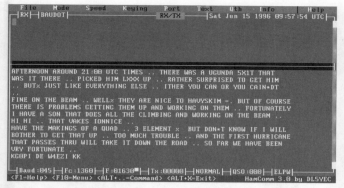

Figure 2—_HamComm_ does an excellent job of decoding several HF digital modes.

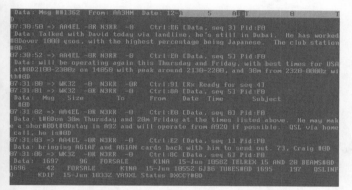

Figure 3—_PKTMON12_ allows you to watch packet traffic from the comfort of your easy chair.

radio software CD-ROMs (see the sidebar "Finding Shareware"). The most recent versions available when this article went to press were _HAMCOM31.ZIP_, _JVFAX71.ZIP_, and _PKTMON12.ZIP_ (older versions of the programs will also work, in most cases). These are shareware or freeware programs that can be freely downloaded. With the interface, your PC, and these software programs, you're now set to explore new signals on the bands.

RTTY and AMTOR

Probably the granddaddy of all HF digital decoding programs is the shareware program _HamComm_ 3.1, by W. F. Schroeder, DL5YEC. _HamComm_ can decode ASCII, Baudot RTTY, AMTOR, PACTOR, NAVTEX, and CW. A wide range of options are included—to change speed, mark/space polarity, shift, and many other parameters. Figure 2 shows _HamComm_ in action.

This versatile software includes several tuning and signal spectrum displays that can be used to tune signals and assess their characteristics. _HamComm_ also is transmit-capable in most of these RTTY modes, using a simple addition to the computer interface circuit.

These digital RTTY modes can be found throughout the amateur, commercial and military bands. Weather data is sent on a number of stations (for example, 10.536 MHz) and AMTOR/SITOR is used for many ship-to-shore communications. A good shortwave reference guide will help you find particular stations, although much of the commercial and military traffic is encrypted.

VHF and HF Packet

If you want to see what is in those packet bursts you hear on 2 meters or on the HF bands, the freeware program _PKTMON12_

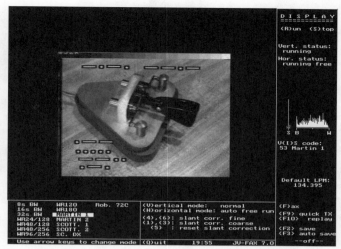

Figure 4—This SSTV "CQ" was picked up with _JVFAX_.

does a good job. It allows you to eavesdrop on 1200-baud VHF or 300-baud HF packet (see Figure 3) using the HamComm serial port interface. _PKTMON12_ shows all of the message fields and time-stamps each message. Messages can be logged to disk and sorted. An option to suppress packets received with errors can also be enabled (tuning HF packet using this program must be done carefully).

For those interested in the fine details of the packet signal, this program's output, coupled with a reference such as _The ARRL Handbook_, can allow you to observe almost the entire transmission protocol.

SSTV and WEFAX

One of the most popular programs for the reception of amateur slow-scan TV (SSTV) and weather fax (WEFAX) is _JVFAX_ by Eberhard Backeshoff, DK8JV. This program can receive most SSTV modes using the same _HamComm_-type serial port interface. Most WEFAX modes can also be accommodated. The program includes a large number of configuration and auto-receive options, tuning aids, and image file logging and management. Figure 4 shows JVFAX receiving a clever CQ image.

If you are using a high-resolution monitor (SVGA with 800×600×256 colors or better) and a reasonably hot video card, you'll see vivid color SSTV pictures with _JVFAX_. It is a popular program with the SSTV enthusiasts, but is a great way for beginners to monitor this mode. _JVFAX_ is also transmit-capable if the interface is modified. Most SSTV activity on HF is located on 14.230 and 14.233 MHz. You may also hear SSTV on 3.845, 7.171, 21.340 and 28.680 MHz. WEFAX stations in the US are found on 3.357, 4.271, 4.346, 6.340, 6.496, 8.080, 8.682, 9.982, 10.536, 10.865, 11.090, 12.730, 12.750, 13.510, 15.959, 16.135, and 17.151 MHz.

Other Programs

HamComm, _JVFAX_, and _PKTMON_ are just a few of the large number of shareware and freeware programs that are available. You can use these shareware routines to try out many of ham radio's other signal modes—that's what the program's authors intended. If one of these modes really lights your fire, you can invest in a multimode controller and go on the air yourself!

PO Box 11130
Washington, DC 20008-0330

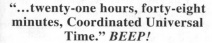

NEW HAM HORIZONS

"At the Tone…"

Enter the world of extreme frequency and time precision. It's as close as your HF radio!

By Steve Ford, WB8IMY
Assistant Technical Editor

"…twenty-one hours, forty-eight minutes, Coordinated Universal Time." *BEEP!*

If you've spent even a few minutes combing the HF bands, you've probably stumbled onto this signal. It's the voice of WWV in Fort Collins, Colorado. Perhaps you muttered, "Oh, it's an on-the-air clock. How nice," just before you flipped the dial and promptly forgot it.

When I began life as a shortwave listener—a couple of years before my discovery of Amateur Radio—my reaction was somewhat different. My receiver at the time was a Radio Shack "Science Fair" kit consisting of a dozen components on a red plastic breadboard. The radio had the sensitivity of a billiard ball and there were only a few stations that I could hear clearly. One of them was WWV.

WWV didn't play catchy songs, but it was interesting in a strange, metaphysical way. The powerful voice of WWV sounded like God's timepiece. It was omnipotent, receivable any time of the day or night. Stranger still, the monotone voice seemed to relentlessly tick away the seconds of the universe itself.

In a fit of teenage foolery, I once slapped on a pair of headphones and listened to WWV for about 15 minutes straight. I had hoped to use it as a kind of electronic mantra. (Hey, this was 1970. What do you expect?) I fell somewhere short of cosmic enlightenment and got a headache instead. When I finally switched stations, I heard the opening strains of Chicago's hit tune, "Does Anybody Really Know What Time It Is?" Well, I sure did—with a vengeance!

Setting the Standard

Now it's twenty-five years later and I've tossed aside the New Age debris. That doesn't make the voice any less interesting…or useful.

There are actually *two* voices: one male and the other female. The male voice belongs to WWV. The female voice originates from sister station WWVH in Kauai, Hawaii. Both stations are operated by the National Institute of Standards and Technology. Note the word "standards." That gives you a strong clue as to what these stations are all about.

Most hams refer to WWV and WWVH as the *time* stations. That's only about half the story. They are really time *and* frequency stations. The time signals you hear are regulated by an atomic clock that uses the oscillations of Cesium atoms as its standard. (9,192,631,770 oscillations equal 1 second.) The clock is accurate to 1 part in 1 *trillion*. The transmitting frequencies are accurate to about 1 part in 100 billion.

Of course, propagation plays a role in fudging the accuracy. Signals from WWV and WWVH take a certain amount of time to reach you, depending on where you live. By the time you receive the signals, as much as 1 ms may have transpired from the moment they were actually transmitted. There may also be a received frequency error of 1 part in 10 million. Despite these factors, their signals serve as the most popular time and frequency standards for engineers, scientists, broadcasters, sailors, pilots and Amateur Radio operators worldwide. (Yes, there are other time-and-frequency stations operated by other nations, but WWV and WWVH seem to hold the top spots in the hearts and minds of listeners.)

If the accuracy is good enough for astronomers, it's good enough for Amateur Radio. I don't think too many hams lose sleep over whether or not their rigs are off frequency by 1 part in 10 million. When I tune in WWV and my frequency display reads 10 MHz, I'm happy in the knowledge that all is right with the world. If, on the other hand, my display read 10.130 MHz, I think I'd suspect a problem in my rig before I'd get on the phone and call Fort Collins!

Services and Frequencies

WWV and WWVH transmit on several frequencies at various power levels:

	WWV	WWVH
2.5 MHz	2500 W	5000 W
5.0 MHz	10,000 W	10,000 W
10 MHz	10,000 W	10,000 W
15 MHz	10,000 W	10,000 W
20 MHz	2500 W	none

Although WWV produces a virtually omnidirectional signal using half-wave dipoles, WWVH uses phased vertical half-wave dipole antennas designed to radiate primarily to the west. That's why WWV is usually the stronger station in the continental US. When propagation conditions are right, you can often hear WWVH's identification and time announcement beneath WWV's signal. It takes place at 15 seconds before the minute, 7.5 seconds before WWV's speech.

The "ticks" that mark the seconds are really tone bursts—1000 Hz for WWV and 1200 Hz for WWVH. Each burst is precisely

WWV, Fort Collins, Colorado

MATTHEW DEUTCH, N0RGT

5 milliseconds in length. There are 10 milliseconds of silence *before* each tick and 25 milliseconds of silence *after* each tick. Every second gets a tick except for the 29th and 59th. In alternate minutes during most hours, 500- or 600-Hz tones are broadcast with each second.

When the WWV announcer says, "At the tone…," that tone frequency is 1000 Hz and you hear it for exactly 800 milliseconds to mark the start of a new minute. (WWVH uses a 1200-Hz tone.) Don't even *think* of asking whether the tones and silent periods are accurate. Do you dare doubt it?

In addition to the tones you hear, both stations broadcast a tone you *can't* hear. A BCD (binary coded decimal) time code is sent on a 100-Hz audio subcarrier. The tone frequency is so low that it's filtered out by most receiver audio circuits. So why bother with it? Well, many users have special clocks that contain dedicated WWV/WWVH receivers. The receivers decode the 100-Hz tones and use them to keep the clocks perfectly synchronized with the stations. Clever idea, isn't it? Heathkit once manufactured such a receiver/clock. It monitored the WWV/WWVH frequencies and continuously updated itself. As a result, the time you saw on the display was the most accurate time available!

WWV and WWVH offer other services including:

❏ Geophysical alerts (solar activity reports and more)
❏ Marine storm warnings
❏ Omega Navigation System status reports

❏ Global Positioning System (GPS) status reports

These reports and warnings are given at specific times during each hour. See Figure 1 for details.

WWVB

If you own a receiver than can plumb the depths of the radio spectrum, you may be able to tune in WWVB at 60 kHz. WWVB is located on the WWV site in Fort Collins. It broadcasts with 13,000 W to a top-loaded vertical antenna installed over a massive radial ground screen.

WWVB's time signals are intended primarily for the continental US. It doesn't broadcast voice announcements. Instead, it uses a BCD time code, sending each bit *by shifting the power of its transmitted signal.* Carrier power drops 10 dB at the start of each second. If full power returns 200 milliseconds later, that counts as one "0" bit. But if full power doesn't return for 500 milliseconds, that's a "1" bit. This scheme is known as *pulse-width modulation.*

Time Stations and Amateur Radio

Now that you know about America's favorite time stations, how can you use them? As I mentioned earlier, one application is checking the frequency of your HF rig. They're also handy for monitoring propagation conditions. Not only can you listen to their hourly solar activity reports, the signals themselves offer clues. For example, if you live in the Midwest and you can hear the voice of the WWVH announcer on 15 MHz, there's

a decent possibility that the 20 and 17-meter bands may be open for long-distance communication—at least to the Pacific. If you're a low-band enthusiast, listen for WWV and/or WWVH on 2.5 MHz to get an idea of how well 160 and 80 meters are doing.

It's also important to have an accurate clock by your radio. This is especially true for satellite operators. Even something as simple as making a "sked" to talk to someone is easier when you have a clock you can trust. Just check WWV or WWVH once a month and set your clock accordingly. What the heck, set *all* the clocks in your home!

If you don't own an HF receiver, you can still get a regular dose of accurate time information. For WWV dial 303-499-7111. For WWVH dial 808-335-4363. Remember that these are *not* toll-free calls! If you get mesmerized by the tones, don't worry. You'll be automatically disconnected after 3 minutes.

And if you're thinking of visiting WWV or WWVH—don't. They used to offer tours in the days before government cutbacks, but this is no longer true. Both stations operate with small staffs and they're far too busy to accommodate visitors. You'll have to be content to view them from afar, listening to their electronic heartbeats as they measure that odd human concept we call "time."

Finally, this article would be incomplete without a "thank you" to Matthew Deutch, NØRGT. Matthew is one of those busy WWV staffers who took several minutes out of his day to answer my inane questions and provide additional information via the mail. Now that I've stopped bugging him, he can go back to measuring those oscillating Cesium atoms.

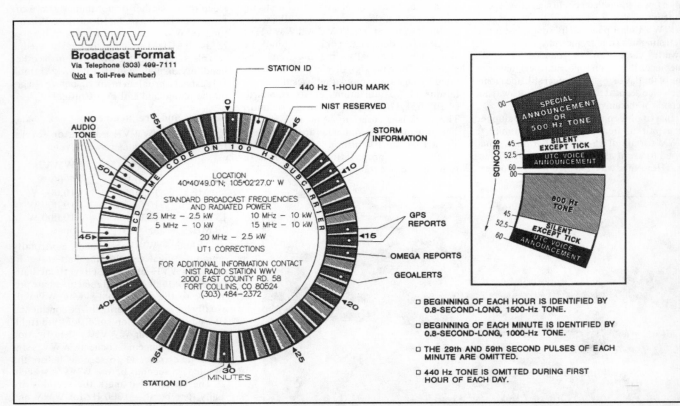

Figure 1—WWV's hourly broadcast schedule (*courtesy of the National Institute of Standards and Technology*).

Understanding Signal Strength

NEW HAM COMPANION

By George Wilson, W1OLP
82 Frazier Way
Marstons Mills, MA 02648

Our sense of hearing often requires a doubling of input before we can detect that a sound has become louder. The exceptions are those practiced listeners who can sense relatively small changes when conditions are ideal. (This is an important skill to develop for DXing or working QRP operators.)

Most of us rely on our ears to evaluate the signals we hear. Because we also like to have visual confirmation, we turn to the venerable *S meter*. Many transceivers feature these handy devices, and yet few hams really understand their place in the overall scheme of things.

On a perfectly calibrated meter, one S unit represents a factor of four in terms of power. This is because the S unit was originally defined as a doubling of the signal voltage as measured at the input of the receiver. If the voltage at the input doubles, the current also doubles. This results in a *four-fold* power increase.

Hams use *decibels* to more easily express ratios (power ratios, in this case). A two-fold power change is equal to 3 dB; a four-fold increase is equal to 6 dB.

For Whom the Bel Tolls

A *bel* is a measure of ratio. It's named after Alexander Graham Bell. A bel is 10 times as large as a decibel. A 3-bel change in power is a factor of 1000! It became apparent that the bel was too large to be conveniently used in radio, so the dB was introduced.

To put the dB in perspective, the human ear has a range of about 130 dB between silence and the onset of pain. We can recognize about 40 distinct changes of sound level. Ears and ham receivers have this ratio factor in common.

Your brain is the best judge of the strength and readability of a signal, but S meters are helpful tools—as long as you don't place too much trust in them. In this article I'll use a *hypothetical* S meter to illustrate a few points about the effect of transmitter power changes on received signal strength—as well as the futility of using your S meter as an absolute yardstick of signal quality.

Take a look at Figure 1. At **A** you see a typical S meter scale. Directly below (**B**) is the power relationship between the markings on the scale. Remember that the smooth, linear response of this S meter is a fantasy. The meter in your radio isn't this accurate.

In scale **C** we assume that a 160-W signal produces an S9 reading. If you reduced the transmitter power to less than one watt, the S meter would read S5. Note that at one-one hundredth of a watt the S meter would read S2. A reading of S2 doesn't sound like much, does it? Depending on noise and in-

> **Your ears and your transceiver have something in common.**

terference, however, this would probably be a perfectly readable signal. No wonder QRP (low power) works so well!

The bottom scale (**D**) vividly illustrates the futility of trying to power your way to success. Here it is assumed that a 200-W signal produces an S2 reading. Our ears tell us that the signal is readable, but noisy. In order to produce an S6 signal and achieve greater clarity, the transmitter would have to increase to over 50 kW! To reach S9, you'd need three *megawatts*! Since hams are limited to a maximum of 1500 W, you can attain only a 1½ S unit improvement by increasing your transmitted power to the legal limit. If power alone isn't the answer to boosting your signal strength, what is?

Antenna Gain

One solution is the *apparent* gain derived from directional antennas. Here the radiated power is concentrated in one (or more) directions. This makes your station "look" to a receiver as if your transmitter power has increased.

Consider the effect on our hypothetical S meter. The apparent power gain is usually stated with respect to a dipole in free space—in its most favorable position with respect to the receiver. Since a dipole is inexpensive and popular, it is a good basis for comparison. The table below compares the results of using several popular antennas.

Approximate Gain

Antenna	Factor	dB	S units
Dipole	×1	0	0
2-element Yagi beam	×2.5	4	0.6
3-element Yagi beam	×4	6	1.0
10-element Yagi beam	×16	12	2.0

As you can see, a directional antenna can make a substantial difference. For example, if we were using a wire dipole and our signal was peaking at S5, we might be able to boost it by two S units—up to S7—by using a 10-element Yagi beam instead.

How Much Gain is Enough?

The answer is simply this: You need as much gain as necessary to make your signal readable by the other station. Experienced amateur operators know that a small power change can put their signals far enough above the noise and interference to make them readable to the ear, if not the S meter. How you achieve that extra gain is the big question. Do you increase power, improve your antenna or both? The choice is up to you—and your budget!

George Wilson, W1OLP, is a freelance writer living in Marstons Mills, Massachusetts. His writing specialties are model airplanes and Amateur Radio. He is a graduate of MIT in Electronic Engineering. George retired to Cape Cod after a long career in the electronics industry.

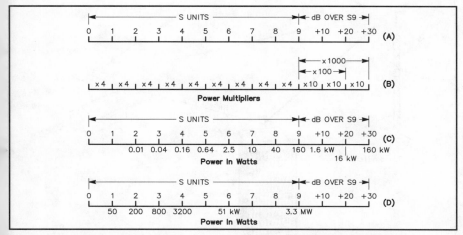

Figure 1—It takes a big increase in power to move our fantasy S meter a short distance. Scale **A** is a typical S meter like the one that's probably in your transceiver. The relationship between power levels and meter readings is shown in scale **B**. In scale **C**, a 160-W signal is shown with an S9 reading. If we reduce the signal to less than 1 W, the meter only falls to S5! Scale **D** shows the futility of trying to power your way to success.

Long Delayed Echoes— A Ham Mystery!

Scotland has the Loch Ness monster. Egypt has the pyramids. Amateur Radio has Long-Delayed Echoes —a puzzle that defies a complete solution to this day!

By Steve Ford, WB8IMY
Assistant Technical Editor

We present for your approval a lone Amateur Radio operator. He's just finished an enjoyable conversation and is about to turn off his radio. As he reaches for the **POWER** switch, a weak signal suddenly appears. It sounds oddly familiar. As he listens, a chill races down his spine. The hair on the back of his neck bristles. The Amateur Radio operator gapes in shocked astonishment as he listens to the sound of *his own voice*!

Better look in the corner of your room and see if Rod Serling is standing there. (Fans of the old *Twilight Zone* TV series will know what I mean.) Is this scenario a fiction, a ham-radio ghost story, perhaps? Not at all. It's *real*, and a number of hams can offer personal testimony to its existence. We're talking about the bizarre phenomenon known as *Long Delayed Echoes*, or *LDEs*.

What is an LDE?

Radio textbooks often show radio waves traveling from transmitter to receiver in thin, straight lines—*rays*. What a nice, clean concept—but then there's reality! When you transmit a signal, it scatters like light from a ceiling bulb, and only a tiny fraction of its energy reaches the receiving station. (Even with a directional transmitting antenna, the signal travels outward in *all* directions— antenna directivity just makes it stronger in some directions than others.)

With your transmitter's energy going every which way, it figures that whatever of your signal gets to the receiver doesn't necessarily all get there the *same* way. Some of the scattered energy may arrive at the receiver after bouncing off reflective objects, or after being bent back toward the Earth by the ionosphere or (at VHF and above) tropospheric ducting. These straggling rays show up a few fractions of a second later than the main signal, creating echoes.

Have you ever seen those annoying *ghost* images on your TV? They appear as faint replicas of the image you're trying to watch. TV ghosts are caused by the echo effect I've just described. Your TV antenna picks up the strong signal that arrives by the most direct path, but it also receives echoes caused by reflections. These reflections take place as the TV signal bounces off mountains, buildings, aircraft, etc. The later they

The Search Continues

Hams and other researchers are still exploring the mystery of Long Delayed Echoes. Several amateurs have conducted carefully controlled experiments on the HF bands and have documented LDE activity, complete with oscilloscope photographs showing the initial signals and their corresponding echoes. The problem with research on the HF bands is the hoax potential. (With modern recording equipment, it's relatively easy for anyone to perpetrate an LDE hoax on HF.)

Many LDE experimenters have moved to the microwave bands to explore the extraterrestrial connection. Using high-gain, narrowly focused antennas, they probe the heavens, listening for elusive LDEs. A concrete explanation, however, is even more elusive!

Some researchers have estimated that an active ham may hear at least one LDE per year on the HF bands. If you're searching for LDEs, you can improve your chances by operating on your favorite band just as it's opening for long-distance propagation. On 10 meters, for example, this would take place at mid-morning. Pause for several seconds between your transmissions and listen for echoes of your own signal. The echoes will be weak and may have a raspy or "watery" sound. Whenever you hear an LDE, make a note of the time, frequency and anything else that may be important—as soon as you recover from the shock!

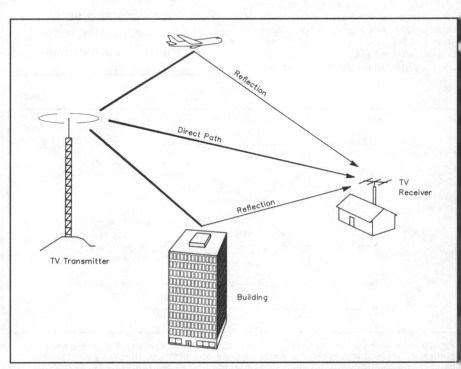

Fig 1—Signal echoes are common and often show up as "ghosts" on TV screens. In this example, the strong direct signal arrives at the TV receiver first. The echoes, caused by various reflections, arrive a fraction of a second later.

arrive compared to the direct signal, the greater the separation between the desired image and the ghost. The echoes take a variety of different paths to get from the transmitting antenna to your television, so TV ghosts are often referred to as *multipath* signals (see Fig 1).

You can hear a similar type of echo on the HF bands. When you're talking to a station in South America, for example, you hear the operator's signal via the most direct path. When propagation conditions are good, however, you may also hear a slight echo. This is the portion of his signal that's traveled a much greater distance to reach you (sometimes all the way around the Earth in the opposite direction!). Since it arrives a tiny fraction of a second later, you hear a hollow, echoing sound.

So what sets LDEs apart from the types of signal echoes we experience every day? An LDE doesn't arrive a few milliseconds after the primary signal—it arrives several *seconds* later. In fact, some LDEs have been observed with delays of as much as 30 seconds.

You don't have to be a genius to pick up a calculator and determine how far a signal could travel in 30 seconds. Try it yourself. The speed of light is 186,281 miles per second. Multiply 186,281 by 30 and you get a total roundtrip distance of 5,588,430 miles!

How can a radio signal travel over such great distances and still be audible in your receiver? What mechanism could be responsible? Welcome to the central mystery of long-delayed echoes!

LDEs Through the Years

Long-delayed echoes are a rare phenomenon, but hams have been reporting them for

Further Reading

Rasmussen, "Ghost Echoes on 1296 MHz," *QST,* June 1976, p 36.

Garibaldi, "Ghost Echoes, Phase 2," *QST,* September 1976, p 31.

Lorenzen, "Long Delayed Echoes on the EME Circuit," *QST,* June 1976, p 36.

Crawford, Sears and Bruce, "Possible Observation and Mechanism of Very-Long Delayed Radio Echoes," *Journal of Geophysical Research,* Vol. 75, No 34, pp 7326-7332.

Clark, "Two Possible Explanations for LDEs," *QST*, November 1971, p 40.

Villard, Fraser-Smith and Cassam, "LDEs, Hoaxes and the Cosmic Repeater Hypothesis," *QST,* May 1971, p 54.

Villard, Muldrew, Waxman, "The Magnetospheric Echo Box—A Type of Long-Delayed Echo Explained," *QST,* October 1980, pp 11-14.

Cohen, Davis and Davis, "Long-Delayed Echo Revisited," *QST,* February 1978, p 17.

nearly as long as radio has been in existence. Some of the first reports of Amateur Radio LDEs were recorded in the pages of *QST* in the late '20s and early '30s. For decades hams assumed that LDEs were caused by rare events in the ionosphere that created *ducts*, allowing radio waves to travel around the Earth many times with little loss. This explanation was especially popular since most LDEs were heard on the HF bands.

Then, in the mid 70's, Hans Rasmussen, OZ9CR, overturned the LDE applecart! Hans observed and documented echoes on 1296 MHz. This frequency is far too high to permit the energy to be trapped or refracted by the ionosphere.

In his experiments, OZ9CR was bouncing

signals off the moon. As any moonbounce enthusiast will tell you, it takes a little more than 2 seconds for a signal to make the journey to the moon and back. OZ9CR was hearing his lunar echoes, but he was also hearing weaker echoes 4 to 5 seconds later. Some strange phenomenon approximately 500,000 miles away was reflecting his signals. Hans' findings caused a great deal of controversy and required some new explanations for LDEs.

Possible Explanations

Ionospheric ducting remains a popular explanation for LDEs on bands below 30 MHz, but the exact mechanism is not fully understood. Some scientists question how a signal could orbit the globe so many times and still be heard by hams with ordinary equipment. It seems to defy our understanding of the physics of radio waves, but perhaps our understanding is incomplete. Just as superconductors exhibit little resistance to electricity under the right conditions, it's possible that the ionosphere occasionally acts as a kind of superconductor for radio energy.

But what about LDEs above 30 MHz? In most cases, the ionosphere is transparent to VHF, UHF and microwave signals. That means the reflecting mechanism must be somewhere in outer space. Researchers have offered extraterrestrial explanations including reflections from plasma clouds, solar wind and streams of cometary dust (see Fig 2).

Some of the more imaginative among us have even proposed the existence of a *cosmic repeater*. If an alien civilization wanted to attract our attention, why not repeat our own signals back to us? They could place automated satellites in solar orbit that would repeat whatever signals they received. This explanation arouses some support since LDEs have been observed by commercial broadcasters and other communications services. (A TV LDE report many years ago turned out to be a hoax, though.) As you might imagine, the alien repeater theory is not taken seriously by many scientists.

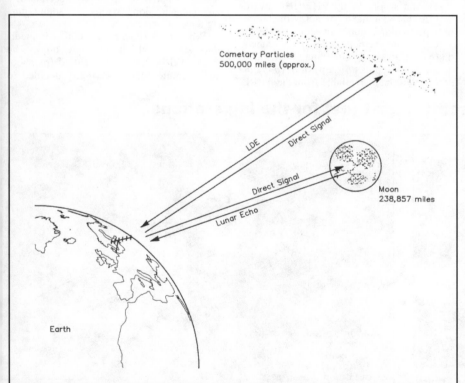

Fig 2—OZ9CR observed 4- and 5-second echoes when bouncing 1296-MHz signals off the surface of the moon. Could a cloud of cometary debris have caused the LDE?

Hooked On Meteors!

By Tom Hammond, WD8BKM
2450 Lea Lane
Ortonville, MI 48462
E-mail: nu-way@ic.net
Photos by the author

With three meteor contacts under my belt, I think I'm hooked!

I'd been active on 2-meter SSB for about three years, but I had never tried to make a meteor-scatter contact. The idea of bouncing my signal off the flaming tail of a meteor seemed absurd. Only the big-gun stations did that kind of stuff. My modest 2-meter setup (a Yaesu FT-736R, a small amplifier and a single Yagi) just didn't have enough *oomph*. Or did it?

Setting Up

It started Monday night, December 12, 1994, while I was listening to the Cincinnati-based VHF/UHF Net. I was hearing meteor bursts with astonishing frequency. The signals would pop out of nowhere for several seconds, then vanish. If I could hear them, could I also *work* them? I jumped into the net and arranged a meteor schedule with AD4FF for the upcoming Geminids shower. We'd try to make contact Wednesday night on 144.143 MHz.

The next day, I posted electronic messages to the Internet *Usenet* groups rec.radio, amateur.misc and rec.radio.amateur.space requesting meteor skeds. I don't have HF equipment, so scheduling contacts on 75 meters (as many scatter buffs do) was not an option. I was happy to get a response from Rupert, N2OTO, on Long Island. We exchanged e-mail and set up a sked for 0330 UTC on December 14, following the sked with AD4FF.

Tuesday night, I listened on 144.200 MHz (the national SSB calling frequency) from 0230 UTC onward. The frequency was buzzing (or should I say "bursting"?) with activity. The meteor bursts were loud, but very short. I heard only partial call signs. I quickly decided that random meteor skeds should be left to the pros.

Timing is Everything

Timing is critical in meteor work. The typical procedure is to divide each minute into 15-second intervals. One station transmits for the first and third interval. The other station transmits for the second and fourth interval.

Each station calls the other giving both call signs (for example, "AD4FF WD8BKM"), repeating the calls over and over during the transmit interval. When you hear a burst with both call signs, you respond with a report indicating the length of the burn in seconds, such as "S2." The other station responds with, "Roger S2." The contact is complete when you exchange "rogers." I like to finish with, "Roger 73," if time permits.

Meteor scatter doesn't support much in the way of conversation, but it's a fascinating way to work distant stations on VHF or UHF. If you're chasing awards, you can pile up *grid squares* quickly through meteor scatter.

The entire world is divided into grid squares based on latitude and longitude. The squares have designators such as FN31, EN80 and so on. Many VHF/UHF awards require that you make contact with stations in a particular number of squares. Before you dive into meteor scatter, I recommend that you buy a grid-square map from Headquarters. Also, pick up a copy of *Beyond Line of Sight*. Both are available from the ARRL.

See the *ARRL Publications Catalog* elsewhere in this issue.

First Contacts

I was all set to go at 0300 UTC. The first sked was easier than I thought. It took about 19 minutes to exchange calls, reports, and final "rogers" with AD4FF. I actually heard him just above the noise on two occasions, indicating some terrestrial propagation was going on as well. Bill is only about 450 miles from me, within range of most well-equipped stations under enhanced conditions.

I calmed my throat with ice water, turned the antenna toward grid FN30 and relaxed in preparation for the sked with N2OTO at 0330 UTC. By the start of that sked, the heat sink on my amplifier had just cooled down. For the next 20 minutes, I called and called and called, until I was blue in the face. I didn't hear a peep from Rupert. Perhaps east-west wasn't the best path for this shower.

I went back to the calling frequency and tried to pull together another contact. There were a lot of bursts, but most were too short to try a random contact. Just as I was about to pull the plug, I heard Gabor, VE3GBA, and decided to ask about his success. Gabor had already worked two skeds and was on his way to another with KB5IUA in grid EL29. From 0530 to 0600, I listened as Gabor and John exchanged reports. I heard John almost every minute of the sked, sometimes with sustained bursts of up to five seconds. It's surprising how long five seconds sounds during a meteor-scatter contact.

When they finished at 0600, I immediately started calling KB5IUA, hoping he might still be listening. I called for about three minutes before I finally decided to

Meteor scatter isn't just for the big stations.

This is my "big gun" VHF/UHF SSB station. There isn't much to it. My Yaesu FT-736R is the workhorse transceiver. A small amplifier boosts my output to approximately 150 W.

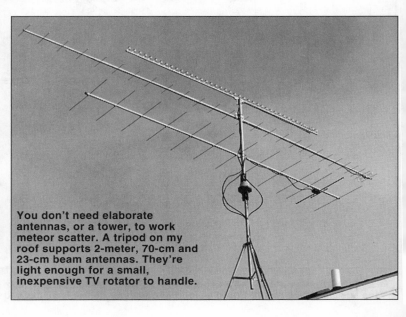

You don't need elaborate antennas, or a tower, to work meteor scatter. A tripod on my roof supports 2-meter, 70-cm and 23-cm beam antennas. They're light enough for a small, inexpensive TV rotator to handle.

reach him by telephone. I have a directory on my computer that lists active VHF and UHF stations. For each station, the directory shows the grid locator, active bands and modes (EME, meteor scatter, etc.) and an optional phone number to arrange schedules. John was very accommodating. I thought he wouldn't be too excited to work another station in grid EN82, but he responded, "I love working the rocks! Let's do it!"

We started our sked at 0608 UTC and were successful within 10 minutes. On one of the last burns I heard John say, "73, Tom. You got it. That's a good one!" Twelve hundred miles on 2 meters via meteor. Amazing!

During our telephone conversation, John said he would be in grid EL18 in the morning at 1100 UTC. Could we try then? *Why not?*

With only 3½ hours of sleep, I was in front of the radio again. This sked took a little longer, with shorter bursts and weaker signals, but we made it. Instead of getting back in bed, I showered and headed off to work. I felt like I had a hangover all day, but it was worth it! **QST**

Q I'm a scanner buff as well as a ham. I enjoy listening to aircraft, but I can't receive them when they're on the ground at my local airport. (I'm using a whip antenna with my scanner.) Is there anything I can do to improve my reception of aircraft on the ground?

A Antenna height is critical in this situation. Radio *line of sight* (in miles) is approximately the square of *h*, where h is the height in feet. Thus, going from 5 feet to 50 feet increases the range by a factor of 3.2! That's why scanners usually give outstanding performance in high-rise buildings—even with rubber-duck antennas. I once talked with another amateur 83 miles away running 1.5 W with a 2-meter H-T and its stock rubber-duck antenna. The path was visual line of sight. If you can do it, put up an outside antenna and get it as high as you can. You'll notice a big improvement.

Q Tommy Robinson, KD4CAN, asks, "When I'm setting up a beam antenna, which 'north' do I use to orient it? Should it be magnetic north or true north?"

A It's best to orient your beam to true north. That way, you can more easily point your beam to the correct great-circle heading when you're trying to communicate with a distant station. The equations for calculating great-circle headings appear in *The ARRL Operating Manual*. If you have a computer and a modem, you'll find programs that calculate great-circle headings on the ARRL "Hiram" BBS (tel 203-666-0578).

You can easily determine true North by using the North Star (Polaris)—if you don't mind working in the dark! Another way is

to obtain the *angle of declination* from a topographic map. Often referred to as the *variation angle* in air and sea navigation, this angle is simply the difference between true and magnetic North at a specified location. By knowing this angle, you can correct your compass reading for true North.

You can learn more about coordinates, great-circle headings, topographic maps and associated computer programs by reading the "Lab Notes" column in the April 1994 *QST*.

Q I'm getting terrible interference to my VHF transceiver from my computer. Is this interference coming directly from the CPU?

A It's rare to have interference *directly* from the CPU, but it is possible. Most computer interference is radiated by the wiring, primarily between peripheral devices (printers, modems, joysticks and so on). High-quality shielded cables are a good start toward solving this problem. Wrapping the cables though large toroids such as the FT-240-61 may also help.

Consider the shielding on your computer, too. The quality and amount of shielding can vary considerably. The better computers have metal cabinet covers that must be removed if you want to replace or add any components. Some hams have even gone to the trouble of lining their computer cabinets with metal foil!

Q A friend of mine said that tubes are completely obsolete. He said that you can't find tubes in any electronic equipment these days. Is this true?

A Not entirely. Unless you're watching an LCD screen, it's an electron tube that creates the images on your TV, computer monitor, oscilloscope and so on. You'll also find tubes in commercial high-power RF amplifiers, especially in the broadcast industry. Specialized ceramic-type tubes (such as the 4CX30000A) are the powerhouses behind many AM and FM radio stations.

In terms of Amateur Radio equipment, you'll still find tubes in linear amplifiers. High-power solid-state amps are growing in popularity. They're costly now, but they are likely to become less expensive over time.

Q I plan to put up an HF dipole and feed it with open-wire line. The output power of my rig is about 100 W. The problem is my small lot. The antenna is 130 feet long and I don't have 130 feet of open space. The best I can do is route the antenna through the trees. Won't that harm its performance?

A Not enough that anyone will notice. Trees are a problem only if you're running high power (more than 200 W), or if you're operating at VHF or UHF frequencies. Running high power through a tree-mounted antenna could create a fire hazard. VHF and UHF signals may be blocked or absorbed by leaves and branches.

In your case, however, there is little to

worry about. You may see changes in your antenna tuner settings during wet weather, or in the summer when the leaves are out. But since you're using an open-wire feed line, SWR and its effects are almost a nonissue. Throw your antenna into the trees and have fun!

Q I recently purchased a new hard drive for my computer, but now I'm wondering if I should take it back. It seems to work well, but I found a label on the case that says it has "bad sectors." How can they sell a hard drive with bad sectors?

A Almost every new hard drive has a small number of bad sectors. They're a byproduct of the manufacturing process. These bad sectors are discovered at the factory during testing and automatically "locked out." That is, your computer is prevented from using them. They don't affect the performance or reliability of your disk in any way.

The label is there for your benefit. If you change a motherboard or swap the drive into another computer, the setup software may need to know the "locations" of these bad sectors. The label gives you this information.

Q When I tune through short-wave broadcast frequencies, I often hear short bits of music—just a few bars—played over and over. If I listen long enough, the stations usually begin sending normal programs. Why do they do this?

A The sounds you're hearing are known as *interval signals*, or *channel markers*. Shortwave broadcasters transmit interval signals between their active programming, as a tuning aid for listeners. Many stations use part of their country's national anthems, or a bit of classical music that has some relationship to the country of origin. For example, the Voice of America repeats a few bars of "Yankee Doodle" while Radio Australia treats you to bursts of "Waltzing Matilda."

Avid shortwave listeners quickly learn to recognize the interval signals of stations throughout the world. This saves time when they're searching the bands for rare signals. If they pick up a familiar interval signal, they won't waste time waiting for the broadcast.

Q I've been told that telescoping whip antennas for H-Ts are much better than the rubber-duck antennas that come with the radios. Is this true?

A "Better" is a relative term! Rubber ducks are convenient; they don't poke your eyes out (unless you try real hard) and they rarely flex the plastic case of your H-T enough to break it. But rubber duck antennas also have substantial loss compared to a bigger telescoping whip. The bottom line is that you won't talk as far with a rubber duck on your radio as you can with a telescopic whip antenna. Physics still applies to H-Ts.

Frank Wolfe, NM7R

A Worldwide Propagation Beacon Network

Which HF band is open—and to which part of the world? The answer may be as close as your general-coverage receiver.

While tuning around our amateur bands, I've often thought about how nice it would be if some benefactor provided a network of propagation beacons to indicate HF conditions to various parts of the world. These beacons would have to be operated continuously, at relatively high power, and placed in far-flung locations. In addition, it would be handy if the beacon frequencies didn't gobble up any of our valuable amateur spectrum, and be exclusively assigned, so as not to be bothered with interference. (Unlike the NCDXF 20-meter beacons, which are generally buried under massive packet interference.) By spending just a little time monitoring these beacons, you'd know which areas of the world were "open" to you on various bands.

Several years ago, to my delight, I discovered that such a powerful, diverse beacon system actually exists. All you need to tap this font of propagation wisdom is a general-coverage receiver (most modern HF rigs have this feature) and a basic ability to copy Morse code. Sounds familiar, doesn't it?

Maritime Coast Stations

The beacons I refer to are *marking signals* transmitted by Maritime Coast Stations. These stations are located all over the world, and are used by ships for commercial radiotelex traffic. The mode used is called Narrow Band Direct Printing (NBDP) radiotelegraphy. Also called SITOR, this is the commercial cousin to our AMTOR mode. The ship station operator uses his transceiver to *connect* the ship station with the shore station. The shipboard operator can then use the worldwide Telex network to send messages to virtually any commercial teletype terminal.

The system operates somewhat like an amateur autopatch, but uses teletype instead of telephone. When a shore station is being used for traffic, you'll hear the familiar *chirp-chirp* sound as data

is transmitted and acknowledged. You'll hear similar sounds when you tune across AMTOR and PACTOR signals in the amateur digital subbands. When the stations are idle, they transmit a marking signal that serves as a propagation beacon for the shipboard operators, allowing them to determine which stations they can work, and whether a particular station is busy or available. The marking signal sounds like a *purr-purr-purr* followed at intervals of a few seconds with the station's call sign, usually composed of three letters, sent in Morse code.

These stations, being commercial, run much more power than hams do—typically 10 to 15 kW. This sounds like a lot of power (and it *is*!), but remember that going from legal-limit amateur power to 15 kW (all else being equal) raises the received signal by less than two S units. This is the same relative power increase as going from 100 W to 1 kW. As a rough guide, a good amateur signal might be two to four S units below the strength of the beacon signal.

Beacon Hunting

I use a wire dipole antenna when I go beacon hunting. Since the frequencies of these signals are well outside the amateur bands, the effectiveness of most high-gain ham antennas is questionable for this application. In addition, their directional characteristics may be unpredictable and entirely different than they would be nearer their design frequencies. That's why you're usually better off with a simple receiving antenna.

If you think you might want to explore other signals outside the amateur bands, consider putting up a multiband shortwave listening antenna. Several *QST* advertisers sell dipole antennas specifically designed for shortwave monitoring. You can connect one of these antennas to your transceiver through a coaxial switch. The switch allows you to select the monitoring antenna when

---

Table 1

Selected Maritime Coast Stations

This is just a partial list of stations to get you started. Look for their signals in the frequency segments noted above. A worthwhile reference is the *Guide to Utility Radio Stations* available from Klingenfuss Publications, Hagenloher Str 14, D-72070 Tuebingen, Germany.

Call Sign	Location	Call Sign	Location	Call Sign	Location	Call Sign	Location
4PB	Sri Lanka	IAR	Italy	NMN	USCG Norfolk, Virginia	VCS	Halifax, Nova Scotia
9VG	Singapore	JCS	Japan	NMO	USCG Honolulu	VCT	Newfoundland
A9M	Bahrain	JOS	Japan	NMF	USCG Boston (intermittent)	VIP	Australia
CBV	Chile	KEJ	Hawaii			VRX	Hong Kong
CUL	Portugal	KFS	San Francisco	NOJ	USCG Kodiak, Alaska (intermittent)	VWB	India
DAN	Germany	KLB	Seattle			WCC	Chatham, Mass
EAT	Spain	KPH	San Francisco	OFA	Finland	WLO	Mobile, Alabama
FFT	France	LGB	Norway	SPA	Poland	WNU	New Orleans
GKB	England	LSD	Argentina	SVU	Greece	XSG	China
HEC	Switzerland	NMC	USCG San Francisco	TAH	Turkey	ZSC	Capetown, South Africa
HPP	Panama	NMC	USCG Guam				

you're beacon hunting, or your ham antenna when it's time to get on the air yourself.

But where can you find Maritime Coast Station signals? They transmit within narrow frequency segments: 4.210 to 4.218 MHz, 6.314 to 6.328 MHz, 8.417 to 8.433 MHz, 12.579 to 12.609 MHz, 16.807 to 16.843 MHz, 19.680 to 19.690 MHz, 22.376 to 22.413 MHz and 26.100 to 26.110 MHz.

Most stations transmit continuously. If you cannot hear a particular station, there is probably no propagation to that part of the world, on that frequency, at that time. Although these frequencies are more or less removed from our bands, they can give you a very good indication as to what Mother Nature (and the ionosphere) is doing at the moment. The conditions you encounter in the 4-MHz segment will generally apply to the 80-meter ham band. Activity in the 6 and 8-MHz segments will give you an idea of what to expect on 40 meters. The 12 and 16- MHz stations show the trend of 20-meter propagation. You get the idea. The assignments at 19 and 26 MHz are relatively new, and therefore not well populated yet.

Use your rig's SSB or CW mode when looking for marking signals. It usually isn't necessary to use narrow filters to pull these signals out of the noise. The stations maintain a separation of about 500 Hz, so the interference is tolerable. The call signs are generally sent slowly. After all, they're a form of advertising for the shore station! The call signs conform to the same international conventions as our amateur call signs do, so the familiar prefixes usually apply (see Table 1).

There are a couple of jokers in the list. The US Coast Guard operates a station on Guam, which is now remotely controlled from San Francisco. When the remote link became operational, the call sign was changed from NRV to NMC, the same as the San Francisco station. This makes it difficult to distinguish the two for the casual listener (although they operate on different frequencies). Similarly, the Australian station VIS in Sydney has adopted the same VIP call sign as the Perth station, making it hard to determine which end of the continent you're listening to.

More than once, after determining that a particular band was probably open to an area such as Europe or Asia, I have tuned around but found few signals. Calling CQ, however, quickly brought a strong reply. Monitoring the commercial signals also gives additional information as to the highest frequency that will actually support communication (the *critical frequency*), and whether the trend is toward higher or lower frequencies. This can indicate when a particular amateur band is about to open or close.

Conclusion

By keeping a log of the stations heard, it's possible to return to those frequencies for a peek at propagation. If your receiver or transceiver features a memory scan mode, you can program the various stations into memory, then scan them anytime to get a quick propagation "analysis."

And many of these stations transmit traffic lists, weather reports and bulletins (in FEC mode) at various times during the day. If you own a multimode communications processor (such as those made by AEA, Kantronics, MFJ and so on), you can eavesdrop on these broadcasts.

Although they're not perfect indicators of amateur band conditions, the Maritime Coast Stations are useful additions to a skilled operator's bag of tricks. And wallowing at the bottom of the solar cycle—as we are at the moment—we need all the help we can get!

Frank Wolfe, NM7R
PO Box 91
Nahcotta, WA 98637

QST.

Q I'm trying to decide whether to upgrade my station computer system to *Windows 95*. What's your advice?

A That's a tough question to answer…and it's one that many hams are asking. If you're running *Windows 3.1* at the moment, it will cost you about $90 to move to *Windows 95*. Some of the advantages include:

Integration: The software that comes bundled with *Windows 95* includes dial-up networking support for the Internet (you still need to contract with an Internet provider for a service connection), a system backup utility, a CD player utility, clipboard viewer, a disk-compression utility, phone dialer, Microsoft FAX, a Microsoft *Exchange* client, system monitor, a more reliable resource meter, various disk utilities previously included with DOS 6.22 and, finally, *WordPad* (a Microsoft *Write* replacement). Many of these new features were *Windows 3.1* add-on programs purchased at extra cost.

Stability: *Windows 95* was designed to be a more stable platform and attempts to correct many of the problems inherent in *Windows 3.1*. Although *Windows 95* makes compromises in memory protection to maintain compatibility with 16-bit applications and device drivers, it appears to be more stable than *Windows 3.1*.

Efficiency: *Windows 95* sports a true 32-bit API, protected address space for 32-bit applications, increased use of virtual device drivers and preemptive multitasking. These are major improvements over *Windows 3.1* and they increase the efficiency of *Windows 95*. *Windows 95* has the potential to run significantly faster than *Windows 3.1*. (Note the word "potential"!)

Compatibility: It installs easily and reliably on a broad range of computers. It can usually auto-sense (automatically detect) installed peripherals such as CD-ROM drives, tape drives, modems, network cards and so forth. It also maintains a very high degree of backward compatibility to standard 16-bit *Windows* applications. This means that you should be able to run all of your present *Windows* software under *Windows 95* without difficulty. DOS is available from within *Windows 95*, but this version of *Windows* does not require it. DOS programs can be run from within a "DOS window." (This version of DOS is called *Windows 95 DOS* and is *not* compatible with DOS 6.22 or lower.)

Before you run out and buy *Windows 95*, however, make sure you have enough computer horsepower to run it efficiently. Microsoft says that *Windows 95* can run on a 486SX 33-MHz computer with 4 Mbytes of RAM. That's true, but many have been disappointed at how slow the system operates. Expanding to 8 Mbytes makes a big improvement, although you'll get much better results with a 486DX-66 computer and the same amount of memory. Of course, a Pentium system with 8, 16, or 32 Mbytes is really slick with *Windows 95*.

But do you need *Windows 95*? If you're satisfied with your computer system and software, the answer is probably no. As time goes on, however, you'll find an increasing amount of software that is written for *Windows 95* exclusively. (You can bet that ham software authors are writing *Windows 95*-specific applications right now.) At some point in the near future you're going to be forced to make a choice: Stick with your present software and accept the fact that it's obsolete (no more support from the manufacturers), or follow the tide to *Windows 95*. No need to rush to a decision now, but keep your options open.

AM Broadcast DXing

By Wayne Heinen, NØPOH
PO Box 473411
Aurora, CO 80013
Internet: nrclog@filebank.com
Packet: NØPOH@KTØH.#NECO.CO.USA.NOAM

Commercial AM broadcasting began in the early 1920s. At first only a few stations took to the airwaves—and many of these were operated by hams. (Yes, hams pioneered radio broadcasting as we know it today.) Many of the people who began listening to this new medium for music and news were among the first DXers. Their preoccupation with DX listening was not by choice, but by necessity. Stations were few and far between. So, for most people in the US, *every* station was DX.

Legions of enthusiastic listeners built their own crystal sets and strung antenna wires between trees in order to hear stations from across the nation. These early DXers would write to the stations and let them know how well they were receiving their signals. In appreciation for these reports, the stations began sending cards or letters of confirmation. The hams called them "QSLs." Listeners treasured these scraps of paper and soon the hobby of QSL collecting was born. A number of these old QSLs are now collector's items, and the lust for AM broadcast verifications continues to this day.

AM DXing Today

Today's AM band still presents a challenge to the broadcast DXer. But the problem isn't scattered signals, it's *too many* signals. From 535 to 1705 kHz, the AM broadcast band is packed with stations.

The excitement of listening to news as it happens, from *where* it happens, is still possible on the AM band. Powerhouses KOMA and KVOO kept most of the Midwest informed on the Oklahoma City bombing, while California's KNX and KFI allowed many to follow numerous natural disasters with local coverage. Another pastime among DXers is following their favorite sports teams during road games. Those who've moved away from the old home town can still follow their favorite hometown teams with a little AM DXing.

To make the most of AM DXing, you need to develop your "propagation sense." That is, you need to understand when conditions will be best for signals over a given range. For example, *gray-line* propagation at both sunset and sunrise offers many new stations in the 400 to 600 mile range. (The signals travel through the zone between daylight and darkness.) Long, cold winter nights enhance propagation and reduce atmospheric noise.

Prowling for signals on the oldest DX band.

Couple quiet nights with gray-line propagation from Europe and Asia and you're talking about *international* AM DX!

Generally speaking, the lower the sunspot numbers, the better conditions are at the medium frequencies where AM broadcasting takes place. This means that we're enjoying some of the best AM DX conditions *right now*. As you're reading this article we're heading into winter at, or near, the bottom of the current sunspot cycle. What a great time to give broadcast DXing a try!

Getting Started

Getting started is easy. The AM DX hobby requires no special equipment. My late father, Bill, W2SIC, sparked my interest in radio in the early 1960s. I started using his old Hammarlund SP-200X receiver. It only tuned 1250 to 1600 kHz in the AM band. Even so, it opened a window to the fascinating world of broadcast DXing. Like many hams, this early listening experience eventually led me to Amateur Radio.

I also used a 9-V pocket transistor radio as my DX receiver. My verifications of clear-channel stations such as KFI and WSM were logged on that little radio. One "state-of-the art" receiver from the '70s and '80s was the Radio Shack *TRF*. These were exceptional DX producers with a price tag of $29.95. The *TRF* offered an inexpensive pathway for many new broadcast DXers.

Quite a few veteran broadcast DXers use the older "hollow state" tube receivers. They're popular because of the ease with

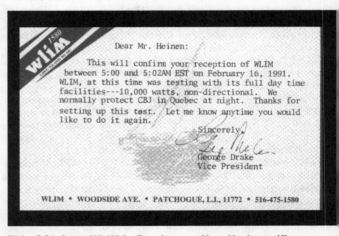

KPNW, a 50-kW powerhouse in Eugene, Oregon, not only welcomes your reports, they encourage them with their "Long Distance Listener Club" cards.

This QSL from WLIM in Patchogue, New York, verifies my reception of their test transmission on February 16, 1991. I helped set up this test and they were happy to comply!

Roots Radio

Try this tonight...

Grab an AM radio, any AM radio, and find a quiet spot in your home, apartment or wherever. (Bedrooms are ideal.) Turn out the lights and relax. Switch on the radio and turn the dial until you reach one end of the band. Now slowly, ever so slowly, tune up (or down) the band.

You'll hear the local stations coming long before you reach their frequencies. Their splattering, crackling signals are easy to recognize. But between the local RF juggernauts you'll find weaker signals. These are the ones you want. Tune them in as best you can, then settle back and *listen*. What are they talking about? What's the hot topic in their corner of the nation? News and weather are especially interesting.

And don't be surprised to hear music, too. Some of the best oldies stations can be found on the AM band these days. You'll even hear jazz, classical music and alternative rock. (Canadian AM broadcasters are excellent sources for jazz and classical.) Listen to the big country-western broadcasters as they fulfill song requests from lonely long-haul truckers.

Yes, you'll also hear squealing interference, fading signals and static crashes, but that's part of the atmosphere (no pun intended!) of AM listening. This is not the sanitized world of FM with its ultra-clear signals and predictable programming. AM is "roots radio," often reminiscent of FM in the "underground" days of the late '60s and early '70s. It's a bit rougher, perhaps a little grittier than what you're probably used to hearing.

Keep tuning and listening. As the sun sets across the country, new signals will rise out of the noise. Listen for the Mexican "border blasters," the stations that pioneered the rock and blues revolution in the days of Wolfman Jack and other famous DJs. At the other end of the power spectrum, you might even hear signals from tiny AM broadcasters who are limited to only a few hundred watts at night.

Better check your watch. While you've been surfing the medium waves, an hour or two may have passed. Grab a snack then head back to the radio with pen and paper. It's time to start a log...and the night is still young!—*Steve Ford, WB8IMY*

which they can be modified. They're also often superior at handling the strong-signal environment encountered on the AM band. Most popular are the Collins R-390A and the older Hammarlund receivers, especially the HQ-150, HQ-180A and SP-600 series.

Portable receivers like the Sony ICF-2010 and the GE *Super Radios* are still popular today. They have built-in ferrite core loop antennas that provide reasonable sensitivity—at least enough to give you a chance of snagging some long-haul DX.

Of course, if you already own a modern HF transceiver, it probably has a general-coverage receiver. Most of these general-coverage receivers include the AM broadcast band. If you want to buy stand-alone receiving equipment, the dealers advertising in *QST* will be happy to accommodate you! All the major ham transceiver manufacturers make dedicated short-wave/medium-wave receivers. You can even find hand-held scanner-type receivers that offer AM broadcast coverage.

Antennas are critical for AM DXing, and they're an experimenter's delight. From homemade loops to ingeniously designed phased-antenna systems, broadcast DXers have always lead the way in improving the equipment they use. By improving antennas and receivers, you can pull those rare DX signals out of the noise and interference.

QSL collecting is still alive and well. Although some say it's harder to get stations to respond, most will do so if you're patient. A simple letter describing what you heard, along with return postage, will often net you a card or letter. My QSL collection numbers over 1500 from around the nation and around the globe.

The National Radio Club

One way of keeping up with this fascinating hobby is through the National Radio Club—the oldest and largest medium-wave club in the world. Founded in 1933, the National Radio Club is currently publishing Volume 63 of its publication, *DX News*. *DX News* is published 30 times a year; weekly during the North American winter DX season.

Many of the dedicated volunteers and members of the National Radio Club are active hams as well. Some, like myself, started out as broadcast DXers and later obtained their amateur licenses. A number of our members are also involved with Amateur Radio at the local level. For ex-

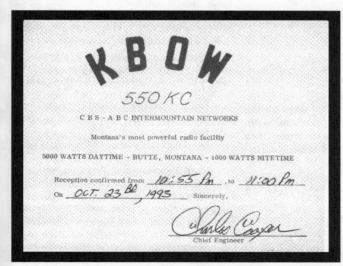

Here's a nice catch out of the Montana Rockies—KBOW in Butte. Their 1 kW nighttime signal isn't easy to hear among all the competing signals on 550 kHz.

Dan Butner, N6DB, was chief engineer of KPAY in Chico, California, when I logged their signal in 1991.

ample, editors Jerry Starr, N8IRL, and John Bowker, WA2WEN, are active in their local VE programs and repeater clubs. Also in our ranks are editors Bill Hale, N5SZC, and Pete Kemp, KZ1Z. Pete was ARRL Professional Teacher of the Year in 1990. Our treasurer is Dick Truax, K8GVU, and our monthly DX Audio Service cassette magazine is published by Fred Vobbe, KB8BMQ. A past editor, and now college student, Mike Hawk, NØOSY, was an ARRL scholarship winner in 1994.

In the late '80s volunteers revived the Courtesy Program Committee of the National Radio Club. This committee writes letters to radio stations and asks them to broadcast special DX "test" programs in the middle of the night when they're otherwise off the air. This makes it easier for DXers to log and verify the stations. This was a common occurrence in the early days of AM broadcasting and its revival has met with great success. In fact, many AM broadcasters use these tests (and your reports) to verify their directional signal patterns.

The National Radio Club continues to grow. Currently there are more than 700 members world wide. As we enter the trough of the sunspot cycle, propagation on the AM broadcast band will continue to improve as the cycle dips to its minimum. As conditions on the HF bands deteriorate, many dedicated DX listeners will once again return to the band that started it all. If you haven't tried your hand at this band, come on down to the medium waves!

The author thanks NRC DX News *publisher Paul Swearingen for his assistance with this article.*

NRC Membership and Publications

The National Radio Club publishes *DX News* 30 times per year, weekly during the Northern Hemisphere DX season. First-year membership is $26 and includes a copy of *Getting Started in Medium Wave DX*, a 69-page book that introduces newcomers to the hobby.

What happens when you turn out to be almost the only source of information for your hobby? As with the ARRL, the NRC became a publisher of reference material.

Starting in the 1960s with reprints of technical articles and the first edition of the *Domestic Log*, predecessor to the *AM Radio Log*, the National Radio Club began catering to the information needs of the broadcast band DXer. Over time the NRC became a wellspring of general and technical information for those interested in AM DXing.

The 16th edition of the *AM Radio Log* is scheduled for release this month. It's the definitive reference of all the AM stations in the USA and Canada. (The 15th edition was reviewed in the September 1994 *QST*, page 45.) The latest edition sells for $22.95.

To obtain membership information and a catalog of publications, send one First Class stamp to:

NRC Publications
PO Box 164
Mannsville, NY 13661-0164

Q I have a packet TNC on a card that plugs into my IBM-PC. When I try to use it, my software says that there is an "interrupt" problem. (There is a reference to IRQ4—whatever that means!) What is an interrupt?

A There are two types of interrupts: *hardware* interrupts and *software* interrupts. Let's discuss hardware interrupts since the message you are receiving appears to be of that nature. They're a common source of problems for PC users who perform board installations themselves.

There are 16 hardware interrupts on an AT-class computer (286s, 386s and 486s). They are numbered 0 through 15 (0 through 7 on XT-class PCs; its data bus is 8 bit versus 16 on the ATs). Any event, such as hitting a key on the keyboard, moving your mouse or communicating with your TNC card, causes hardware interrupts. Interrupts signal the CPU to request processing time. Once the CPU is aware that a component needs attention, it services the request.

Many problems arise when two or more devices try to use the same interrupt. The reference to IRQ4 appears to be an indication that your software is detecting a potential conflict with that interrupt. IRQ4 is commonly assigned to serial port 1 (COM1). You'll need to determine if that interrupt is currently in use, and if the TNC card is also trying to use it. Solutions range from keeping the TNC configured for IRQ4 and disabling the serial port so that it doesn't attempt to use it, or configuring the TNC for another IRQ. Check the user manual or call the TNC manufacturer to determine what interrupts the board can use.

Here are some common hardware interrupt assignments:

IRQ0	System Timer
IRQ1	Keyboard
IRQ2	Cascade to IRQ9-15 (XT: Not Assigned)
IRQ3	COM2
IRQ4	COM1
IRQ5	PC: Hard Disk adapter AT: LPT2
IRQ6	Floppy Disk adapter
IRQ7	LPT1
IRQ8	Not Assigned
IRQ9	Not Assigned
IRQ10	Not Assigned
IRQ11	Not Assigned
IRQ12	Not Assigned
IRQ13	Math Coprocessor
IRQ14	Not Assigned
IRQ15	Not Assigned

Q One Sunday evening I was tuning around on 75 meters SSB, when I heard a bunch of hams who were operating an informal net. Each station on the net would report the *call used* and some sort of *class* such as *single op* (sometimes they added "assisted" to this one), *multi-single*, *multi-two*, *multi-multi*, and so on. Then they would list various numbers, followed by more terms. What's this all about?

A You stumbled upon a post-contest net. It's a meeting place where contesters gather immediately after each contest to exchange "claimed" (or unofficial) scores. Not only do they compare scores, they swap war stories about their adventures during the contest. Of course, they use a lot of contest jargon in the process. Unless you're a contester, it sounds like they're speaking a foreign language. Here's a quick glossary:

Call used: The call sign used by this op (operator) during the contest.

Claimed score: The total estimated score (not officially accepted yet).

Class: Entry classification. (Single operator, single operator with more than one transmitter, etc.) "Assisted" indicates that a spotting network such as a *DX PacketCluster* was also used.

Dupe: More than one contact with the same station. A duplicate contact may or may not count toward your final score, depending upon the rules of the contest. For example, the contest rules might allow dupes if they take place on two different bands.

Mults: Multipliers worked during the contest. A multiplier does what it says—it "multiplies" your point totals. Multipliers are stations located in specific states, zones, or countries according to the rules of the contest.

Qs: The total number of contacts made during the contest.

Run: Working many stations, one after the other, on the same frequency.

Rate: The number of contacts per hour. Many contest programs will give you a numerical readout of your rate. Some will even show this information in graph form.

Search and pounce: Searching the bands for the multiplier stations you need. Searching and pouncing is common when you have difficulty "running" stations on a particular frequency.

By John Teale, N7FKV

Let's Just Listen for a Change

HF broadcasters use brute force to overcome the lack of sunspots.
Here's where to find them.

So the bands are down! So what? Most modern ham rigs aren't restricted to receiving only the amateur bands, as rigs once were. The entire HF spectrum is now our (receive-only) oyster. We can still have fun!

And just because the ham bands seem dead, at least one part of the shortwave spectrum is probably hopping. Remember: Most shortwave broadcast stations are "getting out" with kilowatts or megawatts of power and excellent antenna systems. They punch through when our pedal-powered rigs are in the doldrums.

So Where to Tune?

There are books on the subject…and there are books. Some are explicit and informative and make interesting reading, even without turning on your rig. Unfortunately, most shortwave "guidebooks" have a major flaw: They quickly become outdated. Like last week's *TV Guide* or last year's *Callbook*, they're mostly "yesterday's news" the day they go to press.

One book I purchased on the subject was published in 1994. It's already gone the way of the dinosaurs. Oh, it's good for starters, and it does contain some "timeless" information, but don't expect the frequencies and times stated in the book to be current.

Shortwave broadcasters change their underwear—and their frequencies—regularly! Avid shortwave listeners (SWLers) subscribe to specialized hobby magazines and surf the Internet to stay abreast of shortwave broadcast schedules (see the "SWL Resources" sidebar).

Depending on the part of the country you live in, some stations will be stronger than others. And surprisingly, just because you think you're listening to the BBC direct from beautiful downtown London, it ain't necessarily so. You may actually be listening to the BBC via one of its many relay sites in Singapore, Antigua, Cyprus, Hong Kong, Sackville (Canada), or even from Masirah, Oman (in the Middle East). BBC Broadcasts can even be emanating indirectly from the good old US of A.

The BBC in America?

Yep! The world (and the world of shortwave broadcasting) is shrinking!

The same goes for many other foreign radio broadcasts. Most stations broadcast in English, although many can be heard broadcasting in the language of their country of origin (or in the language of their target area for that broadcast).

Radio Nederland relays its interesting programs via Madagascar, in addition to beaming signals directly from Hilversum, Holland, as you might expect.

It's important to remember that foreign broadcasters—like ham operators—change frequencies regularly throughout the 24-hour broadcast day to accommodate varying propagation conditions on multiple bands. In Table 1 you'll find a short list of popular stations and their favorite frequencies.

Hardware

For the purpose of this article, we're assuming that your shortwave radio is your multimode, wide-coverage ham rig (although using another radio, if you happen to have one, is just fine). Your rig should be able to receive AM and SSB signals.

When it comes to "skywires," your regular Amateur Radio antennas are perfectly adequate for casual shortwave listening (beam antennas may not work as well as simple wire antennas).

Finding Stations

When it comes to finding stations to listen to, there are three main methods. Using the first method, you can "hunt around" in the evening hours between 4.7 and 7.6 MHz. You can also prowl night and day from 9.3 to 13.9 MHz. Frequencies above 13.9 MHz are usually "daytime-only" territory.

Method number two involves looking up schedule and frequency information in SWL magazines (updated monthly), or on various on-line services.

The third, and perhaps more accurate method of ascertaining frequencies, is to write to the radio stations themselves. Even without a reception report, stations will normally send a time and frequency guide. It might help to include a couple of International Reply Coupons (available at your local Post Office) to ensure a reply. You can find station addresses in *Passport to World Band Radio*, available from your favorite dealer or from ARRL Headquarters.

Although most shortwave broadcasters transmit AM signals, more and more broadcasters are using SSB (or a shortwave variant that features a reduced-strength carrier and one sideband). HCJB, for example, broadcasts on 21.455 MHz USB.

Variety Programming

A popular religious station, HCJB, broadcasts directly from Quito, Ecuador. Quito lies almost on the Equator, but fortunately for the staffers, many of whom are nationals of various countries around the world (including the US), Quito sits at a somewhat high elevation. Consequently, the weather is not as tropical as you might expect. In fact, I've heard Quito described as the city of eternal spring!

One interesting program from HCJB is devoted entirely to Amateur Radio. It's entitled, appropriately enough, "Ham Radio Today," and it airs on Wednesdays each week. In addition, HCJB airs an interesting cooking program, too (with an Andean influence,

Table 1
Long-Established Shortwave Broadcast Frequencies (kHz)

5950	Voice of Free China
5960	Radio Japan and Radio Canada International
5965	BBC
5975	BBC (via Antigua)
6020	Radio Nederland
6040	Voice of Germany (Deutsche Welle)
7325	BBC
9435	Voice of Israel
9580	Radio Australia
9720	Voice of Russia
9740	BBC
9775	Voice of America
9820	Radio Habana Cuba
11775	BBC
11820	Radio Habana Cuba
12050	Voice of Russia

Principal Stations and their Mailing Addresses

The following is a list of the principal stations that are normally received clearly in North America. Naturally, there are other stations, too numerous to mention in this article. The principal stations, including their mailing addresses, are as follows:

Australia	Australia Broadcasting Corporation, Box 755, Glen Waverley VIC 3150, Australia
Austria	Radio Austria International, A-1136 Vienna, Austria
Canada	Radio Canada International, Box 6000, Montreal, PQ H3C 3A8, Canada
China	China Radio International, Fuxingmenwai, Beijing 100866, Peoples Republic of China
Taiwan	Voice of Free China, Box 24-38, Taipei, Taiwan, Republic of China
Costa Rica	Radio for Peace International, Apartado 88, Santa Ana, Costa Rica
Ecuador	HCJB, Voice of The Andes, Casilla 17-17-691, Quito, Ecuador
Germany	Deutsche Welle, Voice of Germany, Postfach 100444, 50588 Köln (Cologne), Germany
Holland	Radio Nederland, Postbus 222, NL-1200 JG Hilversum, Holland
Japan	Radio Japan/NHK, Tokyo 150-01, Japan
Korea (North)	Radio Pyongyang, Pyongyang, Democratic Peoples Republic of Korea
Korea (South]	Korean Broadcasting System, No. 18 Yoido-dong, Youngdungpo-gu, Seoul, Korea
New Zealand	Radio New Zealand International, Box 2092, Wellington, New Zealand
Norway	Radio Norway International, Utgitt Av Utenlandssendingen/NRK, N-0340 Oslo, Norway
Russia	Voice of Russia [formerly Radio Moscow], Moscow, Russia
UK(Britain)	BBC World Service, Box 76, Bush House, Strand, London WC2B 4PH, England
USA	Christian Science Monitor, Box 860, Boston MA 02123
	KJES, Star Route Box 300, Mesquite, NM 88048
	KTBN, Box A, Santa Ana, CA 92711
	Voice of America, 300 Independence Ave SW, Washington, DC 20547
	WEWN, Box 100234, Birmingham, AL 35210
	WHRI, Box 12, South Bend, IN 46624
	WRNO, Box 100, New Orleans, LA 70181
	WYFR, 290 Hegenberger Rd, Oakland, CA 94621

Note: With the exception of the Voice of America and WRNO, all of the US shortwave stations listed feature mostly religious programming. VOA, like many other large broadcasters, broadcasts in a number of languages and from numerous locations throughout the world.

SWL Resources

Books

The ARRL Operating Manual: Shortwave listening is covered in detail in Chapter 1.

World Radio TV Handbook: SWL information, schedules, maps; updated annually.

Passport to World Band Radio: Schedules, maps, updated annually.

Magazines

Popular Communications (76 N Broadway, Hicksville, NY 11801; tel 516-681-2922): A monthly magazine devoted to shortwave listening and scanning. Contains updated monthly frequency schedules and feature articles.

Monitoring Times (Grove Enterprises, Box 98, Brasstown, NC 28902; tel 704-837-9200): A monthly magazine devoted to shortwave listening and scanning. Contains feature articles and excellent day-by-day shortwave broadcast schedules, updated monthly.

Internet

You'll find lots of information, discussion and frequency/time schedules in the USENET newsgroup **rec.radio. shortwave**. To find current World Wide Web pages with SWL sections (they change frequently), do a net search on "shortwave listening." You'll be surprised at how many hits show up!

Both *CompuServe* and *America Online* have ham radio/SWL forums that feature information, discussion and software.

---

perhaps). HCJB has its own Official Listeners Club. It costs a nominal fee to join, and paid-up members receive a monthly issue of the club's newsletter.

The BBC airs a regular program devoted to radio plays and book reviews. Recently it was *Dr Jekyll and Mr Hyde*. I can hardly wait for the next episode—same time, same frequency—"next week."

Just like the "good old days," the BBC is heavy on news, too. It provides live reports from BBC reporters around the world (sometimes from the most unlikely places).

And don't forget up-to-the-minute cricket or soccer scores coming to you from Britain, South Africa, India, Australia or New Zealand—all outposts of the former Empire. As long as there are shortwave stations plying the bands with signals, you'll find programs that fit your unique listening style.

Letters, QSL Cards and Signal Reports

One thing foreign broadcasters crave, is letters from you, the listener. Many make it worth your while to spend a few cents on an overseas airmail stamp and a few minutes of your time to send in a reception report from your part of the world.

Unlike Amateur Radio's RST signal-quality reporting format, foreign broadcasters prefer the *SIO* reporting system: S = Signal Strength (1-5); I = Interference (1-5); and O = Overall Quality Rating (1-5), where "1" indicates the worst possible conditions and "5" the best. You assign the numbers according to the definitions in the table below:

	5 (best)	4	3	2	1 (worst)
S	Excellent	Good	Fair	Poor	Barely
I	Nil	Slight	Moderate	Severe	Extreme
O	Excellent	Good	Fair	Poor	Useless

Because foreign broadcasters are even more appreciative of several reports on the various frequencies on which they broadcast, you can use a chart such as that shown in Figure 1 to cover as many as 10 separate reception reports to be filed in a 24-hour period for each station heard.

Some shortwave broadcasts ask listeners to provide signal reports and a brief reference describing the subject of the program

S-I-O Signal Reporting Statistics

Radio Station: _____

Date: _____

Listener: _____

Address: _____

_____

_____

Equipment: _____

Antenna: _____

Frequency	Time

Figure 1—If you need to file multiple SIO reports for a single station, just photocopy this form.

they're listening to. This helps keep listeners "honest," with the broadcasters being sure that the listener was actually listening at the time of the report.

As an example, if the program involved a discussion of a Picasso painting, a brief reference to Picasso should be listed in your report. Keep it short and simple. If you feel moved to provide a more extensive commentary you can write the station a more expansive letter covering just that program. Broadcasters appreciate receiving such letters.

To reduce costs, an inexpensive US Air-Letter form is sufficient. Simply copy an S-I-O chart such as that shown in Figure 1 on your Aerogram. At the very least you can expect a polite "thank-you" note by return mail. More than likely you will receive a picture postcard (QSL card) depicting scenes from the station's country of origin.

Some of the more affluent shortwave stations may provide an extensive reply, along with a station logo decal, bumper sticker or other public relations offerings. These might even include key fobs, such as the one I received from Radio Nederland. Radio Japan sent me a series of beautiful, decorative fans. Collecting QSL cards and other goodies can be a big part of shortwave listening.

After its initial mailing, shortwave stations will often send you regular program and time/frequency guides for the next year or so (annual reception reports usually keep these coming).

Sometimes it's advisable to record the programs you're listening to on a cassette tape. Important information and addresses are often given rapidly over the air. Unless you have an outstanding memory or can write 100 words per minute, the details may be

sketchy. By taping the program, the important information can be retrieved later and the tape retained or erased at your discretion.

Conclusion

Although brief, this introduction to shortwave listening should provide some relief from the "dead-band" syndrome. Remember: However you get involved, whatever your gear, I'm sure you'll come to enjoy shortwave listening in at least some capacity. After all, many hams got started as SWLs—there's no reason why that can't work in reverse! Radio is radio, and DX is DX!

**Box 2865
Silverdale, WA 98383**

QST

Q **I was told that my audio was low on the local repeater. I went into the rig and turned up the audio gain control. Now they tell me that I occasionally drop out of the repeater in the middle of a sentence. Any ideas?**

A Yes, you tweaked that pot a bit too far. When you turned up the transmit audio, you increased the transmitter *deviation*—how far the signal swings in frequency as you talk. The higher the deviation, the louder you sound, until you deviate so far that you go out of the passband of the repeater receiver. If the receiver is set for 5-kHz deviation, and you speak loudly enough to deviate 6 kHz, the repeater will not transmit your audio for that part of your transmission. The result is missing words or sentences. Play it cool—turn the transmit audio gain down or move the microphone farther from your mouth.

Q **My friend is planning to buy a new computer for his shack. We both know the clock circuit in the computer can act as a transmitter, broadcasting signals at the clock frequency and all of its harmonics. He claims that if he buys a 120-MHz Pentium machine, he won't have to worry about interference on the HF bands because the clock and all its harmonics will be at VHF and above. This sounds fishy to me. What do you think?**

A Close, but no cigar! The computer counts the clock down to submultiples, and generates data with varying patterns of 1s and 0s. The result is RF at all sorts of frequencies—from VLF on up. In addition, as the computer does its thing, the frequencies generated will be constantly changing. With a little practice, you can actually get the computer to "play music" through your receiver on any frequency you like.

There are many good reasons for buying a very fast computer, but elimination of HF interference is not one of them! A better approach is to buy a name brand with a liberal return policy if you have problems—and make sure there is an FCC Part 15 certification label on the computer.

Q **The plate on the back of my new rig says "117 Volts, 50-60 Hz." I measured my line voltage and the meter read 119 volts. Is this a problem?**

A Not with today's rigs. Most of them contain a power supply with regulators, and line voltages from 110 to 125 V are usually acceptable. This was a real problem with older vacuum-tube rigs. They used transformers to supply the filament voltages to the tubes, usually without regulation. Often, the tube life was shortened by high filament voltages. Many of the better tube rigs had sets of taps on their power transformers, and you would have to pick the tap for your line voltage—110, 112, 115, 130 V or whatever.

Many newer rigs do have two tap settings—for 117 or 220 V. This allows you to operate the transceiver in many countries that do not use the North American standard of 117 V. Usually, rigs shipped to a particular country have the correct tap connected at the factory, but it doesn't hurt to check before you plug a new radio into the wall socket!

Scanning the VHF Aviation Band

Brad Thomas, KC1EX, flies high above the Barkhamsted (Connecticut) Reservoir. Brad enjoys *aeronautical* Amateur Radio whenever possible. *(photo by Jim Kippen)*

What's going on between the FM broadcast band and the 2-meter amateur band? The sky's the limit!

By Steve Ford, WB8IMY
Assistant Technical Editor

It was a dark, drizzly day. Sheets of gray, ragged clouds stretched from horizon to horizon. I watched as the flashing strobe light atop a local TV tower drifted in and out of view. How tall was that tower? One thousand feet? Maybe more? With such a low cloud ceiling, it was an awful day for flying—which made it an excellent day for scanning!

I knew the VHF aviation band was especially active during bad weather, so I switched on my scanner and began hunting. Sure enough, the airwaves were filled with the chatter of commercial and private pilots. Air traffic controllers were busy with dozens of aircraft attempting to take off or land. As I scanned through the band, one conversation stopped me cold.

"Kansas City approach, this is Cherokee three-two bravo. I'm attempting an IFR into Quincy, but I can't acquire the ILS localizer beacon. Can you verify that it's working?"

Somewhere in the clouds, a lone aircraft was trying to land at our small airport. The pilot was relying on his instruments to guide him safely through the murky sky (IFR stands for "instrument flight rules"). To begin his approach, however, he had to find the instrument landing system (ILS) beacon. The beacon signal was nowhere to be found and the situation was becoming dangerous.

"Cherokee three-two bravo, according to my last update, the localizer is operational."

"Ah...then I've got a problem. I've turned nine ways from Sunday and I'm not getting an indication on my receiver."

"Are you requesting assistance?"

There was a long pause. In my imagination I was *in* that Cherokee. I could hear the roar of the engines. I felt the tension.

"Yeah, I think I need some help. We're getting pretty nervous up here."

For the next 10 minutes the air traffic controller guided the pilot by watching radar echoes. "Make a quick right turn to 180. Keep it steady on that heading. Do you have the ILS yet?"

Each attempt ended in frustrating failure. The controller and pilot were running out of options.

"Can you divert to another airport?" the controller asked.

"Negative. The fuel here is reaching critical. I've got to put her down in Quincy—and soon."

"OK, we're going to have to do it the hard way. Turn to a heading of 270."

"Roger, coming around to 270."

"That heading should put you on the approach path to Quincy. Begin your descent to fifteen hundred feet."

"Fifteen hundred feet. Roger. Cherokee three-two bravo."

As I listened I could see him sinking through the soup, watching his altimeter as it wound down to 1500 feet. If an object popped out of the clouds in front of him, there'd be little time to avoid it. I immediately thought of that TV tower and its blinking strobe light.

"Fifteen hundred feet, Kansas City approach." It sounded more like a plea than a statement of fact.

"Do you have a visual on the runway?"

"Negative. Nothing at all."

"The ceiling was last reported at fifteen hundred. Ease it down to twelve hundred."

There was no response.

"Cherokee three-two bravo. I show you at one thousand feet." It was the controller's way of asking, "What are you doing?"

"I see it!" the pilot shouted into his microphone. "I broke out at 900 feet and I've got the runway right in front of me. Thank you! You really saved my butt."

The relief in the controller's voice was obvious. "No problem. Contact Quincy on 123.00. Good day."

I quickly switched my receiver to 123 MHz and listened as the pilot reported his landing intentions. Somewhere in the distance I heard the whine of an airplane engine. Soon the lucky pilot would be back on terra firma, happy to be alive and no doubt wiser for the experience!

Busy Skies—and Frequencies!

Believe it or not, there are approximately 15,000 commercial aircraft in the air each day in the United States—along with an untold number of private aircraft. Despite the congestion, air travel is extremely safe. Not only are pilots well trained, they have plenty of help. Air traffic control centers sweep the skies with radar, tracking aircraft positions and altitudes.

Individual airports have their own communications systems consisting of automated information broadcasts, special approach and departure frequencies and so on (depending on the size of the facility). It all adds up to a rich mixture of signals between 108 and 137 MHz!

A Brief Tour of the Band

From 108 to 117.95 MHz you'll hear odd buzzes and various tones. These are the signatures of navigation beacons. ILS localizer beacons, for example, are often heard between 108.10 and 111.95 MHz. Don't be surprised if you also hear Morse code now and then. Many of these beacons identify themselves using CW. On pilot maps, the CW IDs are shown in dot-dash format. Of course, most ham pilots don't need to resort to dot-dash tables!

You may also hear Automated Terminal Information Service (ATIS) transmissions. At first you'll think you've found a National Weather Service station, but listen again! The ATIS station is broadcasting detailed aviation weather conditions including visibility and wind direction. The ATIS also lets pilots know which runways are active (available).

121.50 MHz is a worldwide aviation emergency and distress frequency. If your scanner has a *priority* function, make sure to program it with this frequency. You'll want to catch *any* activity that shows up on 121.50.

The Federal Aviation Administration provides an *en route* flight advisory service (called "Flight Watch") with stations scattered throughout the nation. Commercial and private pilots use this service to check weather conditions along their flight path. Listen around 122 MHz and you'll hear these conversations. Not only does the advisory service provide information to pilots, pilots make their contributions, too. You may hear a pilot say, "We're running

into some moderate chop (turbulence) at 28,000 (feet)." That report will be filed and delivered to other pilots traveling in the same direction.

Above 122 MHz you'll discover a hodgepodge of activity. Most of it falls into the category of air traffic control. You'll hear communications with the large air route control centers as well as airports of various sizes.

Small airports usually operate single-frequency *unicom* systems. Unicom frequencies are used by airport personnel to give advisories to incoming aircraft. They're also used by pilots to check on conditions, order fuel or even request a cab! You'll also hear pilots reporting their positions as they approach or depart the airport. For example, as a plane approaches a small airport, the pilot will call the unicom. "Meriden unicom, this is Beech five-three alfa."

Larger airports use a number of different frequencies depending on the activity involved. Approach, departure and tower frequencies are used to communicate with inbound and outbound aircraft. When planes are on the ground, they may use a separate *ground control* frequency. Depending on your location, you may have difficulty receiving the ground control signals. These transmissions are intended for the airport vicinity only.

Air route control centers are often easy to hear. Since they are responsible for controlling aircraft over huge areas, their transmitters are very powerful. They also use *repeaters* to expand their coverage.

The major task of an air route control center is keeping aircraft at safe distances from each other. You'll often hear the control center operators telling pilots to speed up or slow down; increase their altitude or reduce their altitude. You'll also hear pilots requesting new altitudes to avoid bad weather or turbulence.

NEW HAM COMPANION

"New York Center, this is Delta 987 heavy ('heavy' means a wide-body jet). We'd like to climb to 33,000 to get out of this bumpy air."

Some Oddities

As you scan the aviation band, you'll run across some fascinating oddities. If you live near an airport with commercial traffic, for example, you may stumble upon *company* frequencies. These are frequencies individual airline companies use to communicate with personnel on the ground. Most of the time you'll hear pilots reporting their estimated arrival times and fuel requirements. If you monitor these frequencies diligently, however, you may hear something similar to what I heard recently.

"We'll be at the gate in about 15 minutes. Tell security to meet us. We've got an idiot on board who's had too much to drink. He's an obnoxious #$%& and a major pain in the @#$#. I want him off this aircraft pronto!"

Listen around 122.750 MHz for air-to-air communications between private aircraft. Some of these conversations can get pretty lively! You'll occasionally stumble upon air-to-air banter between commercial pilots, too. If you're interested in helicopters, listen around 123.050 MHz. Chopper pilots like to chat with each other on that frequency.

If you monitor often enough, you'll hear military aircraft, gliders and even balloons. The conversations are usually brief, so the trick is to quickly note the frequency whenever you hear activity. If it sounds interesting, add it to your scanner's memory!

Frequency Hopping

When an aircraft prepares to take off from a major airport, the pilot begins by contacting *departure control*. Depending on weather conditions, departure or ground controllers will direct the plane along the taxiways and finally grant permission to turn onto the active runway. At that point the pilot is told to switch to *tower control* for takeoff clearance. The pilot changes frequency and identifies.

"American 671 ready for takeoff."

"American 671, you're cleared for takeoff. Left turn to 270, climb and maintain 3000."

In the terse language of aviation communications, this means the controller wants the pilot to turn to a heading of 270° as soon as the plane is airborne. The aircraft is to climb to 3000 feet and stay at that altitude until further notice. These instructions are usually barked out in rapid-fire order.

When the plane lifts off the runway, the pilot switches back to *departure control*. Depending on how much traffic is in the area, the departure controller may issue additional instructions to the pilot. Soon, however, the plane will leave

the airport's *terminal control area*, or TCA, and must contact the nearest air route control center. Departure control tells the pilot which frequency to use.

"American 671, climb to 19,000. Contact New York Center, 126.50. Good evening."

The pilot quickly changes frequency and contacts the air route center.

"New York Center, this is American 671 out of 12,000 for 19,000." (The pilot is at 12,000 feet climbing to 19,000.)

"American 671, climb and maintain 19,000."

As airliners cross the country, their crews must switch frequencies often as they are handed off from one air route control center to another. When they arrive at their destinations, the same frequency-hopping process takes place in reverse.

By listening to the frequency assignments, you'll be able to track individual planes as they taxi, take off and climb to their assigned altitudes.—WB8IMY

Can I Operate my H-T from an Airplane?

If you're talking about commercial airliners, the answer is generally *no*. FCC rules forbid amateur operating from planes flying under instrument flight rules (IFR). Airliners fly IFR virtually all the time, even in perfect weather.

In addition, many flight crews are concerned that your transmissions will interfere with sensitive electronics in the cockpit. In fact, even using *receivers* is forbidden because of the potential interference generated by their oscillator circuits.

In the case of private aircraft, it's a different story. As long as the aircraft is not flying IFR, you can operate with the pilot's permission.

Many private pilots are also hams and they enjoy operating *aeronautical mobile* from their aircraft. Even if the pilot isn't a ham, he or she may not object if you explain what you're doing. When you're the passenger, observe general rules of courtesy and safety. Don't operate if the pilot is busy talking to air traffic controllers. Keep an eye on the instruments and cease operating at the first sign of interference. Avoid operating during take-offs or landings.

Being an aeronautical-mobile ham is exciting. That stubby rubber-duck antenna that usually operates from an altitude of a few feet is now working at several *thousand* feet! You can expect outstanding coverage with your hand-held, typically a hundred miles or more depending on your altitude. *Don't* operate on repeater frequencies, though. From that height you're bound to trigger many repeaters at once. Instead, call CQ on simplex frequencies and you're sure to stir up some activity!—*WB8IMY*

What Equipment Do I Need?

A basic VHF scanning receiver—hand-held or tabletop—will do the job nicely. Before you buy a scanner, however, make sure it covers the VHF-AM aviation band (not all scanners do). If you use the portable antenna provided with most scanners, you should be able to hear transmissions from aircraft over a wide area. The higher the aircraft, the better your chances of hearing it. Unless you live close to an airport or an aviation communications repeater, you may not hear transmissions from operators on the ground. This can be annoying since you're only getting one side of the conversation.

To hear more than just the pilots, you may need an outside antenna. Several manufacturers offer outdoor antennas for scanner enthusiasts. With a simple antenna on your roof, you'll hear plenty of signals!

If you already have an outside antenna for your 2-meter rig, try connecting it to your scanner. You may be surprised at how well it works!

If you currently own a 2-meter hand-held transceiver, check your instruction manual or contact the manufacturer. Some H-Ts are capable of receiving the AM aircraft bands in addition to 2-meter FM! In many cases a simple modification is all it takes.

Aviation Monitoring is Fun—and Useful Too!

If you have an interest in airplanes, aviation monitoring will give you a special window on the action. As I've already mentioned, it's particularly fascinating to listen during poor weather. That's when pilots and controllers are especially busy. Weekends are good for listening to private pilots, since many only get to fly on Saturdays or Sundays.

I've used my aircraft receiver in other ways as well. Once I was meeting my wife at the airport and it was pouring rain. Her flight was late and I dreaded the prospect of sitting in an airport lounge. Instead, I relaxed in my car and listened to the approach control frequency. When her flight was finally cleared to land, I strolled to the gate. Perfect timing! I arrived just in time to see the big Boeing 767 rolling up to the ramp.

And the next time you attend an air show, bring your portable scanner along, too. You'll be in for a special treat as you listen to the pilots perform!

QST

Q **I'm a new packet operator and I'm hearing an awful lot about TCP/IP. What is it? What are its advantages and disadvantages?**

A TCP/IP stands for Transmission Control Protocol/Internet Protocol. It's been around for a number of years in commercial computer networks. TCP/IP is the foundation of the now-famous *Internet*. What hams call TCP/IP is really an adaptation of the commercial TCP/IP system. If an Internet user saw you operating TCP/IP at your station, he or she would be astonished at the similarities.

Some of the advantages of TCP/IP include:

Intelligent network flow control— Unlike "regular" packet, TCP/IP controls the flow of data for maximum efficiency. When the network is busy, a TCP/IP station will automatically lengthen the time it hesitates between packet transmissions. This allows other stations to easily share the available frequencies. As the network becomes less crowded, the delay is automatically shortened.

Efficient file transfers—Because of its efficient flow control, TCP/IP is well suited for sending large files from one station to another. It's not uncommon for TCP/IP enthusiasts to swap lengthy programs and other files over great distances. This is nearly impossible on standard packet.

Direct mail transfers—On standard packet you post a message to your local bulletin board in the hope that it will arrive at its destination. When you send a message to another TCP/IP user within your network, the message is transferred *directly* from your computer to his (or to a station that's collecting mail for him). No bulletin boards are involved. When you see that the message is no longer in your computer, you can be sure it arrived safe and sound. If the destination station is off the air, your computer will keep trying over and over until the message finally gets through.

Multitasking—You can transfer a file, send mail and chat in real time *simultaneously*.

TCP/IP has a few disadvantages—at least in its present form:

Unfriendly software—If you're not well-versed in computers and networking, TCP/IP software can be baffling. You must acquire a unique TCP/IP *address* (available only from designated coordinators), reconfigure several files for compatibility with your local network, and learn some new terminology (plain-English "help" messages don't exist in most TCP/IP programs). Depending on your level of expertise, the assistance of a TCP/IP buddy is strongly recommended.

Computer requirements—Unlike standard packet where the TNC does most of the work, TCP/IP software does all the processing *in your computer*. Unless you're using *Windows*, *OS/2* or a similar multitasking system, the TCP/IP software will completely utilize your computer whenever you're on the air.

Limited coverage—TCP/IP is still growing. TCP/IP networks can be extensive, covering several states at once, but coast-to-coast, border-to-border coverage is still a dream. Some progress has been made through the use of Internet *wormholes*. Wormholes act like bridges between one TCP/IP network and another. They use Internet or other services to pass data between the two locations.

For more information on TCP/IP, pick up a copy of *NOSIntro* or *Your Packet Companion*.

NAVTEX
and your Multimode TNC

Monitor maritime communications and W1AW bulletins the easy way!

A multimode TNC can do all sorts of wonderful things. Just connect that little box between your computer and your transceiver. In minutes the worlds of packet, CW, RTTY, PacTOR, AMTOR and more are as close as your keyboard. Most hams are so overwhelmed they concentrate on their favorite modes and ignore the rest. The multimode TNCs manufactured by the "big three" (MFJ, AEA and Kantronics) include a curious receive-only mode known as *NAVTEX*. How many of you skipped right over the NAVTEX section of your TNC manual when you were reading it? I thought so. Well, it's time to get acquainted with this little-known function and discover what it can do for you.

What is NAVTEX?

NAVTEX is a method of sending teleprinter bulletins to ships at sea. There is a global network of NAVTEX maritime safety and distress stations and they all transmit on 518 kHz. That's just below the end of the AM broadcast band. Here is an example of a typical NAVTEX transmission copied by Dave Stinson, AB5S:

ZCZC GA63

CG GROUP NEW ORLEANS BNM 0815-93 NO
LOUISIANA - CHANDELEUR AND BRETON SOUNDS
MISSISSIPPI RIVER - GULF OUTLET LIGHT 53 REPORTED EXTINGUISHED.

BT
NNNN
ZCZC GA79
BNM 0312-93
TEXAS - TEXAS COAST NEAR SABINE THE TRLB PREVIOUSLY SET TO MARK THE WRECK OF THE F/V MISS STACY AT POSI 29-39-00N, 094-01-20W, IS MISSING. ALL MARINERS SHOULD EXERCISE EXTREME CAUTION WHEN TRANSITING THE AREA.

BT
NNNN

ZCZC GA85
BNM 0352-93 GA
TEXAS - GALVESTON APPROACHES A LIGHTED WRECK BUOY HAS BEEN ESTABLISHED AT POSI 28-58-24.9N, 094-39-49.5W MARKING THE SUNKEN F/V SEA GULL. DEPTH HAS BEEN REPORTED AS 20 FT OVER THE WRECK. ITS ADVISED ALL MARINERS EXERCISE EXTREME CAUTION WHEN TRANSITING THE AREA.

BT
NNNN

When the Coast Guard discontinued their medium-wave Morse code services, this bulletin was sent via NAVTEX:

ZCZC GA01
EFFECTIVE AUGUST 1, 1993, ALL UNITED STATES COAST GUARD COMMUNICATION STATIONS AND CUTTERS WILL DISCONTINUE WATCHKEEPING ON THE DISTRESS FREQUENCY 500 KHZ, AND WILL CEASE ALL MORSE CODE SERVICES IN THE MEDIUM FREQUENCY RADIOTELEGRAPHY BAND. MORE EFFICIENT TELECOMMUNICATION SYSTEMS ARE NOW AVAILABLE TO PROVIDE THE MARINER WITH OPTIONS FOR INITIATING OR RELAYING DISTRESS ALERTS, AND PASSING AND RECEIVING MARITIME SAFETY INFORMATION. THESE OPTIONS INCLUDE INMARSAT, RADIO TELEX (SITOR), MF/HF SINGLE SIDEBAND AND VHF RADIOTELEPHONE, AND SATELLITE EPIRBS (FOR DISTRESS ALERTS AND TELECOMMUNICATIONS), AND INMARSAT SAFETYNET, NAVTEX AND HF NAVTEX (SITOR) (FOR MARITIME SAFETY INFORMATION BROADCASTS).

BT
NNNN

In the United States, NAVTEX stations are operated by the US Coast Guard. I tele-

By Steve Ford, WB8IMY
Assistant Technical Editor

phoned the Coast Guard district office in Boston and had the pleasure of speaking with Lieutenant Commander Willam Glidden, N6YKB, Telecommunications Management chief. I also spoke with Lieutenant Commander Robert Day, the commanding officer of the Coast Guard Communication Station in Boston. With their assistance I compiled a list of US NAVTEX stations and their transmission schedules (see Table 1). Note that none of the stations transmit at the same time unless they're separated by substantial distances. If you have access to CompuServe, check Library 4 in the HAMNET forum. It contains lists of NAVTEX stations worldwide.

The NAVTEX transmission mode is Mode-B (FEC) SITOR, or what hams know as Mode-B (FEC) *AMTOR*. Nothing too unusual about that. What makes NAVTEX special is *how* the bulletins are sent.

NAVTEX bulletins are coded with specific identifiers that designate the bulletin category and the bulletin number. NAVTEX bulletins always begin with ZCZC followed by the station ID, message class, and message sequence number. For example:

ZCZC FD30

ZCZC begins the message and "tells" your TNC that the station ID is to follow.

F is the ID of US Coast Guard Communication Station—Boston

D means that it's a search and rescue bulletin

30 is the sequence number

By sending the proper command to your multimode TNC, you *choose* the message classes that interest you the most. When a NAVTEX bulletin is sent, you'll see something on your screen only if it's a bulletin belonging to one of your chosen categories (see Table 2).

FEC AMTOR (SITOR) isn't error free. You're not linked to the transmitting station, so you can't request a repeat if a character is garbled. Instead, each character is sent *twice*. Your TNC tests the first trans-

Table 1
US Coast Guard
Maritime Safety and Distress Stations (NAVTEX)

Location	Identifier	Broadcast Times (UTC)
Boston, MA	F	0445, 0845, 1245, 1645, 2045, 0045
Portsmouth, VA	N	0130, 0530, 0930, 1330, 1730, 2130
Miami, FL	A	0000, 0400, 0800, 1200, 1600, 2000
New Orleans, LA	G	0300, 0700, 1100, 1500, 1900, 2300
San Juan, PR	R	0200, 0600, 1000, 1400, 1800, 2200
Long Beach, CA	Q	0445, 0845, 1245, 1645, 2045, 0045
Astoria, OR	W	0130, 0530, 0930, 1330, 1730, 2130
Kodiak, AK	J	0300, 0700, 1100, 1500, 1900, 2300
Adak, AK	X	2340, 0340, 0740, 1140, 1540, 1940
San Francisco, CA	C	0400, 0800, 1200, 1600, 2000, 0000
Honolulu, HI	O	0440, 0840, 1240, 1640, 2040, 0040
Guam	V	0100, 0500, 0900, 1300, 1700, 2100

Table 2
NAVTEX/AMTEX Message Classes

NAVTEX

A	Navigational warnings
B	Meteorological warnings
C	Ice reports
D	Search and Rescue information
E	Meteorological forecasts
F	Pilot messages
G	Decca messages
H	Loran-C messages
I	Omega messages
J	SATNAV messages
Z	QRU—no message on hand
K-Y	Reserved

AMTEX
Bulletin Group

A	ARRL bulletins
C	RAC bulletins (Canada)
I	IARU bulletins
J	JARL bulletins (Japan)
S	AMSAT bulletins
X	Miscellaneous

Message Classes

A	Emergency
B	Priority
D	Reserved
E	DX
G	General
K	Keplerian elements
P	Propagation
S	Satellite
X	Miscellaneous

Table 3
NAVTEX TNC Commands

Note: These commands apply when you are communicating with your multimode TNC using generic terminal software (you see the **cmd:** prompt on your screen). If you are using other software, consult your manual.

Kantronics KAM and KAM Plus

NAVMSG <A—Z>	Designate the message classes you want to see (see Table 2). You can select more than one class.
NAVSTA <A—Z>	Designate the NAVTEX station(s) you wish to receive (see Table 1). For W1AW bulletins, use this command to choose the bulletin groups.
NAVERR <0—10>	Set the maximum *percentage* of errors (up to 10%) allowed in a NAVTEX or AMTEX message before it is considered invalid.
NAVLOG	Displays a list of NAVTEX/AMTEX messages that have been properly received.
NAVLCR	Clears the NAVLOG list.
NAVTEX	Places the KAM in the NAVTEX receive mode.

AEA PK-232MBX, PK-900 and DSP-2232
MFJ-1278

NAVMSG <A—Z>	Designate the message classes you want to see (see Table 2). You can select more than one class.
NAVSTN <A—Z>	Designate the NAVTEX station(s) you wish to receive (see Table 1). For W1AW bulletins, use this command to choose the bulletin groups.
NAVTEX	Places the TNC in the NAVTEX receive mode.

mitted character and determines whether it was received correctly. If you receive it intact, it's printed on your screen. If not, your TNC waits for the repeat. The test is performed on the repeated character and, if it arrived without errors, it appears on your screen. If it fails the second test, nothing is printed. (Some TNCs may print an error symbol such as an X.)

Some TNCs allow you to set a percentage limit on the number of acceptable errors (see Table 3). Other TNCs have a fixed error limit. If you receive a bulletin with *less* than the maximum amount of errors, your TNC considers it *valid*. You can leave your radio tuned to a NAVTEX station for hours or days at a time. The bulletin may be sent again, but nothing will print if your TNC has already marked it as valid. This prevents multiple copies of the same message from taking up space in your computer (or on your printer paper). Clever scheme, isn't it?

Equipment Requirements

You obviously own (or are considering) a multimode TNC. The next item on the list is a receiver capable of receiving lower sideband (LSB) at 518 kHz. Most modern MF/HF transceivers include general-coverage receivers with this capability. A number of general-coverage *communication* receivers will also do the job.

The most important part of your NAVTEX receiving system is your antenna. NAVTEX stations are located in coastal areas (see Figure 1) and usually transmit at power levels of 2500 W or less. Ships enjoy ideal over-water paths to these stations, but you may not be so lucky. If you live more than 50 to 100 miles from a NAVTEX station, you'll need to optimize your antenna setup. Dipole antennas at this frequency are *big*. A $1/2$-wavelength dipole for 518 kHz would be about 903 feet long! Few hams have the necessary real estate for an antenna this size, so the old rule applies: get as much wire as high as possible. The alternative is to invest in a compact low-frequency loop antenna such as those manufactured by Palomar Engineers and others (check the advertising pages of *QST*).

When propagation conditions are favorable, you may receive NAVTEX broadcasts from hundreds or even thousands of miles away. Many NAVTEX enthusiasts switch on their equipment at sundown and leave it running all night. In the morning they may be rewarded with fascinating bulletins from several distant stations.

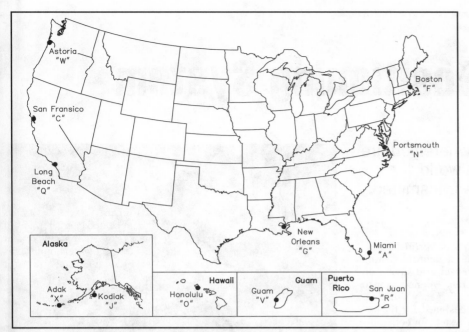

Figure 1—US Coast Guard NAVTEX stations in the United States, Puerto Rico and Guam. The single-letter identifiers are shown along with the approximate station locations.

AMTEX and W1AW

NAVTEX is such an efficient way to send bulletins that ARRL Headquarters station W1AW uses a similar format for its teleprinter transmissions. It's known as *AMTEX* and it works in much the same way.

W1AW AMTEX bulletins are transmitted using FEC (Mode-B) AMTOR on the usual teleprinter frequencies. See the W1AW schedule in this issue for a list of frequencies and times. Each W1AW AMTEX bulletin begins with ZCZC followed by the bulletin group, message class and sequence number (see Table 2). For example:

ZCZC AE50

ZCZC begins the bulletin and triggers your TNC.

A means that this is an ARRL bulletin (this replaces the station ID in the NAVTEX format).

E designates a DX bulletin.

50 is the sequence number.

AMTEX monitoring is a terrific way to keep on top of Amateur Radio news that's important to you. Are you a DXer? Park your radio on a W1AW bulletin frequency and configure your multimode TNC to print (or save) ARRL DX bulletins *only*. If you want the latest Keplerian elements for satellite tracking, tell your TNC to grab those bulletins, too.

This is a convenient, set-it-and-forget-it system. I put it to the test by configuring my Kantronics KAM to receive W1AW propagation bulletins. The transmission began, but my screen remained empty. I busied myself with another project, but soon I saw a flicker of motion. Sure enough, a propagation bulletin was scrolling down my monitor. Next evening I configured the KAM for a couple of bulletin categories, then left to do other chores. I checked the computer before I went to bed and there were several bulletins waiting for me to read. If you're a busy ham who doesn't have time to sit down and monitor live bulletins, or even connect to your local packet BBS, AMTEX is the only way to fly!

To register with ARES, complete ARRL Form FSD-98 and send it to your local Emergency Coordinator. If you don't know who your Emergency Coordinator is, or if you need the form, contact your Section Manager or Section Emergency Coordinator. You'll find names and addresses of Section Managers on page 8 of any *QST*. To register with RACES, you must contact your local Civil Defense office.

Q I keep hearing tales of hams who operate the HF bands by using gutters, fences, and balcony railings as antennas. Is this true?

A Believe it or not, it's true. With a good antenna tuner you can load RF energy into just about any ungrounded piece of metal of reasonable length (preferably ¹/₄-wavelength or longer at your chosen frequency). It may not be a very efficient radiator, but you'll at least put a signal on the air.

Some of these low-profile antenna schemes work surprisingly well. I heard of one ham who seized an opportunity when he discovered that his aluminum rain gutters weren't grounded. He removed a small section in the middle of one gutter, effectively splitting it into two equal halves, each about 16-feet long. He replaced the cut-out section with a plastic piece that was painted to match the gutters. That plastic piece functioned as the center insulator where he attached his 450-Ω ladder line. By using his antenna tuner he was able to load his "gutter dipole" on 20, 17, 15, 12 and 10 meters. A year later he worked his hundredth country and earned his DXCC certificate.

Note that it is *very* important to have a low-impedance connection between portions of such antennas. Otherwise, a semiconducting joint can cause rectification of the transmitted energy, radiation of significant harmonics and RFI to your neighbors. Arcing is another potential problem.

Despite the good fortune of some hams, these types of antennas are best regarded as a last resort. Always keep your output at 10 W or less to avoid RF hazards.

Q Jim Brinson, K4WOP, asks, "I would like to use an outside antenna for my 2-meter H-T, but there is too much interference from paging services. What can be done to eliminate or reduce the interference?"

A Interference from paging services is a common problem for 2-meter operators who live in or near metropolitan areas. Many of these powerful paging transmitters operate not far above the top end of the band. I suggest that you try installing a *band-pass* filter in the line between your antenna and your H-T. As its name implies, a band-pass filter passes only the signals within a particular band of frequencies (2 meters, in this case). It rejects signals at frequencies above and below the band.

Q What's the difference between the Amateur Radio Emergency Service (ARES) and the Radio Amateur Civil Emergency Service (RACES)?

A The Amateur Radio Emergency Service (ARES) consists of amateurs who have registered with the ARRL. (ARES is the emergency communications arm of the League.) All hams are eligible to be members of ARES—whether they're League members or not. The primary function of ARES is to handle emergency messages, including those between government emergency-management officials.

The Radio Amateur Civil Emergency Service (RACES) is similar to ARES in some respects, but it is managed by the US government. RACES is sponsored by the Federal Emergency Management Agency (FEMA). Like ARES, RACES is made up of volunteer ham operators. Its mission is more narrowly focused, however. RACES stations are limited to providing government-to-government communication for state and local civil defense organizations and emergency preparedness agencies. Any ham can become a RACES operator, but he must be officially enrolled in a Civil Defense organization.

By Skip Cubbedge, NØUEI

The Global Positioning System

A GPS receiver can tell you where you are in the world, anywhere in the world, 24 hours a day, using signals transmitted from satellites.

T he knowledge of where you are is a powerful tool indeed. Imagine being able to locate a favorite fishing hole or campsite, determine your exact grid square on a VHF DXpedition, or continuously relay your position to net control while supporting a civic event or emergency situation. The Global Positioning System (GPS) was designed for the US government to provide a personal positioning system for both military and civilian users. With a hand-held GPS receiver, you can determine your position, bearing, and speed, record waypoints and routes, and use a computer interface to plot your course on a map or to transmit your location to others.

Now that hand-held GPS receivers are becoming affordable to the average person, more and more people (including hams) are taking advantage of this powerful technology. How does GPS work? What do you need to know about GPS to intelligently buy a receiver?

How It Works—The Short Story

The Global Positioning System is comprised of 24 Earth-orbiting satellites (Figure 1), each at an altitude of 12,500 miles and moving in orbits inclined 55° relative to the equator. Each satellite orbits the Earth about once every 12 hours. These GPS satellites are essentially orbiting beacon stations transmitting on 1575.42 MHz.

Down on *terra firma*, a GPS receiver must pick up beacons from at least four GPS satellites to determine your location. As small and attractive as it may be, there is nothing "ordinary" about this device. It's a sensitive *spread-spectrum* receiver, an ultra-accurate clock and a sophisticated mathematical calculator.

In spread-spectrum technology, the transmitted signal is spread over a large bandwidth using a fast-coded "message." (If you tuned across a spread-spectrum signal, you'd probably hear nothing more than an increase in the background noise.) A spread spectrum receiver must synchronize itself to the code message so that it can properly detect the carrier signal. This is no easy task!

Once the GPS receiver is dancing in step with the transmitter, so to speak, the receiver grabs the data it needs from the satellite's signal. To calculate the distance to the bird, the GPS receiver must be able to determine the time difference between the moment the data was sent and the moment it was received—the total time required for the signal to travel between the satellite and the receiver. Since the signal moves at the speed of light (300,000 km/sec) the receiver can easily calculate the distance based on the travel time:

Distance (km) = 300,000 (km/sec) × travel time (sec)

The transmission time is sent by the satellite itself (in what is known as a *nav message*) and the reception time is determined by the receiver's internal clock. For this technique to work with the kind of accuracy we expect, however, the GPS receiver needs a clock as accurate as the satellite clocks. This would require a very expensive clock indeed! To keep GPS receivers affordable for everyone, a fourth unknown quantity, the *clock offset*, is calculated from the range measurements made by the receiver.

The clock offset, when combined with the super-accurate time

There's nothing ordinary about a GPS receiver. This is a spread-spectrum microwave receiver, a highly accurate clock and a sophisticated calculator in one package.

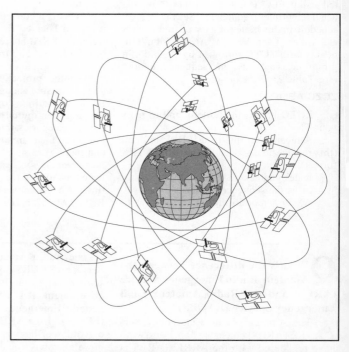

Figure 1—The GPS satellite constellation is a technological marvel, not only because of the satellite complexity itself, but also because of the difficulty of operating such a constellation and keeping the satellites in precisely defined orbits. Because the satellites must transmit very accurate time for the navigation technique to work, each satellite carries highly accurate (and very expensive) cesium- or rubidium-based oscillators as precise time and frequency references.

markers transmitted by the GPS satellites, permits the receiver to display the time to less than one microsecond error, and to perform highly precise ranging. By combining the measured distances between you and the various satellites, the receiver can pinpoint your location anywhere on the globe (see Figure 2).

At a given time, anywhere from five to ten satellites may be in view, depending on the time of day and your location. How does the receiver know which satellites are in view? It keeps an internal almanac of all the GPS satellites, in nonvolatile memory. This almanac is updated continuously via the nav message when the receiver is operating.

Shopping for a GPS Receiver

Great strides have been made in recent years to reduce the size and power requirements of GPS receivers. What was a large rack-mounted chassis 10 years ago now fits in the palm of your hand. Of course, you can choose to "roll your own" GPS receiver, using one of the GPS chip sets or raw circuit boards available (as the AMSAT/

NASA team has done for the Phase 3D satellite; see the AMSAT WWW site listed at the end of this article). For the less adventurous, there are now many hand-held GPS receivers that are available to the general public. Average prices of GPS receivers have been plummeting in recent years with some units selling at less than $200. What sorts of features, performance, and capabilities can you expect to find in a hand-held GPS receiver?

The basic position accuracy of a civilian-class GPS receiver is 100 meters. This is because the government has degraded the accuracy available to civilian users through a technique called *selective availability (SA)*. This is about to change, though. By the end of the decade, everyone will have access to much greater GPS accuracy (see the sidebar, "Government Unleashes Full Power of GPS").

The number of satellites tracked simultaneously is an important cost factor. Usually five to eight satellites is plenty for recreational applications. Some receivers will track up to 12 satellites, which means that they'll track all satellites in view, with spare channels available to acquire new satellites. There are two basic types of receiver architecture: *sequential*, in which one channel tracks multiple satellites by dwelling on each satellite for a short time in a scanning mode of operation, and *parallel,* in which each satellite has its own dedicated channel. Parallel tracking is somewhat more robust, and generally costs more than sequential tracking; some receivers employ a combination of both.

Keep in mind that GPS signals travel at least 12000 miles before reaching your receiver. They're quite weak, making your receiving antenna extremely important. Trees, windshields, hats, backpacks and other seemingly minor obstructions can degrade the signals to the point where they're unusable. Unless you are planning to use the unit strictly out in the open, a *removable* antenna becomes a valuable option. Some receivers come with an internal antenna that is not removable, and have no provision for connecting an external antenna. Make sure that your receiver antenna design fits your particular needs.

All hand-held receivers are battery operated, but shop for a unit with an *external* power option if you plan to use the receiver over extended periods of time. Cigarette lighter plug power cables are available for many receivers. Many GPS receivers are waterproofed by sealing the receiver compartment and filling it with nitrogen— this could be crucial if you are using the receiver in a boat or outside in the rain.

Government Unleashes Full Power of GPS

At the present time, civilian GPS receivers are accurate to within 100 meters. Within a decade, however, we'll be able to enjoy the extreme GPS accuracy used by the military. There could be sweeping economic and social consequences as well. The following announcement was released by the White House on March 29, 1996:

WASHINGTON—President Clinton today approved new guidelines for management and use of the US Global Positioning System (GPS).

"The same technology that helped our troops succeed in Desert Storm will bring us safer air travel throughout the world, improved transportation on our roads and highways and faster response to emergencies by rescue vehicles. And it will help America's industries lead the world," President Clinton said.

GPS technology makes it possible for users to determine their position and navigate anywhere in the world. GPS is increasingly vital to a wide range of civilian and commercial applications ranging from backpacking and pleasure boating to car navigation, emergency rescue, maritime shipping and international air traffic management. The growing demand from civil, commercial, and scientific users has generated a US commercial GPS equipment and service industry that leads the world.

The new White House policy announces the US Government's intention to terminate the current practice of degrading civil GPS signals within the next decade, providing a better signal for commercial and civilian users of GPS. The policy also reaffirms US commitment to providing basic GPS services, free of direct user fees, for peaceful civil, commercial and scientific users throughout the world.

GPS originally was designed by the Department of Defense as a dual-use system with the primary purpose of enhancing the effectiveness of US and allied military forces. The basic GPS, which consists of a constellation of 24 satellites, their navigation payloads, and associated ground stations, data links, and command and control facilities, is operated and maintained by the Department of Defense. GPS provides a substantial military advantage for US forces and currently is being integrated into virtually every facet of US military operations.

Key to the renewed US commitment to GPS is a recent Air Force statement of support for the President's policy on GPS. According to Dr Sheila E. Widnall, Secretary of the Air Force, the Air Force recognizes the tremendous civil and military aspects of GPS, and fully intends to maintain a 24-satellite constellation for the duration of the program.

The GPS policy review was conducted jointly by the White House Office of Science and Technology Policy and the National Security Council and issued as a directive of the National Science and Technology Council.

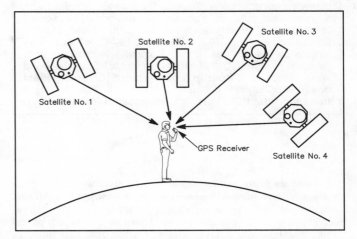

Figure 2—The instant you switch on your GPS receiver, it begins scanning for signals from satellites. Within seconds it acquires the signal from the first satellite (satellite number 1 in this example) and calculates the distance between the satellite and you. It does the same to satellite number 2 soon thereafter. Now it has enough information to calculate a rough latitude and longitude, but more data is still needed. Calculating the distance to satellite number 3 gives the receiver enough information to determine your altitude above sea level. The range calculations to a fourth satellite (satellite number 4) are then added, to determine the clock offset.

Automatic Packet Reporting System

The *Automatic Packet Reporting System (APRS)* was created by Bob Bruninga, WB4APR. *APRS* exploits the ability of a TNC to transmit *beacon* packets that carry short strings of alphanumeric characters. A beacon is an *unconnected* packet. You can think of unconnected packets as "broadcasts." The information is sent to no one in particular and can be received by anyone. An unconnected packet can be relayed through a node or digipeater if you "tell" your TNC to do so.

By taking data from a GPS receiver and incorporating it into beacon packets transmitted by a TNC, you can tell everyone on the network *exactly where that GPS receiver is located.* Any stations equipped with *APRS* software will display the position of the receiver on a computer-generated map. If the receiver moves (let's say it's in an automobile), its position on the map changes with every update.

Although *APRS'* mapping capability was developed to display the movement of hand-held GPS receivers, most features evolved from earlier efforts to support real-time packet communication at special events. Any person in the network, upon determining where an object is located, can move his cursor and mark the object on his map screen. This action is then transmitted to all screens in the network, so everyone gains, at a glance, the combined knowledge of all network participants!

Let's say you're monitoring the movements of rafts during a river race in which each rafter carries a 2-meter FM transceiver, a TNC and a GPS receiver. If your station picks up a transmission from any raft along the river, it will automatically relay the information to everyone else. So, everyone's maps are continually updated with the latest positions of the rafts.

You don't need to own a GPS receiver to enjoy APRS. All you need is the *APRS* software and your normal packet TNC. Just determine your latitude and longitude as best you can. Look it up in an atlas, or borrow a friend's GPS receiver just long enough to determine the position of your station. After you feed the information to the software, your TNC will regularly announce your position to anyone else who is monitoring. You can even use *APRS* to exchange bulletins and enjoy live conversations with others on the network.

Most *APRS* activity is on 2 meters, with 145.79 MHz being the popular frequency. If you do purchase a GPS receiver, you'll need a TNC with *APRS firmware*.

The *APRS* software is distributed as shareware and may be copied for any amateur application. The software includes maps for most areas of the US. You can also edit and add more detail to the maps. *APRS* software is available on many ham-oriented BBSs (including the ARRL BBS at 860-594-0306) as well as various on-line services such as CompuServe. You can grab the latest version of *APRS* for IBM-compatible PCs on the World Wide Web at: **ftp://ftp.tapr.org/tapr/SIG/aprssig/files/dosstuff/DOSaprs/**. If you're a Macintosh user, try **ftp://ftp.tapr.org/tapr/SIG/aprssig/files/macstuff/MacAPRS/**.

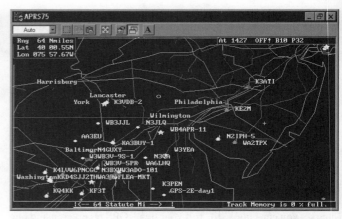

APRS running under *Windows 95*, courtesy of N2IPH from his Web site at http://www.cyberenet.net/~n2iph/bob.htm.

Most GPS receivers compute bearings and speeds for you, using multiple position measurements made as you are moving along. Receivers vary widely as to how this information is displayed, ranging from alphanumeric display to a graphical representation of a "road" in front of you with a compass "dial" indicating the direction traveled. Most receivers will allow you to store locations as *waypoints*, and to group sequences of waypoints together into *routes*. With waypoints and routes, the receiver can prompt you as to what bearing to take and when to make turns. This information can be displayed either as text or graphically. As many display methods are available as there are manufacturers, so you should shop around for what is most appealing to you.

For Further Information

Want to learn more about the fascinating technology of GPS? There are many excellent sources available, both in written form and on the World Wide Web. You can even buy a receiver directly from some Web advertisers. Some of these sources are listed below:

GPS World—A monthly compendium of popular articles on GPS techniques, issues, and applications.

Global Positioning System: Theory and Applications, Vols. I and II, ed. B. W. Parkinson and J. J. Spilker, AIAA, 1996. A very thorough and complete collection of theoretical, historical, and practical information on GPS.

The Global Positioning System, Thomas A. Herring, *Scientific American*, Feb 1996, pp 44-50. A good general article on the technical details as well as some of the social impacts of GPS.

WWW Sites:

http://www.utexas.edu/depts/grg/gcraft/notes/gps/gps.html. A great source of information, tutorials, and other GPS links.

http://www.amsat.org/amsat/sats/phase3d/gps/. The official AMSAT Phase 3D GPS receiver WWW site.

http://www.nmaa.org/navtech.com. Home page of Navtech GPS Supply, a source for receivers, software, books, and other GPS-related materials.

ftp://aleph.gsfc.nasa.gov/GPS/totally.accurate.clock/. A project by Tom Clark, W3IWI, to use GPS as a means to provide extremely accurate time for amateur applications.

If you are planning to use your GPS receiver with the increasingly popular *Automatic Packet Reporting System (APRS)* software (see the sidebar, "Automatic Packet Reporting System"), the receiver *must* have the capability to send position data to your packet TNC. You'll need a receiver with an NMEA 0183 data interface port, which is the standard used by some packet TNC manufacturers as well as the GPS receiver industry. The NMEA data interface can also be connected directly to a computer that is running one of the many popular map database programs. These programs indicate your position on the map, and even drop graphic "bread crumbs" on the street display so that you can track your progress and retrace your steps if necessary.

Skip Cubbedge, NØUEI
2101 Champlain Dr
Boulder, CO 80301
e-mail nØuei@amsat.org

QST~

By Michael Gauland, AA7JF

There's No Place Like Home

Spin your own little corner of the World Wide Web

If you've spent any time exploring the World Wide Web, you've probably thought about setting up your own Web page (popularly known as a *home* page). And why not? Let's take a brief look at what you can do with a Web page. Then I'll give you some tips to start you on your way to creating your own unique contribution to the Web.

Why Create a Home Page?

The answer is obvious. The World Wide Web gives you access to Internet users around the globe, including many hams and potential hams. Of course, your home page will not be interesting to all of them. So, you may want to slant your page to members of your local club, or to people who restore old ham gear, or who share other special interests.

Your club can benefit from having its own home page in several ways. It can serve as an on-line reference for club members, keeping them informed of coming events, providing current lists of club officers and contacts, giving detailed descriptions of the program for the next meeting and so on. Because a Web page is easy to change, it can incorporate up-to-the-minute revisions much easier than a printed newsletter. Your Web page can easily include lengthy descriptions that would take up too much space on paper, and include material that would be impractical in a newsletter, such as color photos, sound clips, and even short video clips! The WWW provides a whole new way to communicate with club members. It's also a good place to provide information about Amateur Radio to potential hams, to recruit new members, and to publicize your community service activities. And, of course, other hams throughout the world can visit your club's page, and be awed by your accomplishments (and inspired to improve their own club!).

You can also set up your own *individual* home page to advance Amateur Radio. For example, if you teach a licensing class, you can not only publicize your classes over the Web, you can provide some general information about the hobby. Perhaps your page can encourage websurfers from other areas to contact the ARRL to find a class in their area (you could even provide a link to the ARRL page). You might also put some of your classroom materials on line to assist other instructors and self-learners. Or, if

you're a diehard Field Day enthusiast, why not describe your most memorable Field Day experiences and show some photos of your Field Day sites? (Maybe someone will learn from your successes—or failures!) No matter what Amateur Radio activity you enjoy, the Web offers you a way to share it with the world!

But what if you're a new ham, or don't have a particular passion you'd like to evangelize? A Web site can still add to your enjoyment of Amateur Radio. A personal Web page can include photos of yourself and your shack, a description of your hometown, your job, and other hobbies you enjoy. You can direct your on-air friends to your Web page (perhaps by including it on your QSL cards), and allow them to learn more about you in a way that just isn't possible over the air.

How Do I Get Started?

If you're already surfing the Web, you probably have everything you need. You'll need a computer, of course, with a text editor (or word processor capable of storing plain ASCII), a Web browser, and some way to get your files to your Web server. (See the sidebar, "Which Web Browser Should I Use?") A Web server is an Internet host that stores your Web files and makes them accessible to other users. You can most likely get this service from whoever is already providing your net access. Some services, such as America OnLine and CompuServe, include Web space with their basic service; on others, there may be an additional charge. Some local Internet service providers offer free Web space for nonprofit organizations, such as your radio club (it can't hurt to ask!).

You'll be using your Web browser to preview your pages as you create them, before you unveil them to the world. To save time, and on-line charges, you'll want to use a browser that lets you open a *local file* (instead of accessing it over the net) without being connected to the Internet or an on-line service. The most popular browsers, *Mosaic* and *Netscape*, let you do this.

Though it's not strictly necessary, you'll probably want some utility programs for preparing graphics (in GIF or JPEG format), and possibly sounds (in any popular format, such as AIFF, SND, or WAV) and movies (in QuickTime or MPEG format).

The last thing you'll need is a basic knowledge of the *HyperText Markup Language* (HTML), which is used to create Web pages. HTML consists of *tags* that describe how your pages should look. Tags control text styles and formatting, indicate graphics files to be included, and provide links to other files and Web sites. There are two types of tags. *Standalone* tags consist of a tag name enclosed in angle brackets (eg, <HR>). For example, the tag <HR> draws a horizontal rule—a line—across the page. Other standalone tags insert blank lines, special characters, and graphics. *Container* tags surround a section of HTML, and affect the way it is displayed. Common container tags are used to create headings, delineate paragraphs, and define links. Table 1 lists some common tags.

How Do I Use These Tags?

It's surprisingly easy to put these tags together into an attractive Web page. Take a look at the HTML file listing shown in Figure 1. Note that the line numbers were added for the following discussion, but are not really in the file. In fact, the file was split into separate lines to make it easier to read, but it would work just

---

July

ARRL Amateur Radio Testing Sessions in Vancouver, Washington
8, Monday Packet Meeting - 7 p.m.
12, Friday Club Meeting 7 p.m.
14, Sunday Bunny Hunt at South End of Vancouver Mall in Sears Parking Lot By Mall Sign
12:30 p.m. For Information on Bunny Hunts Contact NW7L Bill
15, Monday ARES Meeting 7:30 p.m.
19-21 NW DX Convention
26-28 RV Weekend
27 & 28, Saturday & Sunday Walk for Human Race
ARES Net Every Tuesday at 7 p.m.
2 River YL Net Every Wednesday at 7 p.m.
Club Info Round Table Friday's (Except Meeting Night) 8 p.m.

The Clark County (Washington) Amateur Radio Club (http://www.worldaccess.com/NonProfitOrganizations/ccamateur/) uses its Web page to keep members informed of upcoming events.

```
1. <HTML>
2. <HEAD>
3. <TITLE>QST Sample Web Page</TITLE>
4. </HEAD>
5. <BODY>
6. <IMG SRC="mike.jpg" ALIGN="LEFT" ALT="photo
   of a great-looking guy">
7. <H3>Mike Gauland, AA7JF</H3>
8. <P>I'm a proud member of the
9. <A HREF="http://www.worldaccess.com/
   NonProfitOrganizations/ccamateur
10. Clark County Amateur Radio Club</A>
11. , named <B>Club of the Year</B>
12. at the 1995 SeaPac hamfest.</P>
13. <P>I've been a ham since October, 1990.</P>
14. <HR>
15. <ADDRESS>Mike Gauland (
16. <A HREF="mailto:thegaul@aol.com">
17. thegaul@aol.com
18. </A>
19. )</ADDRESS>
20. </BODY>
21. </HTML>
```

Figure 1—Don't let the complicated appearance fool you. HTML files are easy to understand once you learn the various tag statements (see text).

By using an <IMG> tag in your HTML document, you can insert an image into your page. In our example, we use the <IMG> tag to insert a photo of yours truly in JPEG format (mike.jpg).

Table 1
Some Common HTML Tags

<A HREF="URL">text</A>
An anchor tag defines a link to another document or Web page. Replace URL with the name of the local file or the complete Universal Resource Locator of the page you want to link to. Replace text with the text you want the user to click on to follow the link (text can include other tags, including an <IMG> tag).

<ADDRESS>address</ADDRESS>
An address tag is usually used to display information on contacting someone by e-mail, postal mail, or phone. On most browsers, the address will appear in italics. If you want to be sure of this, use the <I> tag instead of <ADDRESS>.

<B>text</B>
This tag tells the browser to display the text in **boldface.**

<BODY>...</BODY>
The BODY tag is the second part of the HTML document, inside an HTML tag, after the <HEAD> tag. Almost your whole document will reside in this tag.

**
**
This standalone tag forces a new line in the text.

<H1>text</H1>....<H6>text</H6>
These tags define six sizes of headers, with H1 being the largest. Usually, a header is displayed in bold face.

<HEAD>...</HEAD>
The HEAD tag is the first part of the HTML document, inside an HTML tag. Normally, it only contains a <TITLE> tag.

<HR>
This standalone tag draws a horizontal rule across the page.

<HTML>...</HTML>
The HTML tag should be the first tag in your document, and everything else will be nested inside it. Inside will be a <HEAD> tag, containing a <TITLE> tag, and a <BODY> tag, containing everything else.

<I>text</I>
This tag causes the browser to emphasize the *text*, usually by displaying it in italics.

<IMG SRC=" source ALIGN="alignment" ALT="text">
This tag defines an in-line image. Replace *source* with the name of the GIF or JPEG file containing the image. As discussed in the text, *alignment* can be LEFT, RIGHT, TOP, BOTTOM, or MIDDLE. The *text* will be displayed if the user's browser can't display the image.

<P>text</P>
This tag defines a paragraph, which browsers usually precede with a blank line. The *text* can include other tags. The closing </P> tag is optional.

<TITLE>text</TITLE>
The title tag is usually the only item inside the <HEAD> tag at the start of an HTML document. The *text* will be used to identify the page in the user's browser, both as the window title and in the "hotlist" or "bookmark" list.

as well if everything were on the same line. Also, the tags are shown in all upper-case letters, but they can be any combination of upper- and lower-case.

Looking at the listing, you'll notice the entire file is enclosed by one <HTML> container tag. This, in turn, consists of a <HEAD> (lines 2 to 4) and a <BODY> (lines 5 to 20). This is the way you should organize all your pages.

The <HEAD> consists solely of a <TITLE> tag. The text inside the <TITLE> tag will usually be displayed at the top of the browser window, and will also be used to identify your page in the browser's "hotlist" or "bookmarks" list. You'll want to make this short, but descriptive. You'll sometimes find other tags in the <HEAD> section, but they are beyond the scope of this article.

The <BODY> tag includes several other tags, which describe the photo, text, and links which appear on the page. The first tag in the <BODY> is an <IMG> tag on line 6. This tag identifies the file containing the image (mike.jpg—the image can be in either GIF or JPEG format), provides a message ("photo of great-looking guy") to print if the user's browser doesn't support graphics, and tells the browser to put the graphic on the left edge of the page, and to wrap the text around on the right. Other options for the "ALIGN" field are RIGHT, TOP, MIDDLE, and BOT-

TOM. RIGHT does what you'd expect; the others insert the graphic into the text stream, lining the text up with the top, middle, or bottom of the graphic.

On line 7, the <H3> tag defines a *heading*. On most browsers, headings are displayed in bold type, using a larger type size. Six different heading sizes are available, with <H1> being the largest, and <H6> the smallest. You don't really have much control over how the heading looks; the specific font, type size, display style, and color are controlled by the user's browser.

Lines 8 to 12 are contained in a <P> tag, which identifies it as a paragraph. Usually, the browser puts a blank line between paragraphs. The text will be automatically formatted by the browser, so that it will fit into the window (that is, you can set your browser window to any size, and the text will not spill outside the window).

Within the paragraph, on lines 9 to 11, is an *anchor* tag, which defines a link. In this case, the link is to the W7AIA Web page, as

Which Web Browser Should I Use?

It's important to use a real Web browser to check out how your page looks *before* you post it to the Web. If you have a choice—which some of us, especially those browsing the Web via LAN-based Internet connections don't—and if you want to see how modern Web pages are *really* supposed to look, I recommend that you *don't* use a browser with the word *mosaic* in its name.

Mosaic on a Web browser is like *Webster's* on a dictionary: It doesn't guarantee what you expect it to. (I'm a diehard *Merriam*-Webster man, thanks.) Although *NCSA Mosaic* (*NCSA* standing for the University of Illinois at Champaign-Urbana's National Center for Supercomputing Applications) began as and remains freeware, it has kept up with neither its competition (*Netscape Navigator* and *Microsoft Internet Explorer*) nor ongoing developments in HTML even though it was updated as recently as March 1996. *Mosaic* variants other than NCSA's own, such as *AIR Mosaic* and *Spry Mosaic*, are relatively old spinoffs that stand to be even more out-of-date in handling modern HTML than *NCSA Mosaic*.

Considering that this is a "getting started" Web article, what do I mean by "out-of-date"? I mean "can't display font size and font color specifications," for one thing. I mean "can't handle <BODY> extensions"—HTML extensions that let you set a document's background, text and link colors, or use a background image. I also mean "can't handle <IMG> extensions"—HTML extensions to the basic <IMG> (image) tag (ALIGN, for instance) that let you specify how text wraps around images.

As we go to press, three browsers were worth serious consideration for those in a position to choose: *Netscape Navigator* 2.02 (production) or 3.0 (in beta), *Microsoft Internet Explorer* 2.0 (1.5 for *Windows* NT) (production) or 3.0 (in beta, so far for *Windows* 95 only) and the browser in *America Online* 3.0. (The AOL browser is active only if you're paying for AOL connect time—a strong drawback when you just want to proof local files.)

Netscape Navigator is arguably the better *proofing* tool of the three in the sense that it's less forgiving of bad HTML—a hyperlink you forget to close with </A>, looks busted because it *is* busted. If you want to proof documents that include frames (a Netscape HTML extension), you'll need *Netscape* 2.02 or higher, or the 3.0 version of *Internet Explorer* or *America Online*. (In case you're wondering, the browser in *America Online* 2.5 is so buggy and prehistoric that I recommend it only as a means of checking how bad your pages will look to visitors using it!)

Specialities may help you narrow your choice among the three. If you're not an AOL subscriber and don't want to become one, *AOL* 3.0 is out, of course. If you need a browser capable of talking to the Internet via a through-firewall protocol called SOCKS, you'll need *Netscape Navigator* 2.02 or 3.0. (The America Online client can do SOCKS with the help of a utility called *SocksCap*.) If there's something compelling for you about the mail, news or FTP capability of a given browser, that may play a part in your decision, too. Or maybe price will drive your decision: *Microsoft Internet Explorer* and *America Online* 3.0 are entirely free, and *Netscape Navigator* is free only to qualified users.

To learn what's available in Web browsers, authoring tools and accessories, watch Stroud's Consummate Winsock Applications at **http://www.stroud.com/**. *Netscape Navigator* is available via **http://www.netscape.com/**; *Microsoft Internet Explorer*, via **http://www.microsoft.com/**; the *America Online* 3.0 installation file, via **http://www.aol.com**.—*David Newkirk, WJ1Z, Electronic Publications Editor,* ARRLWeb *webmaster*

```
<HEAD>
<TITLE>My Page</TITLE>
</HEAD>
<BODY>
<H1>Welcome to My Page</H1>
<P>This is the first paragraph</P>
<P>This is the second paragraph</P>
<HR>
<ADDRESS>To comment on this Web page, send
  mail to
<A HREF="mailto:myaddress@myhost.com">myaddress@
  myhost.com</A>
</ADDRESS>
</BODY>
</HTML>
```

Figure 2—When you're ready to fly solo, here's a basic HTML template to get you started.

specified by the HREF field. The text in between the <A> and </A> tags ("Clark County Amateur Radio Club") will appear on the Web page, and will usually be highlighted by the browser. When the user clicks on that text, the browser will load the file indicated by the link. In this case, it will load the Web page for **http://www.worldaccess.com/NonProfitOrganizations/ccamateur/.** Since we didn't specify a file name, only a directory, the server will supply a default file, commonly index.html, index.htm or home.htm, depending on the server configuration. The anchor could also point to a local file, such as another HTML file, or a sound or image file. The text between the <A> and </A> tags could also contain other tags, such as an <IMG> tag. For example, the HTML directive:

<A HREF="http://www.arrl.org"><IMG SRC="arrllogo.gif"></A>

would display the ARRL logo in the file arrllogo.gif. When the user clicks on the logo, the browser will load the ARRL page at **http://www.arrl.org**. If you use this in your pages, be sure to include an "ALT" field in the <IMG> tag, so the user will have something to click on if his browser doesn't support images!

Line 11 continues the paragraph, and includes some text in a <B> tag. This tag tells the user's browser to display the enclosed text as boldface. A similar tag is <I></I>, which displays text in italics. The paragraph is ended on line 12, and followed by another paragraph on line 13. There will be an empty line between the paragraphs.

The <HR> tag in line 14 is a standalone tag that puts a horizontal line across the page. This is useful for visually separating sections of your page. In this case, the line separates the page from the <ADDRESS> tag on lines 15 to 19. The address tag includes the author's name, and a link to his e-mail address (lines 16 to 18). The e-mail address is set up as an anchor to mailto:thegaul@aol.com, identified by the text thegaul@aol.com. If the user's browser has mailing capability, clicking on the text will let the user send a message to **thegaul@aol.com**. If the browser can't send mail, the text identifies the e-mail address to the user, so mail can still be sent to the page author using a separate mail program. The HTML file concludes on lines 20 and 21 by closing the <BODY> and <HTML> tags.

How Do I Design My Own Page?

To save time and on-line charges, you'll put your page together on your own computer, and only upload it to your Internet host when it's done. To make this easier, create a separate folder or directory for your page. Copy any graphics or other files you want accessible from your page into this folder. For the example page, you'd start with the file mike.jpg in your folder.

Next, fire up your editor, and create a file called index.html (index.htm for DOS/*Windows* users). This is the default file name that most browsers will look for, and is a good choice for your home page file. Start filling it in, starting with the basic template in Figure 2. Use your browser to open this file, and see how it looks. If any of your in-line graphics are missing, check the file names you specified in your HTML file, and make sure the files are in your working folder. Keep in mind that your page will look different on different browsers, depending on the size of the user's window, and the default fonts and sizes used by the user's browser. Of course, you won't be able to check any of your links without actually connecting to the net, so verify those after you've posted your page to your Web server.

Once you're satisfied with the way your page looks, transfer your html and graphics files to your Internet provider. Contact your provider to find out the right procedure to use for their system, but most likely all you'll need to do is to upload your files to the server. *Be sure you use a binary transfer to upload your graphics.* If you're a DOS or *Windows* user, make sure you rename your index.htm file to index.html (or whatever your Internet service provider requires) on the server. Use upper- and lower-case characters consistently in your file names and your HTML file. You may also have to ask your provider how to set the protection on your files so that other users can read them.

Finally, connect to the Internet and try to open your page from there. Try resizing your browser window a few times, and make sure you're happy with the way your page looks. Be sure to test all the links, and make sure they work! If you've put in a mailto field, try sending yourself mail from it, and to verify the address is correct. Once you have it all working, ask a few of your friends to try your page, and make sure it works from their systems as well.

Now that you've got a working Web page, you need to publicize it. If your page is strictly personal, you may want to do no more than tell your friends about it, and maybe add it to your QSL cards. If your page is intended for a more general audience, you'll want to register it with some of the major on-line search services, such as Yahoo (**http://www.yahoo.com**) and WebCrawler (**http://www.webcrawler.com**). A good way to do this is by connection to **http://www.submit-it.com/**.

Moving on...

This article covered only the very basics of HTML and Web page design. No doubt you've seen Web pages that included counters, forms, background images, and other cool features. Those are beyond the scope of this article, but you can easily learn more on your own. Your local library probably has a few good books on HTML, and you can find numerous on-line resources (search for "HTML" using the Yahoo service). Most browsers offer an option to view the HTML source file for the page you are viewing. Usually, you can figure out how an effect was achieved that way. But whether you stick to the basics, or go on to become an HTML guru, the Web can be a great place to promote Amateur Radio.

1165 SE 37th Ave
Hillsboro, OR 97123
e-mail thegaul@aol.com

Q Charles Barkowski, KB2UVG, asks, "I'm a relatively new ham and I want to know more about autopatches. I know they have something to do with telephones, but that's about all. Can you help?"

A An autopatch is a device that allows hams to place telephone calls from their automobiles or even from hand-held transceivers. You'll commonly find autopatches as part of repeater systems, although simplex autopatches exist as well.

While they may seem similar, an auto-patch is not the same as a cellular telephone. They both use RF, but the similarity ends there. Autopatches are comparable to old-fashioned "party lines." When you make an autopatch call, *everyone* hears your conversation. Cell phones are relatively private by comparison. And conventional repeater autopatches are only *half-duplex* devices. This means that you and the person you've called must take turns talking. Cell phones, on the other hand, are *full duplex;* you can interrupt each other at will.

Just because you're able to use a repeater, don't expect free access to its autopatch. Most repeater groups require autopatch users to be paid members. As a member in good standing, you'll receive the "secret" codes that operate the autopatch. If you desperately need to use an autopatch and you're not a member, there is usually a member on frequency who can operate it for you.

The *control operator* has the last word about what takes place on his or her repeater—including the autopatch. For example, some control operators don't mind if you use the autopatch to order a pizza. Others mind very much! Listen for a while and learn the pattern. If in doubt, don't do it until you can speak to the control operator.

Q Ron Cyre, KE4QWP, asks, "I work as a pharmacist, which means I'm confined to the store all day. I'd like to use my 2-meter H-T to relieve the boredom, but I can't reach any repeaters. It's frustrating to watch customers with portable cellular telephones. They never seem to have any trouble making calls from inside the store! What's the solution?"

A It's not uncommon to have difficulty transmitting from inside a commercial building on 2 meters with a hand-held transceiver (H-T). The metal structure attenuates the signal substantially. When you consider that you're only running a few watts, it doesn't take much attenuation to render your signal inaudible to all but the nearest, most sensitive repeaters.

Cellular telephones have the advantage because they operate on much higher frequencies. The shorter wavelengths of their signals are better able to escape through windows and other openings to the outside world. You would get similar results with 33 or 23-cm amateur gear, but you wouldn't have many people to talk to.

If you can afford to make the investment, one solution would be to purchase a dual-band 2-meter/70-centimeter mobile transceiver that offers duplex "crossband" operation. You could leave the radio in your car and use a 70-cm H-T as your link while you're in the store. The dual-band rig would hear your H-T's signal and retransmit it on the 2-meter frequency of your choice. It would also relay 2-meter signals back to you on 70 centimeters.

This is essentially an auxiliary station operation and there are some FCC rules you must take into account. Pick up a copy of *The FCC Rule Book* from your favorite dealer or ARRL Headquarters for complete details.

Q Don Jarvis, VE3FCZ, asks, "I've been a Yagi antenna user for nearly 30 years, but I'm considering a switch to quad designs. How do they compare?"

A The debate over the virtues of quads versus Yagis has been raging for some time, and it won't be settled in this column, either. (The Doctor knows a hot potato when he sees one!) Each antenna has its diehard fans. In terms of performance, they seem to be comparable. From a mechanical standpoint, Yagis are simpler and more durable. (Ice storms in particular are the bane of quad designs.)